Cognitive
Hypnotherapy

Cognitive
Hypnotherapy

"What's that about and how can I use it?"

Trevor Silvester

Matador
5 Weir Road
Kibworth Beauchamp
Leicester LE8 0LQ, UK
Tel: (+44) 116 279 2299
Fax: (+44) 116 279 2277
Email: books@troubador.co.uk
Web: www.troubador.co.uk/matador

ISBN 978 1848765 054

British Library Cataloguing in Publication Data.
A catalogue record for this book is available from the British Library.

Typeset in 11pt Trebuchet by Troubador Publishing Ltd, Leicester, UK
Printed and bound in the UK by TJ International Ltd, Padstow, Cornwall

Matador is an imprint of Troubador Publishing Ltd

To John Peters
Always remembered

Contents

Foreword

Dr. David Hamilton

In my former professional role, I worked as a scientist in a large pharmaceutical company where I was involved in the process of developing drugs for both heart disease and cancer. It was during that time that I became acutely aware of the power of the mind by learning of the benefits patients received after taking placebos.

That period began what has now been, for me, a serious 12-years (and counting) investigation into the mind's ability to shape our health and our lives. I have witnessed many fascinating things. I have come across many therapies and techniques during this time, some promising and even delivering seemingly miraculous transformations. But time and time again I find myself coming back to sing the praises of Cognitive Hypnotherapy, which is what this book is about.

This book guides us to a much greater understanding of our selves and our lives. It so eloquently explains that the limitations in our lives are merely illusions created by our minds. Through its pages, we are guided to a deep understanding of how we use our memoragination to create these illusions. Memoragination - which is an idea I really hope takes root – is a new word that Trevor Silvester has coined that expands the concept of memory from just happenings of the past to include our perception of our present and what we anticipate about the future.

We use our memoragination to create the illusions around us. Our experience of the present depends upon the meaning we have given to events in our past. If we view an event of the past in some negative way then we create negativity around us in the present and also project it into the future.

But most exciting is the fact that our memoragination is mouldable, just as the brain undergoes neuroplasticity as we experience new things and learn new ways in life. Thus, just as we can retrain the brain, we can retrain our memoragination, and in so doing recreate our past, or view it with fresh eyes. And as we do this, the clouds part in our present, and a new sun rises on the horizon of our future.

And in using our memoragination in this way, our sense of self also evolves. This lead us in exciting new directions in our lives as we dissolve the barriers to who we can become that we have constructed in front of ourselves with our thoughts. And thus we begin to recreate ourselves as much grander versions of ourselves. And so, as we change ourselves from the inside out we change our lives.

This book contains both the theoretical and the practical, a balance that makes the topic most attractive because the book appeals to both those who want to understand the science and those who want to know and use the practical tools.

I first met Trevor a couple of years ago and was immediately taken by his knowledge of the subject, his passion in conveying the truths that are evident in the pages of this book, but also his capacity to make explanations extremely clear. Trevor's knowledge, passion, and clarity are expressed throughout the book.

As I read the pages, I had several 'A ha' moments as I made connections that I had not thought of before, both in my own life but also in how I understand the link between the mind and the circumstances of our lives. I am quite confident that the reader will have many 'A ha' moments too.

We are living in exciting times, where scientific discoveries in the field of neuroscience are shining light on why Cognitive Hypnotherapy is so powerful. These discoveries give us faith that we can use our minds to change our self and our life.
And thus, as this book so clearly explains, when we learn to re-pattern some of the events of the past, giving them a new context or meaning, we paint a new picture for our future, one that is much more expansive and fulfilling.

On the whole, Cognitive Hypnotherapy offers us an effective way to untangle ourselves from our thoughts when they have led us down the path of frustration, disappointment, and even dis-ease and then give birth to new thoughts that are much more expansive, fulfilling, and with the potential to bring much more happiness into our lives.

David R. Hamilton PhD

Acknowledgements

When I was younger I never used to bother reading this part of a book. Somehow I thought it had nothing to do with the reader and was only of relevance to the people mentioned. Since then I've come to realise the power appreciation and gratitude has to boost the wellness of the appreciator as well as the appreciated. Now I often finding reading why and who an author thanks - and the way they do it - adds to my knowledge of them, and my understanding of their message. With that in mind, this is my chance to thank a great many people.

It feels right to begin with a friend and mentor who passed away about eight weeks before I was ready to show him what you're holding. You're going to have the opportunity to meet his genius later in the book, but I was privileged to know him as a friend. Gil Boyne will be remembered as a giant in the field of hypnotherapy, deservedly mentioned in the same breath as Erickson and Elman, yet it's his laugh that fills my head on the frequent occasions I bring him to mind. I think he would have approved of the part of the book that describes some of his craft and I hope it adds to his legacy.

Let me continue by thanking people I've never met. Every author mentioned in the book, or listed in the bibliography, have blessed me with at least one of those marvelous moments when a new idea sends a thrill up your spine. I hope I have the chance to thank them personally one day.

Good teachers have been the bedrock of what you read here. In addition to Gil I'd like to thank Tad James and David Shepherd for the brilliant grounding in NLP they gave me, and to Tad for his admonishment to 'read outside of your field'. If you only plough a single furrow you only reap a single crop. Rubin Battino is another teacher who I now call a friend. He lives a simple truth: that only two things matter; people and nature. Base your choices on that and life becomes very much simpler.

Very often my students have been the first to hear my ideas - and shown great patience and forbearance when I sometimes worked them out in front of them - in this instance the students of the Quest Institute Master Practitioner course of 2009/10 deserve particular thanks. However, my life has been blessed by the people I've had the chance to teach, many who I now count as great friends, and I'm grateful to them all for what they've given me.

The people who've allowed me the privilege of helping them have, obviously, provided much of the inspiration for what you are about to read. I've discovered that the act of helping people discover their own strength adds to your own, and that at times we're all fellow strugglers. Confidentiality prevents me from naming anyone in particular, but I hope they would recognise their part as they read this. They are as much a part of this book as I am.

Drilling deeper into the progression of this book from a jumble of thoughts into what you're about to read I come first to one of my best friends, Jan Gilbertson. Jan is the 'go to' girl of Quest and the first person I dared to show the initial draft. She hated it and told me to rewrite it as myself, and I hope I've succeeded in that. I'm also grateful that she was prepared to stop smiling long enough to be the model for my client Helen, who you'll meet in Part Two.

Next is my cosmic sister, Sue Knight. As an ex-lawyer she makes an unlikely mind-match for an ex-cop, but there it is, and I love her. It's thanks to her that it's not a morass of disconnected facts, that you won't find a single joke about George Bush or the French within these pages, or a cluster bomb of semi colons, for which I had developed a particular liking.

My test-readers gave me the confidence to believe I was on the right track, and helped me enormously with the polishing process. Den Laithwaite and Tracy Garnham, known to the world as Manbearpig and Tiny Troll, are wonderful friends and great people with whom we look forward to sharing many more adventures. And Peter Barker, an ex-student who is a more recent friend who shares my love of guitar music, but actually had the discipline to learn how to play superbly. He is also the person who did most to come up with the title. All of them are therapists I hope the world will hear more of.

Ruth Ascroft is another ex-student who has the punctilious kind of nature that made her the perfect editor. Her patience in correcting my English was amazing. Not once did she succumb to the rude acronyms that Sue peppered my manuscript with as she extracted the meaning from a sentence that I'd failed to.

I had the good fortune to make a friend called Marcus Stevenson many years ago. His graphic talents have graced our website from the beginning, but even he will admit that he is eclipsed by the genius of his wife Lisa. I have lost count of the number of rough ideas or vague hopes I have sent her, only to have her send me an image a short time later that far exceeded the poor scope of my imagination. In fact, sometimes it feels like she's mocking me. I asked her to make this book beautiful, and I hope you agree that she completely answered my brief.

The team at Matador have provided a seamless transition from manuscript to published book. It's been a pleasure to join their stable and benefit from their guidance through the transition from manuscript to a real, living, breathing, book.

And finally, if you're still here, a few moments of appreciation that is closer to home. I'll start with my brother Peter, for sparking the Bruce Lee idea you'll be reading about later. And no, that doesn't mean you should have been on the cover. My two sons Mark and Stuart continue to bring joy and fun into my life and it's a source of wonder as I see them develop into the men they are; I'm hugely proud of you. Mark recently married Tara, which has brought that sense of a family stretching out into the future that just makes me feel my genes relax a little. You're very welcome to the family.

My wife Rebecca deserves to be mentioned on every page. At times this book has been a self-absorbing and selfish venture and I know there have been moments when her fingers have twitched when it's been near a source of fire. Yet, despite the challenges this brought to our relationship, she was the only one I went to with my doubts, and what she unfailingly gave always sustained me. Her love, patience, acceptance and understanding have been the oasis within which my life and work has blossomed. Being beautiful too is such a bonus. I love you very much.

And finally, finally, our daemon, Barney, who pretends to be a Yorkshire Terrier. This is probably the last book he'll be around to sleep next to me through. Without his frequent interruptions I would have finished the book a year sooner, but with much less laughter.

This book has had several titles in the four years it's taken to write, and been called many names that would ban it from the shelves of most bookshops. And yet, as with so many things, the right title should have been obvious from the beginning, not emerge bashfully after the first edit. Obvious because the two questions it asks have been central to my teaching of Cognitive Hypnotherapy for at least the time I've been writing, and the 'What's that about?' is the question that is in my head as I listen to clients describe the many and varied ways their lives are inhibited by an undesirable behaviour, whether it's anxiety attacks, phobias, overeating, smoking, depression, anorexia, PTSD or addiction. I believe that all behaviour has a positive purpose, it's just that the inhibiting variety is based on either a cognitive misunderstanding or mistake at an earlier moment of a person's life, or their brain's inability to come to terms with an experience that could occur at any stage.

The solution lies within the problem

By looking for the motivation behind a client's problem, using the tools this book provides, you will find a unique individual world which contains everything you need to help your client create a remedy. The solution lies within the problem, and the pattern of thought that comprises the problem is different for each and every client, even if they share the same label for it. Which leads to the second question, 'How do I use it?'

I was a police officer for 18 years, largely owing to a range of limiting beliefs about what else I could achieve and no clue as to what I might want to do instead. I count myself the most fortunate of men because, largely by luck, I found my calling. Discovering the act of helping people that we variously call counselling, therapy or coaching has improved the lives of many of my clients, but none more than mine. Through my clients I found that Houdini was right when he said that limits are illusions, and I have gone on to realise that so is everything else. Within this book I explore the system that creates our illusions and describe a model that looks at our self-imposed limitations and answers the first question of the title, 'What's that about?' I then go on to explore the best techniques I've found to release us from those limits by using the mental apparatus that creates them - hence the second question, 'How do I use it?' What emerges is a framework that guides the application of what you're using to resolve a problem through an understanding of what the problem is about for that client. The flow that emerges between the answers to both questions is the subject of this book, Cognitive Hypnotherapy.

Cognitive Hypnotherapy is a way of thinking about helping people that has evolved from my falling in love with what I do for a living, and the sheer wonder at how people can transform themselves. Helping people live better lives helps you do the same, and I hope that reading this book provides a catalyst for those who feel there is more inside of them to give.

This is truly an exciting time to be involved in therapy, and I feel blessed to be working in the field at this point in time. Neuroscience is exploding with discoveries and new ideas about how the brain works, and I think great attention should be paid to how these discoveries can be utilised to help people. Neuroscience is involving itself in therapy, so we need to involve ourselves in neuroscience.

Merel Kindt at the University of Amsterdam has demonstrated that injecting patients with a beta-blocker, propanolol, while they are accessing a disturbing memory takes away the negative emotion that memory evokes[1]. They are using the principle of reconsolidation I describe in this book, which I'm going to show you lies at the heart of any work we do with memory, but they are using drugs instead of words. As you will hear me pointing out later, it's not an either/or universe, there is room and need for both. We have a part to play here - we just have to make ourselves more credible to the scientists.

We need to move therapy to an evidence-based procedure where we can see more clearly what interventions work, and which work best in particular situations. By doing so we refine our expertise, expand our range of options and consign to the bin anything that doesn't work. By scientifically testing our art we can bridge the gap that so often exists between our field and science and keeps us limited by the 'alternative' label it brings. We are no such thing. We are truly complementary, but the onus of proof is on us.

If we can't evidence the efficacy of our practice we run the risk of therapy becoming a historical footnote, as the drugs companies turn personal development into a chemistry lesson: *Want to be cleverer? Take this pill. More confidence? That'll be the little blue one.* That, for me, cannot be the best route for our personal evolution. For most people, everything we need is already within us and I work for the day when the practice of therapy will sit comfortably within a culture of individual responsibility, where everyone is taught the tools of self-help and encouraged to use them on a daily basis, and where we, as therapists, become a resource for when life's waves get too choppy, or when a guide is needed to help someone discover their own strength. Everyone would benefit from therapy at some time in their life, but most don't need much, or often. The assistance of pharmacology will always be available, but if we become more skilled drivers of our own neurology it will be needed far less often.

Therapy is about people and belongs to everyone

At times, it seems to me that the institutions of therapy and counselling are becoming focused more on the protection of the helper than helping the want-to-be-helped. They're becoming, like most bureaucracies, organisations that operate for their own continuance, rather than what and who it was set up to serve, leaving within its ranks a lot of talented and frustrated people, dedicated to helping, but kept in a straightjacket of orthodoxy. I hope many of them will read this book. Therapy is about people and belongs to everyone. It shouldn't be the preserve of an academic elite, or a group who see helpers and helped as separate entities. Life can be hard, and at times we're all fellow strugglers, and that should unite helper and helped in a search for a better way of being in the world, within an authentic relationship of mutual respect and exploration.

Therapy should be a unified field bound by a communal curiosity about what can make us more skilled at being human. That's what I want Cognitive Hypnotherapy to be about; permanent revolution driven by curiosity, united by uncertainty, and guided by evidence.

I hope this book inspires you to join our ranks.

The book's journey

In this book I propose a model to explain the mental processing that creates the illusion we call reality. This requires me to take you on a journey, and many of you will enjoy it more if you have some idea of the destination before we begin. So here is the itinerary...

In Part One I suggest that what we call memory is just part of a larger system that I call our *memoragination*. It comprises our remembered past, our perceived present, and our anticipated future. Both our present and future are built from information interpreted from our past experiences and stored as memory.

Our brain uses our memoragination to create a *reality tunnel*, a personal illusion of reality that guides our actions. These actions are geared towards the most efficient use of our resources in pursuit of the most rewarding goals.

To create the reality tunnel the brain has evolved a causal model of information processing that builds relationships between things that have been experienced in our past and given meaning, and things in our present. A match between past and present information causes the brain to construct the most likely consequence and uses it to guide our actions.

All of this is a function of our memoragination. It is usually updated by our experiences and so is necessarily plastic - any feature of our memoragination can be changed - and because our actions are a response to our reality tunnel, changing our memoragination can lead to new behaviours.

Our sense of self is a feature of our reality tunnel. It evolved from the advantage gained by the human brain being able to see its host (our body) in imagined futures in order to select the best actions to reach the most rewarding goal.

From this ability to project a 'self' into our memoragination - to see ourselves in our past and future, emerged the 'I', our sense of being someone separate to the rest of the universe. I'm going to suggest that this is just another illusion. We are an idea that thinks itself real.

My brain doesn't even know I exist: I'm just another source of environmental information that it responds to, and because I'm going to present evidence that our genes are activated by environmental signals, Cognitive Hypnotherapy is a model that contains the possibility of change from the level of our sense of self, all the way down to our cells. It describes a way for mind to influence matter, a true mind/body connection.

We and the World are an illusion we can create ourselves

This model is important for therapists because it shows that our sense of self emerges from our reality tunnel, which is based on interpretations our brain makes of past and present events. If you change the sense of self, you change the reality tunnel; if you change the reality tunnel you re-create the self. The causal model I call *the algorithms of the mind* (TAOTM) is proposed as the means by which these interpretations are made, so they are the means by which the techniques in this book create this level of transformation. We and the world are an illusion we can create ourselves.

Some of you will like to read about science, or need to have reasons behind what you do. Part One is aimed at you. Others either don't like science, or don't need much of a rationale behind what you do, you accept it as long as it's effective. I've designed the book with the intention of satisfying both types. Having read this far you could go straight to Part Two and still get a great deal from the book without reading further about the theoretical underpinning, although you will need to use the glossary at the back on occasion. If you'd like a little more, but not too much, you could just read the sections at the beginning and end of each chapter of Part One headed 'What's this about?' and 'How can I use it?' to get a more detailed synopsis of the overall theme. It's down to you, and I won't be in the least offended; but for the fact that she loves me, my wife would never have read Part One, and she still manages to be a great therapist.

In Part Two I show you techniques that can create transformation, and a framework to guide your use of them. My intention is that, taken together, parts one and two of the book create a fusion of theory, philosophy and practice that provides a coherent model that can capture the best therapy practice that emerges, guided by the best available science.

I am going to argue my case with passion, but no certainty. I was strongly influenced by a saying of Paul Saffo, head of Palo Alto's Institute for the Future, which is, "have strong opinions, weakly held."[2]

In this book I suggest that the brain seeks certainty, and that much of the workings of the brain are dedicated to finding it with the greatest degree of accuracy possible. The attraction of certainty for us is stronger than gravity and has been the cause of more strife in the world than anything else. The certainty that my religion is the true one, that my politics is the best course to take, or that what I am doing is justified, has been the starting position for most people who've led others to war. As Bertrand Russell once said, "The trouble with the world is that the stupid are cocksure and the intelligent are full of doubt."[3]

Perhaps the most difficult thing I ask of my students is to remain unsure. Cognitive

Hypnotherapy requires a tolerance for uncertainty, as I think does success in life, and I know my asking you to have the courage of a lack of conviction is counter-intuitive, but I hope you will see its value by the end of the book.

In Susan Jeffers book *Embracing Uncertainty* she tells how in India the Jains have a word that means "to the best of my knowledge at this time." The word is Syat[4]. I've done my best throughout this book to avoid presenting something as if it's true. Nothing in this book is; hopefully it's just useful. In one hundred years time the most I hope for this book is that it provided a stepping stone to where therapists of the future have got to. So please put Syat at the end of any sentence where you feel I've been too certain, because nothing I am about to tell you is true.

Permanent revolution requires uncertainty to drive it, where any model is open to adaptation or be superseded the minute something else is shown to work better. The only way for practitioners to avoid being part of yet another therapy dogma is for them to embrace uncertainty as a position of strength, not of weakness.

With that in mind, I very much hope you enjoy the trip.

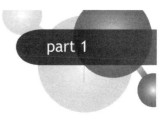

part 1

The Science of Ourselves:
A Strong Theory, Weakly Held

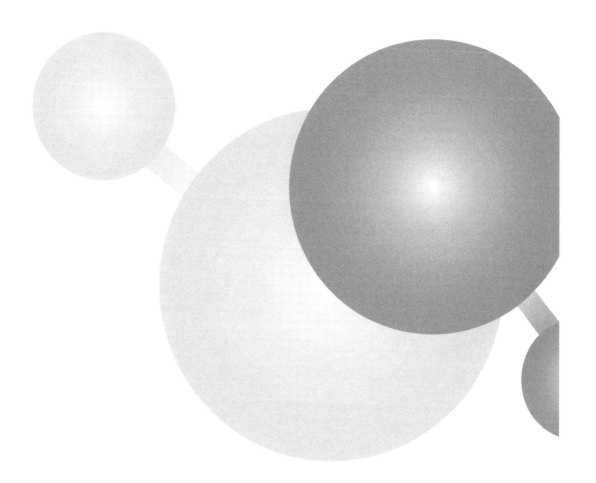

It's just my memoragination

What's This About?

In this chapter I'm going to build a case that our memory exists, not just as a reservoir of things to blame our parents for, or to warm our twilight years with fond remembrances, but as a dynamic pool of interpretations and meanings that are used as building blocks from which our brains build a version of a relevant present, and most likely future.

What I'm suggesting here is that we need to broaden the meaning of memory to encompass a mental system that, at a conscious level, creates a version of the present moment and a version of ourselves intended to best survive that moment, and, at an unconscious (or less-conscious) level, exists in an interpreted past and a multitude of predicted futures all at the same time.

You are living in a tunnel you call reality that is actually an illusion created by your brain to guide your actions. And each of us has a different tunnel.

The Hellmouth of Old London Town

My wife and I run a certification course at Regent's College in London most weekends. The college is one of those marvellous surprises that can be found in all great cities. By some accident of history it sits in the middle of Regent's Park itself, and at the end of a day teaching, it is one of our great pleasures to walk through the park to the place where we stay just off Baker Street. You can guarantee being mugged by portly squirrels, ignored by snotty cranes, and entranced by half a dozen other contacts with nature in the heart of a big city.

One evening in winter we left the college a little late and decided to risk getting locked in. The gates shut at dusk, and the light was rapidly fading. As we neared the bridge that crosses the stream I suddenly became aware of a strange creature emerging from the gloom. It was about eight feet away from us and was moving with a weird kind of random scuttling motion. It was whitish in colour and strangely disturbing in the ambiguity of its shape. And it definitely seemed to be heading for us. I couldn't believe that my wife hadn't noticed it, but she was striding towards it quite blithely.

It paused, I was pretty sure preparing itself to attack, and I couldn't resist blurting, "What is that?" and pointing at this devil-crab which had obviously recently emerged from a Hellmouth and was needing to feed on fresh souls. I was quite proud how steady I kept my voice, but what can I tell you, I'm pretty brave.

Rebecca gave me a look she saves for certain special occasions and said, "It's a plastic bag", and in a moment of shrinking manhood I recognised the obviousness of that simple fact. It was a carrier bag being wafted by the breeze.

This chapter of the book is about that bag, and all the other illusions that haunt our, and our clients', lives. Because the question occurred to me as I walked past the house of Sherlock Holmes, how much of what I'm seeing around me, how much of what I'm trusting is there, and how much of what bothers me, is actually what my brain is making it, and not how it really is? And the answer I currently believe is - all of it. To us the world is not as it really is, it's what our brain makes it appear to be. So we're the root of our problems, and our solutions.

The survival calculator

All organisms that move are faced with issues of choice. Every action, or inaction, has a consequence to it, so evolution has invested heavily in an exquisite mechanism of prediction, and it's called the human brain. A great deal of its 3lb weight is engaged in evaluating present information and making decisions that guide its – and hence our – next actions. Every choice our brain makes potentially has a consequence that makes survival more or less likely, and survival – known as the *biological imperative* – is the key concern that drives us.

We can think of our brain as a survival calculator, and the best on the market so far. It has no need to 'know' reality' because there's too much of it. If we had time to fully process all the information present in a single moment we'd be dead before our brain had finished – certainly from old age, but more probably at the claws of a predator who sneaked up on us while we were still licking the end of our pencil. In the main this is what evolution has shaped our brains to contend with: physical threats to our survival. For most of *homo sapien's existence* life has been what Thomas Hobbes said it was, "solitary, poor, nasty, brutish and short"[5]. From the beginning of life the overwhelming experience of every creature has been that the survivors survive, but life is desperate. Resources are limited, uncertain and competed for.

> *Every brain on this planet is a survival calculator*

Resources are limited *and* we run on batteries, so the basic imperative that drives us is, in the words of computational neuroscientist Read Montague, "Recharge or die."[6] In his opinion every creature has to answer a big question: "what is the value of my available choices, and what does each cost?" OK, that's two questions, but you can see what he means: what will what I do bring me, and what will the cost to my energy be? Choosing is not optional, because even not choosing to do anything is a choice that will lead to an outcome. Every brain on this planet is a survival calculator and has evolved, along with the body it's housed in, as its own response to those questions. In the arms race of survival, species have evolved with ever more complex equipment with which to calculate their choices. And the human brain has made us the current super-power.

Building our calculator

Every generation has tended to describe the workings of our body and brain according to the technology that existed at the time. In the 18th century it was clockwork mechanisms, while Freud's seething unconscious full of repressed energy and venting devices emerged from the age of steam. Currently, computers provide a popular analogy for brain function, and it seems to me that if we're precise about what we mean by the word 'computer', then it's still the best available. To be precise, by computer I mean a device that manipulates data according to a set of instructions. By that definition, a computer can be made of any material, including grey matter, which makes our computer something very special. It is estimated that within its small mass are somewhere in the region of 50-100 billion neurons, connected to each other via approximately 100 trillion synaptic connections and about 160,000 kilometres of myelinated axons.

There is nothing more complex in structure in the known universe, and I don't think many would dispute that most of what it keeps itself busy with is processing and organising information. It consumes about a third of our calories every day, and to be worth such a drain on our batteries this activity must confer a significant advantage to us – and one that only we appear to have. So if our brain is busy computing, what is the data it manipulates, and what is the set of instructions it follows that enables it to survive on this particular planet?

The starting point for the data is the information that surrounds each brain – the world. Over millions of years our brain and body have evolved instruments that harvest that information – our five senses. These evolved not to observe reality, but to filter

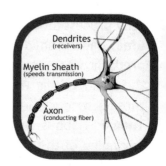

Dendrites (receivers)

Myelin Sheath (speeds transmission)

Axon (conducting fiber)

When I was at school we always seemed to have a flower bulb growing on a windowsill in a clear pot that allowed a view of the roots as they grew.

A brain cell looks a little like this, a bulb-like middle with a single long shoot at one end and lots of thinner root-like fibres extending from the other. These 'roots' are called dendrites and bring electrochemical impulses from other brain cells. The 'shoot' is an axon and is the cell's only channel to the rest of the brain. Axons can be anything from a fraction of a millimetre to 2 metres long. When a cell is coaxed into 'firing', sending a signal up its axon, it does so as a distinct pulse that lasts about 1/1000th of a second and travels at a speed of anything from 2 and 200 miles per hour. They are sheathed in a substance called myelin. Without this sheath the message cannot be passed.

Having travelled up the axon the pulse reaches a dendrite of another brain cell. This point of contact is the synapse, where chemicals called neurotransmitters ferry the impulse across the gap between axon and dendrite.

This reaction continues, a chain reaction involving hundreds, thousands or even millions of cells across the three dimensional matrix. At this very moment reading these words is causing just such a cascade. In order to understand these words patterns of neurons fire in recognition.

Learning is about the simultaneous firing of patterns, where new experiences are added to patterns that already exist.

it. Aggressively. It is estimated that our senses process between two and eleven million bits of information at every moment.[7] The overwhelming majority is discarded, left at the periphery of attention, leaving only, according to George Miller[8], between five and nine bits to be attended to fully. Our brain is a reducing valve and our senses are the first level of filtering.

We're hardwired to 'care' about things that have proved beneficial to care about, like food, sex and power, and to pursue them in the most efficient way

What is the basis of the choices that are made? How does the brain decide what is worth paying attention to and what isn't? Read Montague suggests that our choices about what to pay attention to are guided by goals we've evolved to pursue and a reward system that minimises the drain on our batteries. We're hardwired to 'care' about things that have proved beneficial to care about, like food, sex and power, and to pursue them in the most efficient way.[9]

If it's not relevant it's not relevant

The basis of how we choose what we pay attention to is *relevance*. The highest goal that our brain pursues is survival and from that emerges a stream of sub-goals that each person's brain deems relevant to that goal, based on their interpretation of what happens to them in their life.

These sub-goals are guidance mechanisms whose relevance will depend on current opportunities, contexts and needs. In the spirit of Freud's Pleasure Principle, some guide us towards certain actions and situations that are deemed rewarding, and some guide us away from others that are held to be painful. Each person's set of sub-goals are unique to them, which means that one person's reward can be another person's pain.

Universal sub-goals with which I suggest we all come pre-equipped are food, sex and power. These three have proven themselves so strongly relevant to our survival that their genes have been selected for, but the way each person pursues them is unique to them in many ways, based on the experiences they have in connection to them. One person's pursuit of the goal of sex can lead to a life of promiscuity, while another's could be a life of self-created abstinence. The pursuit of power could lead to a Hitler or a hermit. Each drive contains within it the possibility of such polarised responses simply because of the way the brain works. If you imagine two boats leaving New York on a parallel course, each pursuing the same goal of taking their cargo to London, and then you nudge one of them off course by a tiny margin, they'll appear to share the same journey for many miles. But come back to them a few days later and they'll be miles apart, and weeks later hundreds of miles apart. So it is with our experiences; I'm going to show how something called the Butterfly Effect means that every event deemed relevant to your survival is a potential 'nudge' that will move you further and further along a life course that is experienced by you alone, and with a destination that couldn't be anticipated at its outset.

Reality is just an idea

The connection each individual brain makes between its present environment and its unique collection of goals and sub-goals, determines which goals will become active, and what behaviours are generated in a goal's service in each situation.

For that to happen, for the brain to determine what presently around you is relevant to its goals, it has to give things meaning. I believe this is at the heart of why we haven't evolved to be aware of reality: most of it doesn't help us choose 'what next?', so it's a waste of energy to process a perception of it.

80% of the information you respond to from your environment comes from within you

Perception is the means by which we attain awareness or understanding of sensory information. Some people can speak comfortably in front of a group that someone scared of public speaking would run away from. Some of you *are* those scared people. If people respond differently to the same information, then it's not what's in front of them that's causing the problem. And that's

Meteorologist Edward Lorenz first noticed that in complex systems, such as the earth's weather, small changes can have major effects. It's officially called 'sensitivity to initial conditions', but the simple explanation that a butterfly flapping its wings in the Amazon can lead to a storm in Australia three months later led to its popular title.

because it's not - in front of them, I mean. 80% of the information you respond to from your environment comes from within you.[10] The audience in front of me when I speak isn't solely the physical audience made up of flesh and blood, it's predominantly an idea I have about them. I'm seeing an idea I call an audience, made up of ideas I have about people in that context – detailed ideas if I know them, vaguer ideas if I don't - which lead to an idea I have about the meaning I give to the moment I'm having with them. And the strings of ideas *you* have in that situation are likely to be very different to mine. Our past experiences are the greatest influencer of these ideas and perceptions. In fact, when we are faced with something outside the scope of our experience bizarre things can occur: In 1797, when a haberdasher called John Hetherington donned a new item of apparel for a stroll down The Strand it led to him being charged with a breach of the peace and incitement to riot. Women had fainted, dogs barked and a child was knocked over by the crowd. His new creation was a 'tall structure having a shiny lustre, and calculated to frighten timid people'. Any guesses? It was a top hat.[11] I wonder what it would take now to cause such a stir? And legend has it that when Columbus first landed in the Indies the natives were unable to see his ships, so far from their map of reality were they.

What I'm saying is that the world we're surrounded by is an interpretation invented by our survival calculator. The data being processed is a mixture of 20% of information from our senses and 80% of existing information (our memories) provided by our brain. The means by which the brain matches the 20% to the 80% is a set of simple instructions I call the algorithms of the mind (TAOTM, which we cover in detail later) and our reality tunnel emerges from this process. Everything we perceive in our world is an idea we have about it, and that idea contains meanings we hold for it and even actions we plan for it. Nothing in our world is allowed to be devoid of meaning, and any meaning is a product of our life-to-date. Forget reality, forget the truth of things. You're living in a hologram of your brain's devising which is made up of its ideas about the world, ideas the brain feels help it navigate the future most beneficially. Often it gets it right, but sometimes it gets it spectacularly wrong.

> *You're living in a hologram of your brain's devising which is made up of its ideas about the world*

So, when I saw the plastic bag in the park my brain tried to match it to previous experiences I'd had. Clearly none matched precisely enough to identify it as accurately as Rebecca did (I wasn't wearing my contact lenses, alright?), but clearly it resembled something (probably from an episode of Buffy the Vampire Slayer) enough to get the feeling of a need to do something about it. The brain hates uncertainty, so it settled on the idea of the bag as a creature to be ready to fight or run from. Which is particularly embarrassing, in retrospect, because it wasn't even one of those tough 'bags for life'.

The nature of memoragination

Our ability to casually recall our past is one of the abilities that we take most for granted. But, really, what's the point of that? Why would evolution invest in the facility of memory? The latest research suggests that it forms an intrinsic part of how we create our perceptions. Our past is what we build our present and future out of.

We tend to think of our memories and our thoughts about the future as being different, but fMRI scans show that the brain thinks otherwise. Karen McDermott, of Washington University in St Louis Missouri, asked subjects to either recall or imagine a future common event – such as a birthday party. It was expected that past and future thoughts would create different patterns of brain activity but, in fact, both tasks produced very similar patterns. The conclusion from this, and other studies, is that there is no specialised brain module dedicated to episodic memory, but that it is part of a more general module which handles both past and future[12], a mental network dedicated to time travel that doesn't compartmentalise past and future in the way we think of them - as separate parts of our experience - but as parts of an interconnected and interdependent system. I've called it our *memoragination*.

It's probably true to say that since 1848, when Phineas Gage survived a steel spike being driven through his skull, neuroscience has depended for many of its insights about the biological basis of personality from the study of individuals suffering from various debilitating conditions. A subject known by the initials K.C. is one of them. For more than 20 years he has been studied by Endel Tulving of the University of Toronto in Canada. K.C. is able to recount facts, but he has no recollection of his personal past. Something else has also been noted by Tulving, K.C. can't conceive a personal future.

Other researchers have found links between past and future thoughts. A man who lost his episodic memory after suffering from oxygen starvation couldn't remember a single day at work, although he could say what he did for a living and where he did it. Interestingly, while he could conceptualise about the future in general, he couldn't imagine anything about his own.[13]

Other studies show that deeply depressed people experience a reduction in their ability to recall their personal past, and an equivalent reduction in their ability to imagine a future with them in it.[14]

All this seems to point toward a relationship between our personal episodic memory and our ability to imagine our future, but why? How does data from our past connecting to data we imagine about our future guide our choices about what to do next?

Well, to know what to do next, we need to be able to assess consequences. When my son Stuart was a toddler he was what you might call a spirited child, and as he prepared to do something I'd forbidden I would say, "If you do that I'll…" (add your own punishment). I could see his little cogs turning and, as often as not he'd continue with his action, and then come back to me for his punishment. Obviously he'd decided the juice was worth the squeeze. Clearly I had helped with his calculations for the future, by providing him with a clear consequence, but just as clearly he must have been able to imagine the fun he was going to have up until I turned into the angel of justice. By balancing the two together he made a decision.

Imagining outcomes "permits our hypotheses to die in our stead."

To assess consequences we need to be able to run what are often described as *counterfactual futures*: simulations of possible future choices, and from that we come to a decision. As Sir Karl Popper once said, imagining outcomes "permits our hypotheses to die in our stead."[15]

But from what can we weave such futures? Without being able to reference our past it would be impossible – well, not impossible; we could imagine a future without using the past, but how accurate could it be? If I use nothing from my past as reference experiences my brain might imagine a chair made from ice cream to assess whether to stand or sit. I guess Stuart used past experiences of the crushing nature of my wrath to run simulations of the likely consequences of defying me, and decided they weren't so bad.

So, here's the great advantage in being able to remember the past. Our memory is a storage facility for ideas we use to decipher the way the world works that we then use to create a tunnel to walk through. The richer our store of ideas from our past the more material we have to weave our possible futures, the more possible choices we can compute, and the more accurate our final choice is likely to be. "In many ways intelligence is really a measure of our capacity for prediction," says Steven Johnson.[16]

Evidence to support this use of memory comes from an experiment conducted at University College London by a team led by Eleanor Maguire. They took five patients who suffered from amnesia as a result of brain damage and asked them to imagine a future event in detail, such as meeting a friend. Compared to control subjects their scenarios were much less detailed and more fragmented[17]. Added to this is the fact that children start to begin to be able to talk about the past and the future at the same time – about 4 years old - and that as people age they're less able to remember their past with such clarity, and become sketchier about their future. There seems to be an indisputable link between our ability to access the past *and* project the future.

This makes evolutionary sense of memory, as a resource that enables us to plan and assess choices. It also explains the way memory works.

Things aren't ever what they used to be

For many years it was thought that the brain was like a video recorder, laying down memory tracks in a concrete, unchangeable way. We now know this isn't so. Memory is malleable – Ernest Rossi asserted in the '70's that you can't access a memory without changing it because your present perspective influences the emotional colouring of the event in mind[18] – and it seems he was right. Memory is not a flawless replay, it's largely constructive, i.e. in large measure we make up what happened to us. As Steven Johnson puts it; "In a sense, when we remember something, we create a new memory, one shaped by the changes that have happened to our brain since the memory last occurred to us."[19] But you already knew that. How many times, when you reminisce with your family, do you all have a different recollection of the same event? As a police officer, I was very aware of differences in recall from honest witnesses – and the fact that by asking, "How tall was the mugger?" instead of, "What was the height of the mugger?" I would increase the height of the mugger in their memory.

Joseph LeDoux has proven that every time we recall a memory it renders it 'unstable', in the sense that it can be changed, so the mood we're in when we remember something could affect the way we recall it the next time.[20] This, for me as a therapist, is very important. If memory exists to guide our choices and help us choose our goals, then it makes sense that it would be more effective if it could be updated in response to current experiences, otherwise we'd still be trying to interpret the world using information unchanged from our childhood. However, in cases of strong emotional events, childhood information can become so powerfully imprinted that it remains a source of comparison with present events. In psychology this is known as 'accessibility', and in the words of psychologist Timothy Wilson, a "determinant of accessibility is how often a concept has been used in the past. People are creatures of habit, and the more they have used a particular way of judging the world in the past, the more energised that concept will be. Our non-conscious minds develop chronic ways of interpreting information from our environments."[21]

This can have both positive and negative effects. Imagine that, as a child, you have a series of positive experiences and are supported within a loving, non-critical environment. This is likely to lead to you developing as a confident and outgoing person. Future scenarios based on past experience involving strong emotional examples of being loved are likely to be similarly positive and optimistic, and you'll feel motivated to put effort into creating them in your life (in that respect Freud was bang on with his *pleasure principle*: we move towards things we perceive as rewarding, and freeze or move away from things we perceive as punishing or painful). What we have here is a situation where the world we live in becomes the one we anticipated and we become the kind of person who lives in such a world. And as that person, we influence and change our memory of the past whenever we look back, which in turn influences our future, which then influences the person we need to be to fit into that world. Our memories, past and future, create a feedback loop that creates...us.

> *The world we live in becomes the one we anticipated and we become the kind of person who lives in such a world*

Because now instead imagine a child who grows up in a critical environment and has some strongly negative experiences. These will also be used to anticipate future events, which are likely to be imagined as having a negative outcome; so this child still has choices, but the choice they select will still only be the best of the bad possibilities. Invoking Freud's pleasure principle again, the motivation to move towards something unpleasant, or even just bland, is pretty low, and may often actually become an active movement *away* from the future – which may be a reason for depression, ME and anxiety disorders; an unconscious attempt to keep away from the bleak future choices the mind is imagining. The same feedback loop applies; they become the person who fits into this version of the world, and they change their memories of the past by looking at them through the eyes of the person they've become.

The older we get, the happier or sadder our childhoods are likely to be remembered, depending on the balance our personality has between the two extremes described above. After all, for most of us life has been a mixture of positive and negative events and influences, so we'll tend to be a mixture of both. Different situations we experience will be responded to according to the similarities our brain finds between the situation and other events from our past, and these contextual 'loops' continue to build as the years go by, so that we become more and more habitual in the behaviour we exhibit in particular situations. In that regard, who we feel we are can be the result of which environment we inhabit most often.

What this means is that, while it feels as if we live in *now*, actually now is only a part of the equation the brain is working from. The brain lives in an environment it creates from information taken from the remembered past, the experienced present and the anticipated future. It's hard to grasp the intricacy and extent of this. The metaphorical graphic of a memory loop may help:

Down the rabbit hole

Imagine that this feedback loop is hollow and you are inside it at the point of now. From what we've learnt so far, this tunnel you are in is your present reality, but it is created from an interpretation of information flowing through your senses, and the basis for that interpretation is its matching to meanings given to past events by your brain. Every moment your brain matches incoming data from your senses with data already experienced and given meaning. As a consequence of this matching, a percept (a moment of perception) is created: a multisensory projection that surrounds you, in every sense, and which we call reality, but which is really just the sum of our ideas about what's present. We live in a reality tunnel, built from the bricks of our past, and given direction by the beckoning mirage of the imagined future selected as the most likely outcome of this matching of past and present.

Now - and this is the truly amazing bit - I've described that reality tunnel in a single, momentary slice of its existence, but each succeeding moment requires an adjustment according to the changing information being matched. While life seems to be a video, actually it's thirteen snapshots per second that somehow our brain stitches together to create a faultless stream of reality.[22] Rarely do we suffer the tunnel wall dissolving into computer code in the way that Neo experienced it in the film The Matrix, but it's there.

> *As our reality tunnel shifts moment-to-moment, so potentially does our behaviour*

As our reality tunnel shifts moment-to-moment, so potentially does our behaviour – the person we need to be in that reality. In the vast majority of cases this transition of 'selfs' is seamless too, because most situations are similar enough for the 'person' to feel they're the same. However, if a situation flips rapidly, or something is thrown into the mix, some new piece of data which is evaluated as being similar to something with a strong emotional charge, then the shift in our reality tunnel can be so great that we become a noticeably different person within it.

For example, John is a sensible, intelligent man in his thirties. He's walking down the street, thinking of nothing much, while his brain, in the background, is busy deciding on the meaning of everything passing through his idling senses: other people, a pigeon, a bus, the smell of bread coming from a baker's, the feeling of one of his new shoes pinching a bit. All familiar, mundane and undistracting – well the girl walking towards him is a bit distracting, that's quite a skirt she's wearing. But what's that by her ankle? Instantly John is transformed from the suave, man-about-town about to give the girl a cheeky wink. His eyes focus exclusively on the Chihuahua walking beside the girl, his breathing increases rapidly, a light sheen of sweat covers his forehead and a feeling of terror grips his chest like a vice. Bruiser the Chihuahua is an example of a stimulus that leads to an avoidance behaviour (remember the moving away from pain or its anticipation that Freud called the *pleasure principle*?).

In a blind panic John dashes from the street into the nearest shop. The ladies in the shop selling underwear for the larger lady are surprised to see him, but welcoming. What the hell happened? How did suave John become weird John? A grown man running from a Chihuahua? Simple. John's brain found a match between the data that

> *Our present is just a rehashed mix of bits from our personal history*

equalled the dog with data from a memory of him aged five when he was bitten by a Poodle. The metaphorical bricks from that memory are hurled into John's reality tunnel to recreate the Poodle (from the perspective of a frightened five-year-old) in place of the Chihuahua. Nobel prize winner Gerald Edelman describes the reality tunnel as "the remembered present"[23] – reflecting the fact that our present is just a rehashed mix of bits from our personal history.

Suddenly John's behaviour makes sense, doesn't it? His problem is that he isn't aware of the work that went into this response to little Bruiser; all he's consciously aware of is the dog and his fear. He doesn't know that his brain foresaw the consequence of Bruiser as being the pain of being bitten (or possibly death, to a five-year-old), and simplified his choices down to the flight option. No other reality existed than the one containing a danger to his life.

Of course afterwards, as he leaves the shop clutching a 52FF brassiere for his...er... mother, the input information is different, and the John who leaves the shop is living in a reality tunnel that now connects his behaviour with the dog (in the absence of Bruiser) to an embarrassing incident at a party when he was eight, and his brain foresees people laughing at him as he walks up the street. That reality creates the percept of a street where everyone is looking and laughing at him as he hurries away. He probably doesn't revert to the 'usual John' until some time afterwards. And the feedback built into the memory loop is likely to strengthen his fear next time around, as well as his belief that he's stupid for running from something so harmless.

We all become different people in different situations, some as markedly as John, some not. Have you noticed that you can be one version of yourself, say, with your family, and another alone with your partner, and yet another with your friends or at work? We like to think of ourselves as being stable; you know - 'take me as you find me', as if you're the same person whatever, but the truth is it's much more a case of 'take me *where* you find me'. We appear to become the self that seems to offer the best choice to us in any given moment, rather than the singular identity we feel ourselves to be.

Now, sometimes the choices this leads to can seem strange, even bizarre. How can running away from a small dog be the best choice available when nobody else is doing the same thing? You can tell from my example of John that I argue it's because some memory has caused the brain to anticipate a negative consequence from not running away. And I don't think it's much of a simplification to suggest that any behaviour you want to change, but find you can't, is for the same reason. Let's try a few common ones:

You want to stop smoking but always give in when you're with your mates, or bored, or upset, or stressed.

Physiological addiction apart, for many the key factor is an emotional attachment. In certain situations the brain foresees a certain negative outcome – usually related to self-image – and runs simulations of choices available to reduce the unpleasant emotion. The memory string that becomes active is the one that contains cigarettes as the corrective behaviour.

Think of that and substitute a person wanting to lose weight, and replace the cigarette with food; it's much the same.

The same pattern also fits behaviours in relationships – take jealousy. One partner is presented with a situation: let's suppose their other half comes home late from work and smells of alcohol. If the waiting partner has memories of past rejection, then the consequence of the partner's lateness is likely to be imagined as them having an affair, or not loving them, etc, and the person he or she is, in that situation, is likely to be very different from the person they appear to be in most other situations.

> *Our memoragination is made up of this system of memory loops, countless numbers of them, that interact moment-to-moment to create a reality tunnel which guides our responses*

What I'm proposing is that our memoragination is made up of this system of memory loops, countless numbers of them, that interact moment-to-moment to create a reality tunnel which guides our responses, and that the presence of a self forms part of the choice-making apparatus of the brain (I think it began as just another bit of the tunnel, but at some point became aware of itself. I'll return to that later).

Memory loops are not independent, operating in isolation; they are engaged in a constant exchange of information, much like Sherrington's description of the brain as an 'enchanted loom'[24], morphing in and out of existence in response to the brain's interpretation of its environment. Some loops will hardly ever be fired, others, ones that become key determinants of our personality, become a recurring theme in the loom's weave.

Gerald Edelman has a model that supports this idea in some of its aspects. He calls it *global brain theory*. Intriguingly his model utilises evidence from fMRI scans that an output from the brain – such as picking up a glass, or noticing the colour red, while utilising the same areas of the brain each time (visual cortex, motor cortex etc), recruit different arrangements of neurons to carry out the task. He attributes this to something he calls *re-entry*, the ability of the brain to not just create patterns of connections, but to create patterns from within those patterns by recruiting neurons from different loops to do the same task.[25] Perhaps this is why we can lose millions of brain cells each day, and yet not experience the sudden winking out of a memory; the memories aren't stored in any one cell, but stored as an idea within a vast network that is constantly changing its shape yet maintaining its purpose.

How can I use it?

What Edelman's idea suggests to me, is a situation where our memoragination is in a constant state of creation and re-creation, weaving patterns from past, present and future that become our awareness of the world and ourselves.

As therapists this gives us a focus, and in Part Two I show the different ways we can change our memoragination for the better. Reinterpreting our past can change what our brain makes of our present, and I show you how in Part 2.4 of that part of the book. Restructuring our past can achieve the same thing, and I describe techniques for that in Part 2.4. Changing our present perceptions and behaviours will cause a reappraisal of our past, and tools for that are in Parts 2.5 and 2.6, and imagining our future deliberately will shape our feelings and behaviours in the present, which will then ripple back to our beliefs about the past. That is the subject of Part 2.7. And because the sense we have of ourself is predominantly the product of our responses to our historical environment, changes in any and all of these areas of our memoragination can change our 'self'. We become the creators of our own chosen identity.

Therapy no longer needs to be seen as changing our client's reality, just their imaginations. Because reality is our imagination. Or, more precisely, our memoragination.

2

The bricks of the reality tunnel

What's this about?

The purpose of our memoragination seems to be to provide a means of calculating what is the most rewarding action for us to take, and the reality tunnel the means by which our brain guides those actions. Most of what we do day-to-day is a response to the situation we feel we're in.

The reality tunnel is an illusion, in that 80% of what we perceive around us is interpreted information drawn from our past. In this chapter, I label the mental phenomena the brain uses to create this illusion, and describe how these phenomena can be harnessed by us to create a better tunnel to guide us to what we choose to be the best reward.

It seems odd to talk of the world we're constantly interacting with as something we're mainly making up, doesn't it? The book you're holding is obviously what it is, it's real. But is there only one way of experiencing it? If an ant walks across the page, what is it experiencing as the book? How about if you had the eyes of a fly, what would you be looking at? If you look at the sky on a nice day it's a beautiful blue. Isn't it? Not if you're an owl, which is colour blind. And even with your eyes you're not seeing a sky that is blue, you're seeing the consequence of the different wavelengths of light from the sun being absorbed or reflected from the atoms that make up the atmosphere. The particular construction of our eyes interprets that activity and leaves us with the impression of blue – but philosophers have worked themselves into asylums trying to prove that your colour blue is the same colour I call blue. It can't be done – yet.

What we are aware of from the world comes through our five senses, and is limited by the capabilities of each sense. If we could hear like a bat, see like a hawk, and smell like a dog, our world would seem amazingly different, but no more or less real or true.

What information does get through, then gets processed and interpreted and the conclusion of that interpretation gets projected back out onto the world. The world around us is a perception, everything we see is a version of what it could be, as is everything we hear, smell etc, and our brain is the agent of the interpretation – it makes up your universe - what I've called your reality tunnel.

The reality tunnel is made up of perceptions from all of our five senses, distorted in particular ways to give the meaning that the brain thinks is most useful. In Cognitive Hypnotherapy we call these distortions trance phenomena. So I'd better start by talking about trance.

There's no such thing as hypnosis

For some time in the field of hypnosis there has been an argument that has come to be known as the 'altered state' debate. Debaters fall into two camps labelled *state* or *non-state*; i.e., is trance a special state that you're 'put into' or go into, or is it just part of the continuum of consciousness that is part of our everyday experience? The public largely go with the first camp because the media have more fun portraying it as such, so many clients come to therapy expecting to be 'put under', and fear losing control or being forced to blurt out intimate details. Stage hypnotists are particularly skilled at projecting this view of hypnosis, but many traditional hypnotherapists also talk of 'putting you into a trance'.

I was in this camp until I learned of the other one, through the writings of Steven Wolinsky. He did more than open my eyes to the everyday nature of trance, he made me realise that trance states are a natural part of many experiences – including the ones we think of as being problems.

"In my breakthrough moment, those puzzle pieces came together in an entirely new pattern: I saw that although trance states can be used to evoke resources and change at an unconscious level, they can also be – are used – to create the symptomology with which we all struggle. I saw that the person who brings his or her problems and symptoms to me is already in a trance state, and that it is this very trance state that is interrupting his or her experience of the present moment, blocking unconscious potentials and resources, and creating problems and symptoms."[26]

Does that sound like the reality tunnel to you? We're always in it, only its construction varies.

One of life's great illusions is that we're present in the here and now most of the time - it's just how it feels to us. However, research has shown that for up to 90% of the waking day we are not strictly conscious[27] – our attention is not in the moment, it's somewhere else, usually somewhere in the past or in one of the counterfactual futures we create. In the 'non-state' camp, those moments when your attention is elsewhere is a trance state. Think of when you're daydreaming about your next holiday during a meeting, wondering what's for dinner on the way home, or worrying on the train to work about the row you had with your partner last night: they're all examples of trance. In terms of your reality tunnel, your attention has shifted, from now to some place further along, or further back.

In most situations this is a perfectly normal part of our life - so normal that people don't even notice that most of the time they're physically present in the world, but mentally absent. Watch someone staring into space, deep in thought and oblivious to what is going on around them. It's a trance, dude! It led the wonderful Steven Heller to declare "There's no such thing as hypnosis." He went on:

"If we use hypnosis to imply any transaction and communication that causes an individual to go into their own experiences and call upon their own imagination in order to respond, we will have a map that will allow us to become aware of hypnotic transactions occurring around us. These transactions can be triggered by not only words, but also visual cues, tones, people and things."[28]

Now think back to the example of John, walking down the street quite happily until

Bruiser turned up. The pattern match between Bruiser and the dog that bit him in his childhood causes the reality tunnel to rapidly shift from 'normal world' to 'dangerous world'. In response to this 'different' environment, his brain shifts into survival mode and John loses the ability to control his actions. All he's aware of is the fear roaring around his body. His focus has narrowed to Bruiser, he's lost control of his actions and his body seems to be doing what the hell it wants. He's in a trance.

Wolinsky calls the 'self' that emerges at these moments, and runs our behaviour independent of our control, a *trance identity*.

> *Every occasion when we lose the sense of ourselves being an active agent – being responsible for what we are doing – is a trance*

In my model of trance, every occasion when we lose the sense of ourselves being an active agent – being responsible for what we are doing – is a trance. If you are trying to diet but can't stop that biscuit passing your lips, if you're trying to quit smoking but find yourself reaching for the offered cigarette when your head is shouting no, if you get ridiculously angry every time your partner does that thing you've told them not to do, if you get achingly sad and burst into tears when nobody else does, you're in a trance. It's not you, it's your trance identity. So, in a very real sense, Cognitive Hypnotherapy is often about waking the client out of a negative trance to allow them to retain control in the moment they 'should' be doing their problem, or helping them create a more pleasant tunnel to have a trance in.

The term 'trance phenomena' describes nine different ways we can describe the way our reality tunnel gets distorted in order to create a world within which we feel we need to act in a particular way. Please bear in mind that these nine terms are slices of a single phenomenon – which is our projected reality tunnel. Because of this the differences can sometimes appear blurry. They're useful labels, but no more than that.

Positive Hallucination

A positive hallucination is seeing something in a way that those around you may not. From what I've said earlier, you can see that we are all walking through a world that we see through the lens of this particular phenomenon. Seeing Bruiser as a scary dog is one example, someone standing in front of an audience and seeing a crowd of unfriendly people waiting to ridicule him or her is another. And thinking a plastic bag is a hell-creature is another...

At the banal end of the scale, it can account for differences in opinion over which film star you find more attractive than your friend does, what clothes look nicer, and what you see in modern art. Preferences of this kind are subjective and the end result of what you project onto what you're looking at, not what you're looking at itself. At the more extreme end of this phenomenon we can sometimes see things that aren't there at all. Stage hypnotists utilise this in highly suggestible subjects to get them to see the audience naked, for example. People seeing ghosts might be another.

> *Because reality is an illusion, we don't help clients to see the world as it 'really is', we help them create a nicer illusion.*

The word positive doesn't denote a quality – you can have good positive hallucinations, like sucking in your stomach in the gym mirror and seeing yourself as you were 20 years ago, or bad positive hallucinations, such as seeing the look of disapproval in the eyes of your boss, when actually they just have a hangover. Because reality is an illusion, we don't help clients to see the world as it 'really is', we help them to create a nicer illusion.

Imagine someone with a fear of speaking in public standing in front of a group of people and only seeing in their faces whatever it is that makes her comfortable enough to speak. Or a child scared of spiders seeing them looking small and frightened. Or someone with low confidence beginning to notice around them the things that make them realise their self-esteem is growing. By manipulating the walls of the reality tunnel this becomes possible. The effect of any successful technique is such a change in the fabric of our reality, and hypnotic suggestion is an approach that works directly through trance phenomena. I'm going to talk more about that at the end of this chapter.

Negative Hallucination

Ever lost your keys, turned the house upside down, and then found them in the place you looked originally? Attention is selective and our brain deletes most things that come through our senses; it's common for things that are actually useful to see to be ignored as well. Probably the most famous example that demonstrated this phenomenon was conducted by Daniel Simons and Christopher Chabris. They got subjects to look at a film of a group of people passing a basketball amongst each other. Half were dressed in white T-shirts and the other half black T-shirts. The observers were given the task of counting how many times the white T-shirts passed the ball to each other. Afterwards they were asked for the answer, which varied by two or three. They were then asked how many had noticed the gorilla? As you might expect, many were dumbfounded by the question. The film was replayed, and halfway through the game a person in a gorilla suit walked from right to left between the players, stopped and waved at the camera, and then walked off. Typically 50% of people don't see the gorilla.[29] It's called *inattentional blindness*, but the point is that the blindness is caused by the person's attention being on something else.

In survival situations, panic often makes people blind to the emergency exit, grieving people don't notice the smiles of support that surround them, and smokers don't see their children hold their breath when they hug them.

Imagine how useful it is for clients not to notice the cigarettes for sale in the service station, not to see the look their mother gives them that makes them feel useless, or the spider in the corner of the room. Utilising negative hallucination gives us the ability to take bricks out of a negative reality tunnel and replace them with something better.

Sensory Distortion

This phenomenon refers to any sense other than visual. It's exactly the same as positive and negative hallucinations, but it refers to information from the auditory, kinaesthetic, olfactory or gustatory senses. I coach a boxer who doesn't hear anything being shouted during a fight except his father's calls; somehow he manages to create a near-complete deletion of sound. This is the auditory sensory distortion version of a negative hallucination. On the other hand, I worked with a promising young golfer who used to fluff important putts. When I questioned him closely about what happened just before he hit the ball, he reported that he heard his father's voice saying "Don't f*** this up!" - a sound that isn't really there, just like a positive hallucination.

Like most other things, taste and smell are illusions in the sense that what we like or what causes us to wrinkle our noses is largely subjective - what did you like or avoid when you were a child that you now love or loathe? It's your interpretation of the taste that has changed, not the thing itself, so it's comparatively simple to change the taste of a cigarette (or piece of chocolate) into something that makes you want to vomit.

And finally our sense of feeling. If you're an experienced parachutist, then jumping out of an airplane probably induces a feeling of excitement in you. If we took a blood sample from you at that moment we'd be able to identify a cocktail of chemicals that you've labelled excitement. However, if you suddenly realised that the nagging feeling you'd forgotten something was right and that you'd left your parachute behind, the feeling would probably be better described as terror, but if we took another blood sample the chemistry would be nearly identical. Excitement and fear are near-identical states – it's the meaning we give them that provides the label. The reality tunnel of the parachutist with the parachute includes a future with a safe landing because the tunnel is built from the bricks of previous successful jumps, so it's safe to feel excited. Without a chute the future is built from an entirely different set of reference experiences which don't provide for a happy ending; cue the terror.

Trance phenomena operate to create our reality tunnel, and our body is part of that tunnel

You'll notice that I'm including distorted information that is both external – seeing things around you in a particular way, and internal – images in our imagination, or feelings within our body. Trance phenomena operate to create our reality tunnel, and our body is part of that tunnel (we may feel fat/ugly/unattractive when we look no such thing, for example) and thoughts about the past and future aspects of the tunnel obviously have to happen in our imagination, so we experience both internal and external trance phenomena.

If you think about the implications of the feelings we get from our body being hallucinations too, it means that we can choose any feeling we want to have in any situation we want it, and we can guide our clients' perceptions to 'feel' whatever is more useful to change their problem. A client wanting to lose weight could feel full sooner than they anticipated, someone with anorexia could feel more comfortable about the food in their stomach. Someone else could hear a reassuring voice in their ear before they play their stroke.

Time Distortion

Time is another aspect of our life that we take for granted. Time feels like it passes, although quantum physicists will tell you otherwise. Someone once said that time was invented to stop everything happening at once, and certainly we feel as if we are living in a stream of time that takes us from cradle to grave. Our many time-pieces

> *Who says that the time we carry on our wrist is any more true than our invidiual sense of it?*

and calendars also give us the sense of a regularity to its passing. But that disappears the minute we actually examine it. Remember as a child how quickly the school holidays passed? Notice how it feels the opposite now you're a parent? Remember how long it took to get to something you were really looking forward to, and then how quickly it passed? Time tends to drag or fly. We can say that this is just a subjective experience, because clocks will always correct your impression, but who says that the time we carry on our wrist is any more true than our individual sense of it? Isn't it just more convenient to have a yardstick we can all agree to? But is the universe counting with us? Somehow I don't think so.

Within our own lives life will slow down and speed up until we run out of it. It happens automatically, but we can manipulate it ourselves. How useful would it be to create a reality tunnel that gets the trip to the dentist over with quickly? How much would you like a reality tunnel that slows the ball down enough to give you time to hit it? How useful would it be to go for longer and longer without thinking of a cigarette or for a craving to pass in moments? For good times to pass slowly and boring times to pass quickly? All are possible through the skilful manipulation of this phenomenon.

Age Regression

This phrase tends to bring on the heeby jeebies in people more than just about any other within hypnotherapy, mainly because of its association with past life regression, which is a shame because we probably regress several times an hour at least. Did you have a nice evening yesterday? To be able to answer that question you have to regress to last night. As we've explored, our brain is constantly shuttling back into our past to make sense of our present in what must be a constant journey-loop. Edelman's use of the term 'the remembered present' makes this point. In therapy, the term *transference* is used to describe the situation whereby a client projects onto a therapist the attributes of someone from their past and begins to respond to him or

> *Often you respond to people because of who they remind you of, rather than who they actually are.*

her as if to that person from their history. We all do this quite commonly. Often you respond to people because of who they remind you of, rather than who they actually are. People get into intimate relationships owing to projections of this kind and end up falling in love again with the person who dumped them last time, not with who the new person actually is. And the cry goes up after it's run its course, "They weren't who I thought they were!"

Age regression is one of the core trance phenomena, because our past is the pile of bricks from which our present understanding is built, so a central part of the process of therapy is to train the brain to select positive past experiences from which to create our present reality tunnel and the direction it points towards. Working directly with age regression is covered in Part 2.4

Age Progression

This is also called *'pseudo orientation in time'*, but not by me because, well why would you, given a choice? It labels our ability to take ourselves to a future time-frame and run a counterfactual outcome – ie how might things turn out? This is one of the occasions when the labels of trance phenomena overlap somewhat, because if I ask you to imagine something in the future – like a holiday you haven't been on yet – and you begin to picture it, that's an age progression, but you're also seeing something that's not there, so isn't that a positive hallucination? Yes it is. A simple rule, once you think about it for a bit, is that nearly all age progressions will be positive hallucinations (I say nearly all because some people will imagine a future without seeing it), but not all positive hallucinations will be age progressions (looking in the mirror and seeing how good or bad you look, for example).

We get the future we expect

In Part 2.7 I talk at length about the many uses of this phenomenon, because it's so powerful. Age progression within our reality tunnel tends to have the nature of a self-fulfilling prophecy, so we get the future we expect to get. A client who foresees their job interview going badly is likely to enter the room with adrenalin running through their system because their unconscious is preparing them to run away or fight. That's hardly likely to leave them silver-tongued. Instead, if they see themself walking away from the interview punching the air in satisfaction, the state they present to the panel is likely to be much more impressive than the adrenalin shakes.

Dissociation

Association is the experience of life through your senses - it's a first-person, 'through my eyes' perspective. Dissociation is the perception of experiencing life from a disembodied point of view – watching what is happening to you, rather than feeling that it is. The dissociation can be a complete out-of-body experience – I have often helped pregnant women leave their bodies during the most painful moments of labour, and then reconnect during the easier moments so they can have a natural birth and experience the wonder of it. Dissociation can also be partial. When I severed the tendon of my thumb trying to open a bottle of champagne with a table knife (as I said to the surgeon, "when I say it out loud like that it sounds kind of stupid, doesn't it?") I used a dissociative technique to numb it which worked so well the doctor thought I had nerve damage...because I was in shock and had forgotten I'd done it. (That's an example of the next phenomenon.)

> *Victims of violent and/or sexual abuse often learn to dissociate themselves from the moment in order to protect themselves*

Victims of violent and/or sexual abuse often learn to dissociate themselves from the moment in order to protect themselves, which can lead to all sorts of relationship issues. More generally, people whose tunnel uses this phenomenon a lot, for whatever reason, feel more of an observer of life than a participant in it. An extreme tendency toward this has also been suggested as a cause of multiple personality syndrome, where the dissociation has been so complete that whole new, independent, personalities arise.

Positive uses for this are obviously in pain control situations like childbirth, but also in performance situations where the aim is for the conscious mind to get out of the way of the body and let it operate freely.

Amnesia

Bizarrely, this is the trance phenomenon that my students always remember. We forget things all the time, indeed most of what passes through our senses is instantly forgotten because it isn't deemed relevant, and when a particular reality tunnel is active, memories not connected to it tend to be inaccessible. Ask a client who has been talking about how bad their

> *What's not on your mind isn't readily brought to mind*

life is for the last hour about something that made them happy in the past and they usually take some time to come up with an answer. What's not on your mind isn't readily brought to mind. This is a very important tool in our armoury. If the memory loop that initiates a problem behaviour isn't active, then neither will be the problem behaviour, so utilising amnesia to forget an association between something happening now and something that happened in the past would prevent the problem from coming to mind. So, it doesn't matter if the client remembers to forget, or forgets to remember.

Post Hypnotic Suggestion

This is different from the others, in that it is something that invokes other trance phenomena to distort a reality tunnel rather than having a direct effect itself. Any suggestion made to a client that causes them to respond to that suggestion later fulfils this category. If I suggest to a client "as you begin the meeting you may notice the feeling that makes you realise how much more confident you're feeling," I'm using a sensory distortion (making whatever feeling comes to his awareness mean he's feeling confident), timed to go off at a point in the future. It's like setting a 'happy trap' in their future, waiting for the right moment for them to step into it. Essentially, most suggestions you make are post-hypnotic suggestions, mainly because you want the effect of them to be noticed outside the session rather than just within it.

> It's like setting a 'happy trap' in their future, waiting for the right moment for them to step into it

Many students get this phenomenon mixed up with age progression. If you take the above example and change it to "go out into the future and notice the feeling that makes you realise how much more confident you are," you're using age progression: at this moment you're getting them to imagine something in their future. With post-hypnotic suggestion they notice something in their future - when they get there.

Parents give us post-hypnotic suggestions - "All the women in the family struggle with their weight", "You're going to come unstuck one day" ,"You'll never make anything of yourself unless you...". We do it for ourselves as well - "I'm bound to muck my interview up", or "I always find the seventh hole difficult". We create the future we anticipate, so be mindful of your language.

> *Life isn't a package holiday you have to put up with because you've paid for it*

The nine trance phenomena I've just described are ways in which we can describe different facets of how the brain creates our perceptions, each of which we can use to guide our perceptions when creating the reality tunnel we enjoy travelling down the most. Life isn't a package holiday you have to put up with because you've paid for it so it's too late to change; you can adjust any part of the experience you want to by manipulating the trance phenomena from which it is created.

Submodalities

Digging deeper into the substrata of perception, we come to submodalities. If trance phenomena are the means by which sensory information is adapted to create *reality*, submodalities provide the fine detail. The word modality can be used to describe one of the senses - as in visual modality, auditory modality, etc. - and sub-modalities (smds) are the bits of information from which each modality is formed. They are the building blocks of thought. For example, if you get a picture in your head of someone you know, is that picture in black and white or colour? Is it a moving image, or a still picture? Does it have a frame around it, or is it panoramic? These are visual submodality qualities. If you imagine that person speaking, is the voice loud or soft? Which direction does it come from? Is it inside or outside your head? These are auditory smds. There is a fuller list of them on page 182.

Later in the book I propose a causal model of how the brain makes sense of the world. One of its planks is something called equivalence - there's a brief explanation in the glossary. The theory of submodalities is that the individual qualities that make up a thought - whether it's in black and white or colour, where the sound contained within it comes from, whereabouts in your body you feel the feeling associated with it - are the code from which the emotional meaning of a thought derives. In other words, if you have a thought that scares you, pleases you, angers you or arouses you, it's the particular combination of submodalities that creates the equivalence of that thought equalling that meaning. This means that if you change the submodalities of a thought, it can change the meaning of it: it can make

> *If you don't like the thought you're having, you can change it. It's only a thought.*

the meaning stronger, weaker, or give it a completely different meaning altogether. No longer are we slaves to our thoughts, people. If you don't like the thought you're having, you can change it. It's only a thought.

Not all submodalities in a thought are critical to its meaning; you don't have to change all of them. Typically three or four will tend to be the ones that make a difference, and they will be unique to each thought - just because changing one person's negative thought into black and white eliminated the bad feeling doesn't mean it will do the same for anybody else, or even another bad thought of the same person. Each thought has to be targeted and the submodalities elicited, and then the important ones identified. These are typically called 'critical' smds, or drivers.

However, while I've just said how individual they are, there are some which tend to be pretty universal in their ability to make a difference to the emotional content of a memory. In the structure interventions (Part 2.5) I go into this in more depth, because most interventions based on smds are particular combinations of 'universal' drivers, which is what makes the techniques work on a high percentage of people. However, this is also why they won't work on everybody - because they're only 'nearly universal', which probably means they work for about 80% of the population. If you understand this as a principle, when you use a structure intervention from the book and it doesn't work you'll know to check on what effect the smd combination has on the client, and be able to play with others to get the effect you are after.

How can I use it?

Our reality tunnels guide our actions, and we gain a lot of our sense of who we are from the things we do, so changing the nature of the tunnel is an intrinsic part of changing ourselves.

If trance phenomena and submodalities are the means by which our brain creates our reality from our memoragination, then using them gives us the power to create reality in the way that rewards us most. In Part 2.5 I'm going to teach you several techniques which use the power of submodalities for their effect. I said earlier that trance phenomena are utilised most directly through the use of hypnotic suggestion. My first book, *Wordweaving: The Science of Suggestion*, describes a model that I think harnesses trance phenomena within suggestion in the most powerful way I've yet come across. To explain it again in this book is beyond its remit, but in appendix one I have given a synopsis of it which I hope will encourage you to read further. Wordweaving™ is a skill that takes effort, but I believe that it's the difference that makes most difference in my work.

The Tao of the Mind

What's this about?

Our brain creates our reality tunnel from our memoragination by creating connections between meanings stored in our memories and information we encounter in the present. On the basis of this connection, it then runs a simulation of the most likely consequence of that match - our anticipated future. In this chapter I present the system I suggest the brain uses to make these connections, how it creates these patterns of recognition, and then how it calculates the likely outcome of the meaning it gives to a current situation.

I left the police in 1998, after nearly eighteen years, to pursue a career as a therapist. I walked away from a job that was secure and which would pay a healthy pension in just twelve years time, as my friends kept telling me, for something I wasn't sure could earn me a living. I just knew it was what I was here to do. I had spent about half my service not wanting to be a police officer. I had lost any sense of meaning in what I was doing, and saw myself as merely part of a system that worked for the benefit of lawyers and judges and did little in the way of serving justice. Like so many others I was going through the motions and mistaking it for life. And I didn't have a clue what I wanted to do instead. Becoming an instructor at Hendon police training school opened my eyes to a different world and had led, by a string of coincidences and synchronicities, to my discovering hypnotherapy and NLP. It transformed my life because I had found my thing. And when that happens anything becomes possible.

For the next three years I built up a practice, and earned extra money teaching elements of other people's hypnotherapy courses. I wasn't making a lot of money, but I was making enough. At that stage, though, I had no real long-term plan for where it would take me. My then girlfriend, and now wife, Rebecca, was also looking to leave the police and join me, but we were concerned about putting all our eggs in one basket. I still had two boys to support, so we dithered for some time.

One day, with this very much in our minds, we had a day out to one of our favourite places with the idea of coming to a decision. Avebury in Wiltshire is a magical place, home to a vast neolithic structure dating from 3500BC. It includes an earthworks, a henge and several stone circles and it takes about 40 minutes to walk around it. It's so large there is a village lying within it. Avebury is a great place to go to contemplate decisions. Just up the road is Silbury Hill, the largest man-made hill in Europe which also dates from the neolithic, and a short walk from there is my favourite place of all, the West Kennet Long Barrow. This is a tomb dating from 3600BC, about 400 years before Stonehenge was begun, and in use for over 1100 years. To step down into this barrow is to become aware of the smallness of your concerns. This is a space that was filled with the remains of people who had worries too, and 5000 years to put them into perspective. Maybe it's that sense of perspective that causes us to always bring a candle and light it when we leave, maybe just a desire for connection to a past. I can't say; it just somehow fills you with something, even an atheist like me.

As we left on this particular summer evening into the last of the sunlight we were greeted by two deer running together across the front of our position. They stayed in sight for the best part of a minute, swapping the lead, jumping fences and leaping the stream that runs between Silbury Hill and the Barrow. In the harmony of their movement it felt as if the ancients had sent us our sign, and Rebecca resigned from the police that week. We started the Quest Institute and the rest is history. You're reading this book because of two deer.

This chapter is about those deer, and the demon carrier bag, and all the other things that result from the way the brain seeks relationships between things and distorts our reality tunnel to give them meaning...even when there is none, and even for people who should know better.

The world is a piece of computer tape

In Part 1.1, I suggested that the brain can be described as a computer, but not everyone agrees. Edelman is one of those who speaks against this viewpoint. In his emphatic words: "The brains of higher-level animals autonomously construct patterned responses to environments that are full of novelty. They do not do this the way a computer does - using formal rules governed by explicit and unambiguous instructions or input signals. Once more, with feeling: the brain is not a computer, and the world is not a piece of tape."[30]

I gulp as I say it, but I think he's wrong; I think the brain is a computer and, while the world isn't a piece of tape, the version of the world we create to help us navigate the real world safely, is. If 80% of what we perceive around us is our brain's interpretation of the information flowing through our senses based on its previous experiences; once more, with feeling: we're not living in the world, we're living in a simulation of it made from ideas that emerge from our memoragination. I see no reason why those ideas can't be woven using a set of calculations but on an ever-changing loom, and I'm going to recruit one of my heroes in support.

Algorithms all the way down

Alan Turing is one of the key figures in the history of computing. He first became famous for his part in saving civilisation with his code-breaking work as part of Bletchley Park during WWII, and then subsequently his suicide following his harassment by that same civilisation for his homosexuality.

Turing's early insights into the nature of computing led to the Computational Theory of Mind (CTOM)[31]. Essentially it tells us that our mind is not the same thing as our brain, or the interaction of its parts. Our mind is equivalent to the information

> *We are the total sum of the ideas processed by our brains*

processing - the computations supported by our brain. All things 'thoughtlike' are ideas stored, processed and transformed by physical mechanisms in our brain. Our mind emerges from the brain, the sum of our ideas, like software emerges from our hard drive; we are the total sum of the ideas processed by our brains. In Turing's model, a computer could be made of anything, it's simply a mechanism for methods of information processing. Nothing says the mechanism should comprise the same parts every time something is calculated on it.

A criticism levelled at this model is that it doesn't account for the meaning thoughts are given; the information of our thoughts is greatly richer than the simple identification of what is being processed. We look at a sunset and we don't just see the colours, we imbue it with beauty.

> *The calculation gap is the playing field of change*

One person looks at a dog and sees a friend, another a danger. How does one thought carry a meaning that is different to another's thought when it's based on the same information? The answer is that in the gap between the information arriving from the outside and the thought we have about it is a calculation that can change anything into anything else; something good can become something dangerous, and vice versa. Our subjective experience is the result of the calculations our brain makes to interpret the world, and I'm going to argue in this book that so are we, the 'I' having that subjective experience. This is the home territory of the therapist, because this *calculation gap* is the playing field of change.

Read Montague suggests that, if we want to understand how what happens in this 'calculation gap' has the power to create our world, we need to understand that Turing's model operates at every level of biology. The structure of every molecule defines its function, and its structure depends on an algorithm (a set of rules for solving a problem in a finite number of steps) to create it.[32] As a consequence, for biological structures to evolve, so too do their algorithms.

When your body produces a new cell, it does so by following an algorithm, when you tie your shoelaces the same way each time it's because your body is following an algorithm for how to accomplish it, and when you respond to a situation in a way you can't control, there is an algorithm working in the background that's causing that response.

Complex biological systems possess many layers of physical structures, from DNA-to genes-to-proteins-to-organs/bones/hair, so, in Montague's words "it's information processing all the way down"[33] and, because Turing's model suggests that the mind emerges from the biological structure of the brain, it's information processing all the way up too, from cell to thought.

In that sense, algorithms are the mechanism of evolution, so the struggle that characterises the survival of the fittest is the struggle of competing computations. And our thoughts are the fittest computations ever to emerge from the primordial soup…except for the thoughts of the people who inhabit reality TV. And the fittest set of algorithms are those that humans use to create the world we recognise around us.

Because, because, because…

We are surrounded by chaos and yet, somehow, our brain creates an ordered world from it. How? How does it create choice from chaos? How does it decide, from everything present in the reality it can be aware of, what isn't chaos or irrelevant, and create our individual reality tunnels from what remains?

From the first moment we heave ourselves into the light of day our brain begins to build an elaborate model of 'how things work in the world', what NLP refers to as a person's *model of the world* (MOTW), which I suggest encompasses both past, present and future. From this model of the world is created our reality tunnel, that takes us from our first moment of light until our last in one apparently continuous stream of experience.

> *Causality is the architect of the reality tunnel, it determines which bricks get laid where, and when*

What makes this possible is the set of instructions the brain follows to come to a conclusion, and I think the root of these instructions is the notion of causality – the idea that effects come from causes, and specifically, belief systems about *which* effects come from *which* causes. Causality is the architect of the reality tunnel: it determines which bricks get laid where, and when. I think it's probably the biggest idea that's ever come out of our brain, except perhaps the idea of a self.

This facility is crucial to our survival because to be able to predict how changes in some things lead to changes in other things gives us a mechanism of choice.

Causality also leads us to be able to create imagined worlds in which different choices are made in order for us to be able to choose which effect is most likely to lead to whatever goal is being pursued – if I say 'please' is it more likely Mummy will give me a sweet than if I don't? If I wear this particular brand of aftershave is it more likely that girls will want me? If I save this money now, will I be safer if something goes wrong in the future? In Cognitive Science these alternative universes are called *counterfactuals*, a means of having ideas about worlds that are not the one that currently surrounds you. They can be worlds we spend time pleasantly daydreaming in - perhaps one where you're discovered on X Factor and become the next Madonna, or unpleasant ones not entirely divorced from your current world, where you imagine the boss walking towards your desk with an envelope in her hand which leads to you sleeping on a park bench beside a Tesco trolley containing all your worldly goods.

One of the things that define us as human is the ability to identify and pursue goals. In a very real sense, all creatures that move pursue goals; it's one of the consequences of the choice that locomotion brings you. But we are the most developed when it comes to what is called 'agency' - the ability to deliberately intervene and change our situation. At least, isn't that how it feels to us, that we are in charge of our choices? It is so entrenched in our mentality that it's as obvious as breathing, and central to our experience as a person and our success as a species. If I see the possibility of ending up on a park bench because of getting the sack, I can begin to plan to avoid it. We create a causal framework that enables us to construe the world (and its alternative versions) in a particular way that guides our choices of action - if I do this, that will happen, which will lead to...

This ability to create causal models forms the framework for how the brain creates our notion of reality that I call TAOTM, *The Algorithms of the Mind*. You can tell from how I put it in capitals that I think this is a big idea, and just to drive home the point I pronounce it as Totem, because it sounds sexier.

There are just three algorithms used by the brain to give meaning to the world

In this model I propose that there are just three algorithms used by the brain to give meaning to the world, and I realise that's a bold claim. Just three calculations account for us understanding everything around us? Yes. Nature doesn't have time to be complicated.

The big three

1. Causation is the assumption that objects and situations are connected through time, so that one thing precedes another. It is usually written as C ▶ E (Cause - then- Effect) You were caused by your parents having sex, WWII was caused by Adolf Hitler, and wearing a particular aftershave will make the girls swoon. Causal relationships don't have to be true, they just have to be plausible, because our brains are highly susceptible to mistaking correlation for causation. Correlation is where two entities share some form of relationship based on complementary, parallel, or reciprocal factors. An example would be the fact that in every school the children with the bigger feet will be the better readers. If we attribute a causal relationship to those two facts, then it would be a good idea for parents to listen to my patented 'make your feet bigger' download, and I'm on my way to being a millionaire. But of course the reason for this correlation is age – the older you are the bigger your feet will tend to be, and therefore the better reader. The urge to make one thing the cause of the other is strong because of our desire to create a world that is predictable, and history abounds with costly causal mistakes, such as:

- The Mayans, Aztecs and Incas all believed that human sacrifice was necessary to continue the existence of the universe. From the success of their crops to the sun rising, the ripping of a beating heart from a victim was deemed a necessity.

- For nearly 2000 years, until the late 19th century, blood letting was thought to be a way of clearing out illness. In one textbook it was prescribed for acne, asthma, cancer, cholera, coma, convulsions, diabetes, epilepsy, gangrene, gout, herpes, indigestion, insanity, jaundice, leprosy, ophthalmia, plague, pneumonia, scurvy, smallpox, stroke, tetanus, tuberculosis, amongst a long list of others.

It can also lead to magical thinking errors, such as touching wood to prevent bad luck, astrology and tarot card readers.

Without meaning to step on anybody's spirituality, the search for an explanation for the natural world, in the absence of science, soon leads to superstitious explanations for why things happen when they do - volcanoes are caused by Vulcan working in his forge, storms are the angels moving the furniture and bad luck is caused by doing something wrong and God extracting a tithe, or mercury rising in your fourth house. In our brains habitual search for patterns, in the absence of a human or natural explanation for an effect, every culture has invented an external causal agent. And, as Bertrand Russell pointed out, "Man is a credulous animal, and must believe *something*; in the absence of good grounds for belief, he will be satisfied with bad ones."[34]

We all carry beliefs that affect our behaviour because of our having made this kind of error. I have a belief that I cause the England football team to lose if I watch them. I even know that it stems from 1970, when we were beating Germany 2-0 and I turned to my grandad and said to him, "There's no way we can lose now." He interjected quickly, "Don't say that, it's bad luck," and I then proceeded to watch us collapse to a miserable 3-2 loss. Of course supporting England all of my life has made it easy for this initial event to be reinforced, and I really must get around to doing something about it. Strangely my wife seems reluctant to help...

Spend some time thinking how often we shape our thoughts with 'if I do this, that will/won't happen', 'because I'm X, Y is bound to happen'. Watch adverts - they are nearly all based on cause and effect: buy this product and *this* will be the great consequence. Anytime you're using the word 'because' or any form of the verb 'to make', or someone is using them on you, you're deep within the causative model.

2. Equivalence – To discern order and create meaning requires the ability to find patterns - relationships between objects and situations that exist in the moment or across time. Equivalence permeates all aspects of our life. Rapport is based to a great degree on unconscious connections being made based on similarity. Listen to people meeting for the first time at a party and much of the conversation will be a search for similarity, in musical taste, politics, holidays or children. If we find a basis of similarity we tend to 'click' with that person. If the exchange predominantly exposes differences we're likely to find that person harder work. In the main, we like people who are like us, which makes sense. For most of history the only safe humans were the ones within our own small group of hunter gatherers, all others represented a threat. We are great mimics of other's behaviour and mannerisms. Watch in any office how members of a team begin to adopt a common language, borrow mannerisms and turns of phrase – particularly from the boss. It takes a remarkably short time for group of strangers to form groups of 'them and us'. We are pre-programmed for it, and vital to the formation of such a connection is some expression of similarity.

I think equivalence explains why we tend to have favourite writers and actors. We look for things in them that we either see as a similarity between them and us, or a similarity we'd like to think exists. Themes in films and books will often attract you time and time again to the same genre because of some link you perceive between the character or the storyline. An example is my attraction to the myth of King Arthur; I've been hooked since I was a boy. I saw something in the experience of the hero that resonated within me: A boy who didn't feel he belonged in the family he was raised in, and whose potential was recognised only when Merlin revealed him to the world. Such is the power of ourselves as a story that I recognise now that I waited until I was about 32 for Merlin to find me. I finally got the point that you have to be your own magician. And no surprise that The Matrix had such a profound effect on me; Neo is Arthur, Morpheus is Merlin, and off we go again. My associating Arthur's story with my own had been a major contributing factor in keeping me stuck in the police all those years; I was waiting for someone to rescue me.

At the back of the book as Appendix Two is an exercise I developed as a result of this personal insight. I call it the Trackdown Exercise, and I know a lot of people who've had light-bulb moments because of it.

The consequences of our brain searching for equivalences affects us every day. If you've ever waved at a stranger thinking them to be a friend, you've been the victim of your brain trying to save time by taking a short cut. It happens because the more you know someone, the less you actually 'see' them. To save time your brain just projects who you expect that person to be. It's why we don't notice people ageing or putting on weight day to day, but will if we don't see them for a while. Psychologists call this the *difference threshold,* and if changes in information passing through the brain fall below it in terms of similarity or difference, the changes go unnoticed. Mark this page because it's a 'get out of jail free' card the next time you fail to notice your partner changing something about their appearance.

This equivalence-matching of snapshots of people in the present with others extends into our past as well. You know sometimes you meet someone for the first time and you get a feeling of already knowing them? It's likely that your brain has just spotted a similarity, in features, mannerisms, accent or phrasing, with someone from your past. If you get a good feeling about the new acquaintance it's because you liked the person matched to them, and if

Often what we say we like or dislike about someone is just a conscious realisation of a decision your unconcisous has already come to

you feel uneasy, it might be because they remind you of the school bully. We like to think of ourselves as objective but often what we say we like or dislike about someone is just a conscious rationalisation of a decision your unconscious has already come to.

Equivalence is represented in our speech by people saying something is *like* something (not including our current crop of teenagers, and most Americans when they say "It's so, like, cool!") or something *means* something. It can be as simple as the sight of a swallow means that spring is here, my suggestion that your chair being comfortable means that you can relax really deeply, or using a certain brand of cosmetic means "you're worth it."

For millennia, stories, fables, myths and legends have been passed from one generation to another as a means of communicating important information; about the role of people in their society, the right way to behave, or the values that their society wishes to inculcate into their citizens. When Victorian boys were read the epic story of Scott of the Antarctic it was in the hope of the boys projecting themselves into the hero's role and imbibing the qualities of sacrifice, bravery and steadfastness that were so valued by that society. This projection into the hero is the same phenomenon that caused my association with Arthur, and it's a potent way of transmitting important ideas because TAOTM renders us so sensitive to finding equivalences between things – even when they're not there. The same goes for the two deer at Avebury, I was seeking some kind of external sign, and my brain created the connection between Bambi and his mother and our dilemma.

Earlier in the book I mentioned how people often form an equivalence between an object, like cigarettes or food, and a positive emotion like love. This is how it occurs: being given chocolate as a child by your mother can easily become a symbol of her love for you if given over time (or in a single powerfully emotional moment) and in the right circumstances - "You're such a good girl darling, have some Chocolate Buttons." No wonder, then, that as an adult, whenever she doesn't feel good about her life she asks Doctor Cadbury to make a house call, an equivalence error that can have serious consequences for her adult waistline.

Anything can end up meaning anything, it just depends on how the equivalences are reinforced by experience after the relationship is first formed

An equally dangerous equivalence can be formed between the same object - food - and a negative emotion, which can lead to anorexia. The ability of two brains to create an equivalence between an object and emotions that are polar opposites just shows the ambivalent flexibility of the brain's reward system. Anything can end up meaning anything, it just depends on how the equivalences are reinforced by experiences after the relationship is first formed.

3. Difference - Anything you perceive through any of your five senses is filtered through your brain as being similar to something already experienced, or different. Essentially the process of therapy is to cause the brain to stop ascribing similarity or causation between a past event that had a strong emotional signature (we call them Significant Emotional Events, or an SEE) and a present situation - for John to see Bruiser, and any other dog in his present and future, as being different from the dog that bit him when he was five, for example.

> *TAOTM is how we assign meaning to things*

I would imagine that just about every creature on the planet uses TAOTM in varying degrees of complexity in order to assess the reward or pain potential within each situation. TAOTM is how we assign meaning to things. It's why things appear to be the way they are, even when everyone is finding the same situation different to your experience of it.

All creatures are selective in what they pay attention to. All attend to the information that serves their goals while ignoring that which is deemed irrelevant. Perception imposes structure so that we don't pay equal attention to everything. Most information is useless, and paying attention to it would merely clog our minds.[35] Selective attention solves a problem: it helps us to find those aspects of the environment that move us towards our goals.

TAOTM is how our brains select what to attend to. It seeks pattern matches between stored information from our past and our present situations, which then cause us to pay attention to whatever is tagged as relevant as a result.

> *Expertise in anything requires the ability to spot patterns of invariance*

Our mind uses these algorithms to create a model of the world that presupposes invariance in many of its qualities. We expect the ground to be solid, water to be liquid, gravity not to forget to do its job and politicians to lie. Expertise in anything requires the ability to spot patterns of invariance – things that are relevant because experience has shown them to be so – and to ignore everything else. That is what enables experts to work faster and more accurately: invariance enables them to discard the irrelevant. Our brain's overriding goal is to become an expert at survival, so we all develop models of invariance as we grow up, the vast majority of which work well.

This is important to us as therapists, because the problem at the heart of any problem is mostly the result of clients' reality tunnels being built from inaccurate invariants; if an invariant belief is that people don't like you, you can guess the lonely walk your brain will build for you and the actions you'll be led to take. Our well-being in an uncertain environment is fundamentally linked to the degree to which the brain can accurately identify invariance – the systematic relationships between objects, events and symbols from which we derive our perception of the world: a place of meaningful simplicity.

This is no easy task, because we are surrounded by the world's fluid complexity. Everywhere things are changing moment to moment and so the existence of uncertainty seems more trustworthy than its opposite. Yet its opposite is what our mind determinedly roots for, and causal relationships have so far turned out to be the best means of assessment of certainty yet devised by evolution. This is why we're so exquisitely sensitive to them – and sometimes see them even when they're not there, especially when we're young (remember me and England?). Actually, not especially - we mistake correlation for causation throughout our lives, it's just that these early mix-ups tend to lead to the greatest difficulties in our adulthood.

I suggested earlier that the causative model may be the best idea the brain has ever had. TAOTM enables the brain to save time by using pre-stored meanings it can project onto present situations and build patterns of invariants that form a basis for prediction. In this context, another word for invariants is beliefs. As we grow up, we form beliefs about how the world works, and who we are within it. Everything we believe to be true is based on our brain having established a pattern of similarity, cause and effect, or difference between objects, people or situations. The benefit is the confidence that comes from certainty; the danger is the certainty that comes from certainty. If our beliefs are based on miscalculations, we can firmly believe to be true things that are utter nonsense - like "I'm not loveable", "I'm not good enough", or "I don't deserve good things to happen." And the cleverest trick beliefs have, is that they feel true. It's what they evolved for.

> *The cleverest trick beliefs have is that they feel true*

How can I use it?

Our ability to recognise and give meaning to anything in our lives is wholly dependent upon our brains use of TAOTM. Inaccurate invariants that lead to a negative reality tunnel are the root of many client issues, and identifying them and returning them to a state of flexibility is one area to focus on in therapy. In Part 2.4 I teach several approaches that focus on limiting beliefs and how to transform them.

Information received through our senses, that is presented in the form of an equivalence, difference or cause and effect is automatically more acceptable to the brain than something that is not. In Cognitive Hypnotherapy we utilise TAOTM in every session by making the work we've done the cause of anything that is evidence to the client that they are moving towards their solution. Every difference they notice and every similarity they find that reminds them of what they want, is used to build the momentum of their change. TAOTM is the architect of our reality tunnel, and thus of our personal development, and I explain how to utilise it in Part 2.7.

If all behaviour has a purpose why do I do stupid things?

What's this about?

In this chapter I explore how the calculations our brain makes leads to emotions that are turned into actions and how this process can lead to the mistakes clients call issues or problems. It's about why we sometimes do stupid things for what feel like good reasons, or good things for what seem to others like stupid reasons.

Getting to see the Pyramids was a big tick on my bucket list. Since childhood I'd been fascinated by the ancient civilisation of Egypt but, despite visiting Egypt several times, they'd remained just beyond my reach. Finally the day dawned when my wife Rebecca and I stood before them. And their magnificence didn't disappoint. Although, I have to say, there being a Pizza Hut in front of them certainly did. How far we have travelled along the road of civilisation; from Pyramid to Hut.

One of the surprises that made the day special was the opportunity to climb down into the Queen's pyramid, down a steep wooden slope with dowel steps, a testament to the admirable Egyptian resistance to the notion of health and safety. The tunnel was only wide enough for people to travel in one direction at a time, and was controlled by a guy at the top who was carefully keeping track of how many were travelling down – in-between fag breaks, charging for photo's of him, selling bits of cardboard as fans, or asking for baksheesh if all attempts at trade failed. Girded with our intrepid spirit we descended into the bowels of the tomb until we finally emerged into the final resting place of the Queen. Completely undecorated, devoid of sarcophagus, really just a hole in the ground, but a man-made space that, like West Kennet Long Barrow, had sat in its own silence for 4000 years, so impressive for all that.

After a while we became aware that the space was becoming crowded, with no letup in the numbers descending. This triggered a number of reactions: the British started to queue, arranging themselves in tidy ranks along the back of the tomb – a national form of meditation - others just milled. Some found it amusing, increasing numbers began to become anxious. Not the Brits, obviously, they had yet to lay themselves like firewood, so there was still plenty of room.

Eventually the tension snapped. People started calling on the people descending to stop, for the guard to do something. Finally one tourist shouted something colonial like "We're out of here," and climbed out on his own, barging those descending out of the way. Obviously he was using the royal we.

What struck me later, as I helped unstack the British, was the great range within which the brain operates. The same brain that was capable of building the Pyramids, of working out the geometry, creating the necessary technology, of harnessing 100,000 people over thirty years of sustained effort, was the same brain that could react with panic to a situation where the actual danger was minimal – eventually the congestion would have caused the guard to realise the space was full, certainly before we ran out of air or water. How can we think so clearly and well in some situations, and so badly in others? Why do we have a rational brain capable of such wonders, and an irrational brain capable of such stupidity? My answer is that, to the brain, it's not stupid at all, it's the best response possible given the information it's using to calculate the most likely future. Irrationality is just a point of view.

If you put the cells of any organism in a petri dish and add a nutrient, the organism will move towards it. If you put a toxin in the dish, the cell will move away. Bruce Lipton, a developmental biologist, suggests that genes have two classes of programs. One is for growth, and the other is for protection. In response to the environment we are in, genes are selected for one or the other. And that means that, with our brains creating 80% of our environment, it is our perceptions that cause our bodies to either be in a state of growth or protection. Even just as a metaphor, this is a very powerful idea, because our behaviour is one of the strongest pieces of evidence we use for who we decide we are. If we live in a state of protection, we become people who need protecting in a world to be protected against. If we live in growth, we live a life of infinite possibility.

> *Both growth and protection utilise TAOTM, the problem is that the protection system tends to shoot from the hip.*

Our memoragination exists to guide our choices, and evolution has reduced the choices to those two classes: in response to the match it makes between present information and our stored past it calculates a future that involves an opportunity for growth, or one that requires protection. The more often the calculation favours the latter, the more we'll find ourselves living in a limited world of constricted choices; a world most of our clients are all too familiar with.

Both growth and protection utilise TAOTM, the problem is that the protection system tends to shoot from the hip.

You're either with me or against me

My suggestion that the algorithms of the mind are the architect of the reality tunnel might seem to be too simplistic, because in the way I've described them they are pretty blunt instruments, but the survival arms race every creatures brain is involved in has led to TAOTM developing sharper and sharper edges. The great Swiss educationalist Piaget, described a model of mental development that showed how children develop over time a finer and finer capacity to judge causal relationships.[36]

Piaget identified four stages the young brain goes through in the development of its ability to recognise invariants (beliefs), and to build patterns of similarity and difference. The model fits the idea of a maturing person (or computer) applying greater and greater degrees of subtlety and shading to the relationships it finds between things it experiences. The first level is **nominal** processing: this is seeing things in stark contrast. Something is black or white, right or wrong, good or bad. It is the level the brain uses for knee-jerk reactions, and all it has time for in moments of threat or danger. Children are limited to this level of thinking until they are around ten years old.

The second level is called **ordinal**, and allows information to be processed within a hierarchy. So, where black and white were opposite ends of a nominal continuum with nothing in the middle, ordinal allows a more textured comparison. For example, at five you might have won or lost the egg and spoon race and that's all there was to it, but with ordinal you understand the principle of ranking, so coming second becomes meaningful to you.

Interval processing is the next increase in sophistication and allows a finer means of measuring relationships between things – such as how close you came to beating the winner of the race. And finally comes **ratio** processing, which takes into account the three previous levels, but brings in more flexible perspectives, like, does it matter who won, and does it have to mean anything about you as a person that you came second?

> *The more time the brain has to conisder a course of action, the finer the degree of pattern matching it can apply*

The more time the brain has to consider a course of action, the finer the degree of pattern matching it can apply. Given time, the brain can come up with exquisitely complex or creative ideas. More great discoveries in science have come from 'aha!' moments of insight that have arisen from periods of pondering, than have come from the relentless application of conscious logic – think Aristotle shouting *Eureka!*, Newton and the apple, or Kekulé, who famously saw the formula for benzene emerge from a fire he was staring into as a dragon circling to bite its own tail. Knowledge emerging, almost as if it's the result of osmosis, tends to be a feature of the unconscious having the leisure to ponder – and the state of *growth* tends to be a fertile opportunity for this. Interestingly, the brain becomes busier when we consciously cease to use it[37], and perhaps this is what it is doing. Maybe there is a benefit to watching soaps?

However, protection is also a prime consideration of the brain, and time has more often been a threat to it than a friend, so our protection system tends not to ponder, it wants us to act, and quickly. In addition to this, our brains seek to save energy in all situations (because we must 'recharge or die') including their own computations, so our thinking tends to be as imprecise as the brain can get away with and survive. This makes nominal processing the perfect level of thought for protection-thinking. It is both quick and simple, and in situations of threat that is most likely all you have time for. This has echoes of Joseph LeDoux's description of the brain's survival system's response to threat as being 'fast and dirty'.[38]

Suppose you're walking across the garden and see a length of hosepipe poking out of the grass. If your brain matches it to the stored image of a snake the brain might trigger an emergency response before the conscious spends the extra half a second 'making sure' it's a hosepipe. *Fast* because it acts faster than the conscious can interrupt, *dirty* because limbic system connections (the part of the brain that is responsible for emotional responses) to the cortex outnumber cortical connections to the limbic system by two-to-one, so when your protection system shouts *emergency*, any other part saying 'let's not be hasty here', is drowned out. To your

To your protection system, getting it wrong a thousand times is better than getting it fatally wrong once

protection system, getting it wrong a thousand times is better than getting it fatally wrong once. Respond in haste, be able to repent at leisure is its mantra – and an anxiety disorder is one visible negative consequence of this; in simplistic terms it's your protection system becoming over-sensitised to normal situations, causing it to act in circumstances when there is no real threat. Of course, not getting bitten by snakes is the visible, and more highly prized, positive.

It's a jungle out there

We share about 97% of our DNA with chimpanzees. They are our closest relation in the animal world, and we separated from them about seven million years ago. If we took this moment of separation as the starting point for our species and called it midnight of the single day we've been on the planet, then homo sapiens, clever old us with this marvellous brain, made its first appearance at about 11.20pm. Overwhelmingly, the protection responses the brain has developed have been geared towards what

> *Protection responses the brain has developed have been geared towards what was relevant for our ancestors*

was relevant for our ancestors, not modern man; we simply haven't been around long enough.

I think it's safe to say that most of the survival challenges our ancestors faced would have had to do with trying to avoid being some other creature's lunch. Behaviours that maximised our efficiency in the pursuit of that goal would have been selected, so it's no surprise that they are the ones that surface in situations where the brain calculates a present threat in its environment, even though the environment they're intended for no longer exists.

The mechanism that evolved to prevent this is commonly termed the *fight or flight response*.

Since its description by Walter Cannon in 1915,[39] it has been realised that his catchy title is too simplistic. Organisms respond to threat in many ways, ranging from the simple to the complex. For some creatures, flight is achieved by freezing, or by changing colour – like chameleons and some fish. Flight can also be away from a predator, or towards safety. Similarly with fight, clearly it can be attacking the source of the threat, but it can also be various forms of display to threaten the threatener – I'm thinking of my in-law's cat Psycho (they call him Coco, but I've looked in his eyes). Our dog Barney only has to move towards him in his typical desire for friendship, for the cat's back to arch and the spitting to start. A more accurate term might be the *protection response*, in tune with the idea of us always being in a state of growth or protection.

Physiologically, what happens when the protection system kicks in is that adrenalin gets released into the body which has immediate effects: our heartbeat increases to drive more oxygen to our muscles, our temperature increases because muscles are more effective if they're warm, our stomach feels funny because blood is diverted to our arms and legs and our digestion shuts down (which may cause your mouth to go dry, and to make it feel like we need the loo – emptying our stomach reduces the chances of blood poisoning in the event of a wound, and, I'm guessing, makes us less appetising to eat). As a result of this diversion of blood we may shake because our blood pressure increases in our arms and legs. Finally, blood flow is reduced to our pre-frontal cortex, where we do most of our higher level thinking and planning. In ancient times, those humans who responded to a sabre-toothed tiger by scratching their chin and saying, "now then, what shall we do?" got eaten. The survivors survived because they reflexively responded by offence, defence or freezing, not by taking time to think through the options. Many of you will recognise these physical responses as symptoms. Many conditions – such as phobias, anxiety disorders and even PTSD are just particular uses of this basic response. As I often say to clients, their symptoms are a sign that their body is working perfectly, it's just that their survival system is basing its *protection* calculations on nominally processed information from their past – i.e., it's inaccurate in its conclusion. Change the information, and you remove the need for the response.

Strong emotions make us stupid

Put simply, our brain seeks simplicity, especially in situations of uncertainty. Unfortunately, that can also mean that strong emotions make us stupid.

This is one of the reasons why our behaviour has the intention of protecting us but we sometimes behave in ways we wish we didn't. If our brain makes a 'fast and dirty' decision believing itself in danger, especially when we are young, it may be used as a reference experience in the future that guides our responses - like John and Bruiser. That's a straightforward processing error - all dogs are dangerous - designed to protect us from a physical danger. Such nominal processing errors are at the root of most of the emotional problems people have – the emotion is fired in response to a match between a present situation and an historical miscalculation.

Our protection system gets stuck in nominal (black and white) processing when strong emotions are present

But if our memoragination is constantly being updated, why aren't these processing errors ironed out? I think it's because our protection system gets stuck in nominal (black and white) processing when strong emotions are present.

When John sees Bruiser, his memoragination creates a connection and a consequence, and his reality tunnel undergoes a sudden reorganisation which drives his behaviour in the direction dictated by prior experience - he runs for it. This particular memory loop is driven by nominal processing and, in my opinion, restricted to it. Memory loops connected to the protection system (i.e. those containing a strong negative emotion) are examples of what Argyris and Schon described as 'single loop learning'[40]. In this scenario, all that is available for the brain to learn from is what is available within the loop, and because it contains an invariant belief - 'all dogs are dangerous' - and thinking is limited to nominal processing, all that can happen is that the invariance is reinforced. Our fears become more *real* the longer we hold them unchallenged. Because it fits what I'm describing more easily and is easier to fit into a sentence, I'm going to call this *closed loop learning*.

With Argyris and Schon's double and triple loop learning, information external to the loop can be admitted, as well as the higher levels of processing (ordinal, interval and ratio). For new meaning to be given to an experience, or for alternative responses to be considered, the single loop of a protection response - which I think lies at the root of most clients' problems - needs to be opened up so it can 'breathe' some fresh ideas. This form of learning I'm going to call *open loop learning* - because all other memory loops can be drawn upon for new perspectives: like a loom that can create a fresh pattern, as opposed to one that keeps churning out the same old thing. In open loop learning we can grow, in closed loop learning we stagnate.

What may prevent a memory loop being open to new information could be the consequence of the brain being what the Americans call a kluge, and the British call a bodge, defined by Jackson Granholm as, "...an ill-assorted collection of poorly matching parts, forming a distressing whole."[41]

I mean this in the respect that the brain wasn't 'designed', it's a patchwork of fixes to solve problems as they arose, selected from random mutations on the basis of the survival advantage they gave us. The more recent the addition to the structure the more bug-ridden it tends to be, and the more imperfect the communication between it and older systems.

Our protection system is predominantly sited in the limbic system - our emotional brain - which evolved millions of years before our cortex - the source of our higher thinking processes. Joseph LeDoux suggests that

Closed and Open Loop learning

Imagine your reality tunnel is a balloon and you are inside it. This is the situation where the information being used to create it by the memoragination is an example of closed loop learning. The strong emotion that provides the context for the connection between past and present has meant that the calculations made about it are limited to fast and dirty nominal processing. The end result is that all future understanding is limited to what is contained within the closed loop - so the walls of the balloon will remain unchanged in appearance, other than the possibility of getting more inflated (the response to that reality becoming more pronounced).

On the other hand, in an open loop the reality tunnel is more like a kaleidoscope, where information from all other loops is available for causal comparison, and open to ordinal, interval and ratio level thinking, so any new perspective can cause a shift in the walls of the kaleidoscope, which could change the whole tunnel - ie your reality.

memories connected to our primary survival emotions - fear and anger - are stored in a part of the limbic system called the amygdala, not with other memories in the cortex.[42]

This is just speculation, but perhaps strongly emotional memories that are only nominally processed remain stuck as a closed loop because higher thinking processes which evolved later within the cortex simply don't have access to them under 'normal' circumstances because they are stored in the limbic system where the cortex can't get at them. It's a programming kluge.

I think this is why therapies that emphasise rational thinking and intellectual insight often fail to produce a change in the problem. Simply talking or thinking about a problem is not engaging the right system - the words just bounce off the walls of the closed loop. But, by the same token, approaches that simply encourage reliving, or re-accessing the feelings about the memory (i.e. the 'and how does that feel?' approach) are also likely to be less effective because all that is being accomplished is another lap of a closed loop, which could actually reinforce it (i.e. inflate the balloon - see textbox on page 60). The memory loop needs to be firing in the memoragination **and** new ways of perceiving it introduced into it. The information used by the TAOTM calculations driving the emotional response are what need to be changed, only then can the loop open and new perspectives gain access. How we do this is the stuff of Part Two.

It's been emotional

> *It's through our emotions that we know what to do*

When the brain, using the memoragination, has finished its deliberations about the meaning of the present moment, and chosen the course of action it wants to take, it creates a reality tunnel in a form that causes us to act, and it uses emotions to do this. Our emotions move us into actions that take us towards a goal or away from a threat. It's through our emotions that we know what to do.

Antonio Damasio is one of the world's foremost neurologists, and some of his greatest discoveries about brain function have come from patients who have lost part of their normal function from accident, injury or illness. One of his most famous examples was a man called Elliott, a man who had been a model citizen. Previously a successful business and family man before an operation to remove a tumour in the frontal lobe of his cortex, Elliott presented with a major psychological flaw post-surgery. Despite his IQ remaining the same, he had lost the ability to make a decision.

We take this ability for granted to such an extent that it is really hard to grasp the scale of the problem this causes. What to have for breakfast could task him for hours. What to watch on television, which tie to wear to the office or what job to do first, all became impossible. He could spend hours working through the options, and weighing the pros and cons, and still he'd be incapable of coming to a decision. It wasn't long before he lost his job. And that was just the start of his decline. Every business he started failed, he was conned out of a lot of money and became bankrupt. His wife left him.

Imagine that happening to you. You would imagine depression would be an almost inevitable consequence. Not with Elliott. Ever since the operation Elliott's world had been washed clean of emotional colouring. He talked of his circumstance with total dispassion. In Damasio's words "Nowhere was there a sense of his own suffering...I never saw a tinge of sadness...no sadness, no impatience, no frustration."[43] He was an emotional vacuum.

Damasio's conclusion from the many hours of experiments was clear; a brain can't make up its mind if it can't feel. How ironic, when, since Descartes, we've placed so much emphasis on removing feelings from our decision making processes.

The part of the cortex destroyed by Elliott's tumour, thought for so long to be the repository of dry logic, is called the orbitofrontal cortex (OFC). It is responsible for integrating emotions into our decision making. It connects areas from our limbic system – the so-called emotional brain – to our conscious thoughts. It's a significant connection between two parts of the Kluge that spans our evolution from a feeling to a feeling/thinking creature.

When we are at the moment of making a choice, from buying a pair of jeans to whether to run from a sabre-toothed tiger, the unconscious is using emotion to nudge us (or throw us) in a certain direction – emotions are a guidance mechanism. It's no wonder that emotion and motivation share the same latin root *movere*, 'to move'. Emotions are calls to action, and they can be subtle sirens, or in an emergency situation they can be deafening, irresistible klaxons. But whatever their call is, it always has a

All behaviour has a purpose. Everything we do is aimed towards one goal or another

point. All behaviour has a purpose. Everything we do is aimed towards one goal or another.

If you don't know where you're going how can you know how to get there?

I remarked in Part 1.1 how, since the beginning of time, the overwhelming experience of every creature on the planet has been that the survivors survive, but life is desperate. Resources are limited, uncertain and competed for. Every choice we make has a consequence that makes survival more or less likely. We are currently the most successful complex organism on the planet, and it could be argued that, from the perspective that we are 'information processing all the way up', our thoughts are the crowning achievement of that processing. 30% of our bodies' calories are consumed by our brain, so evolution has clearly invested heavily in its output. For that investment to be worthwhile our brain must help us be what the response to desperation needs us to be: *efficient*.

> *Our client's brains are often more comfortable with the certainty of misery than the uncertainty of happiness*

Efficiency is the best long-term return from the least immediate investment. In the view of Read Montague this lies at the heart of how our thoughts became meaningful; how they came to 'care'. They came to care because it made them more efficient, and, in his opinion, what thoughts (computations) care about are goals.[44] And in my opinion, that's because goals reduce uncertainty. Our clients' brains are often more comfortable with the certainty of misery than the uncertainty of happiness because it's what their computations have led it to. Unhappiness becomes an invariant. It's the world it's grown used to seeing, it's got you this far, and from within its closed loop it finds it hard to see what it hasn't experienced. Growth becomes the scary thing, and protection safer. And remember, uncertainty is the enemy. This is a phenomenon that often gets labelled as resistance. In my model, resistance is just the pressure of existing invariant beliefs to stay within the familiar.

> *Resistance is just the pressure of existing invariant beliefs to stay within the familiar*

In order to reduce uncertainty our brain evolved the capacity to plan, which involves being able to anticipate, and to measure, progress towards outcomes. Our single-celled ancestors had the most basic ability to plan, and successive evolutionary progressions have raised the bar all the way to us. Not only does our brain have goals, but the means to mentally calculate the path to their fulfilment with a sophistication beyond that of any other organism.

Goals are necessary to answer the questions that Montague suggests all creatures have to answer in order to survive: "What is the value of my available choices, and what does each cost?"[45] Having goals enables us to attribute a value to an action, and to assess its efficiency in achieving it. And in man, evolution has equipped his computations with the most sophisticated algorithms to calculate value; the memory loops I talked about earlier, operating within the memoragination.

As much as I disagree with him, I can quite see Edelman's reasons for dismissing the brain as a computer. My PC works to very specific goals; its outputs can be varied but are narrow in their final actions, they either output a spreadsheet, or a graphic or a word document. Life isn't like that. I might have a goal of going to the supermarket, but each trip will present different challenges that need to be adapted to. This flexibility is something we take for granted, but it has flummoxed artificial intelligence designers for many years. The truth is that the specific hard-wiring of goals is an inefficient way of achieving them, species unable to adapt have become extinct, while those that are capable of the required degree of flexibility in the face of environmental uncertainty have survived. Our brains have managed the trick, while remaining computers, to guide us flexibly towards the goals we come pre-equipped to value, or which our experience has led us to value. Key to this valuation system may be a single chemical that appears to guide our choices.

The chemical of choice

Many scientific discoveries are the result of great diligence, persistence and investigation, but most still require a dollop of luck. So it was with James Olds and Peter Milner. In 1954, while working at McGill University, they implanted an electrode into a rat's brain. By complete chance, the electrode ended up next to a brain structure called the *nucleus accumbens* (NAcc).[46] Whenever you see a friend for the first time in ages, or sip that perfect glass of wine, or watch your team score a goal, it's your NAcc that brings you the happy feelings.

My Nan always used to say that a little of what you fancy does you good, while a Roman playwright she went to school with called Terence, advised "All things in moderation". It turns out they were both right; too much happy can kill you. The scientists ran a small current through this electrode, keeping the rat – and the others they repeated it on – continually happy. The rodents lost interest in everything, food, water, sex, everything. They just huddled in a corner, lost in their bliss. Within days they had all died of thirst.

It took many years before the chemical responsible for this was isolated and identified as dopamine, and the massive release of it by the stimulation of the electrode had led to the rats being overwhelmed by ecstasy. I'm sure you'll have already thought of the similarity between what I've just described and the experience of drug addiction. It's because heroin and cocaine work in exactly the same way.

However, dopamine is much more than simply the happiness molecule. Researchers now know that it helps to regulate every emotion we experience – both positive and negative - and helps us to decide between alternative choices.

We can largely thank the persistence of neuroscientist Wolfram Shultz for unravelling how dopamine achieves this. While at Cambridge University he began investigating Parkinson's disease and experimented on the brains of monkeys to find which cells were involved in controlling body movement. For many years he was unsuccessful. One of the experiments involved rewarding the monkeys for moving in a particular way, often by giving them a piece of banana. One day he noticed that dopamine neurons fired just before the monkey was given the food, which was odd, because you'd think dopamine would be released when the reward was given, it's the happiness molecule, right? "At first I thought it was unlikely that an individual cell could represent anything so complicated as food," Schultz says. "It just seemed like too much information for one neuron."[47]

Dopamine is the means by which your brain gets you to go toward pleasure and away from pain

After hundreds of further experiments Schultz bowed to the weight of his evidence and concluded that he had found the reward mechanism in the primate brain; dopamine is the means by which your brain gets you to go toward pleasure and away from pain.

The experiment that Schultz used to get his data was simple. He sounded a tone, waited for a few seconds, and then squirted some drops of apple juice into the mouth of a monkey. While this was going on, the electrical activity in the dopamine cells was being monitored. At first the dopamine cells fired only when the juice was squirted – as you'd expect. However, once the monkey paired the tone with the imminent arrival of the juice – which only took a few repetitions of the exercise – the cells began to fire with the tone, instead of the reward of the juice. Shultz called these cells 'prediction neurons', since they appeared to be more involved with predicting a reward than the reward itself. What is also interesting is that this process can be indefinitely extended: the dopamine neurons can be trained to respond to a smell that precedes the tone, then a light that precedes the smell, and so on.

Schultz proved that, once learned, dopamine neurons become extremely sensitive to variations on such patterns. If the predictions proved correct and the reward arrived as expected, then the monkey received a brief surge of dopamine – the pleasure of being right. However, if the tone was played and the juice didn't arrive the dopamine neurons decreased their firing rate. The term for this is a *prediction-error signal*. In human terms the monkey felt 'upset' because its prediction of reward was wrong.

From our point of view, what is particularly relevant about what is being described here is that it's all about expectation – what is most likely to happen? And the patterns the dopamine neurons reinforce in order to refine predictions are mainly based on 'if this, then that'. That is why I've taken the time to describe the reward system in such detail: because dopamine appears to be the chemical that drives TAOTM, and why wouldn't it be, if TAOTM is the means by which the brain calculates what to move towards or away from?

> *Dopamine appears to be the chemical that drives TAOTM*

The monkeys learned that the tone predicted the juice, or that the smell preceded the tone that predicted the juice. Out of the chaos of information that surrounds us, the reward system distils patterns of causation that allow the brain to predict the immediate future.

One of the features of this system is the feedback that is built into it. The brain compares its predictions against what actually happens. Once a pattern of expectation has been learnt – such as juice follows a tone – the monkey's dopamine cells monitor the situation. If the prediction goes to plan the monkey gets a burst of 'happy stuff'. But if the juice doesn't arrive, the dopamine cells withhold their reward. The brain is designed to amplify the shock of these predictive mistakes. In the words of Jonah Lehrer, "Nothing focuses the mind like surprise."[48] We keep getting rewarded if we

> *We keep getting rewarded if we avoid surprises*

avoid surprises. Now, apply this to our survival system's closed loops. John keeps getting a dopamine reward every time he reacts to a dog according to the invariant contained within the loop - 'all dogs are dangerous' - while reward is withheld if he tries to change his response, because no new learning is admitted into his closed system. No wonder change can feel so difficult for our clients.

The dopamine system is an exquisite mechanism that enables us to adapt our causal models in response to the changing circumstances of our environment, and our experiences, but only if the memory loop is open to adaptation, otherwise all dopamine does is reinforce existing behaviour. Strong emotions don't actually make us stupid; they can just lead to us repeating a behaviour based on a wrong conclusion, and the reward system is completely ambivalent about what it rewards, it can be trained to reward unnecessary protection just as easily as joyful growth.

This is the reason why an identical event in our past can lead one person to live a life of fulfilment, and another one of addiction, depression or anxiety, or one person to under-achieve and another to strive. In both cases, the polarity responses are the end result of a reward system being trained through miscalculation to release dopamine for behaviour that is either harmful or at least detrimental to the person's quality of life. And we like the feeling of dopamine, it's why it works, so in many respects one of the things therapists have to work on is the client's addiction to their problem, because dopamine rewards certainty.

We have to wean the client onto a solution that may initially feel less rewarding than the certainty of their issue, and train their brain to begin to reward the choices that take them toward their desired outcome.

We don't like to think of our brains being a bodge, but Gary Marcus is right to point out that if it were designed it could only have been by an unintelligent designer. As the brain evolved, it adapted to the challenges the environment set it, and new systems were able to run more and more sophisticated versions of the causative algorithms that had proved so successful. Ordinal, interval and ratio processing were harnessed by our cortex to take our abilities to predict our most productive choices to new levels of accuracy. Given time to consider options, our unconscious can create wonderfully creative ideas and solutions to problems. Given time. But residing beneath this shiny new software is the old soldier, our limbic survival system. It has no time for time, it's a gunslinger that shoots first and asks no questions afterwards.

Because it operates within a closed loop learning system, initial mistakes it makes with its nominal processing can become locked into lifelong limiting behaviour that the reward system amplifies the longer it continues. We may do stupid things, but they're really just a stupid way of trying to do a good thing.

How can I use this?

If we understand that the problems clients bring us (or we ourselves experience) are the result of a memory loop that is stuck in closed loop learning, then we can focus on how to introduce new information into it that will cause the brain to reassess the loop's actions, which we cover in Part 2.4.

We can also change the structure of the thoughts contained in the loop that create the emotion contained within it. By removing the emotion we remove the need to take the action they existed to drive. That's in Part 2.5.

And if our client's reward system has made him or her addicted to her problem, we need to pace their withdrawal and initiate a dopamine response to actions that move them towards their desired outcome and away from their problem. That's in Part 2.7.

Our present complexity emerged from a beautiful simplicity that still runs in the background to protect us from physical threats, but the story of the last 200,000 years has been of the growing importance of our ability to interact with each other. Our increased reliance on the group we belong to has reduced the physical danger we face, but made any threat to our position within the group a danger in itself, and one the protection system will respond to with its big guns. We may perceive rejection, humiliation, embarrassment, sadness, guilt or worthlessness as a result of the actions of others, but all the protection system sees is a sabre-toothed tiger. The difficulties this adds to the mix are the subject of the next chapter.

It's all about me

What's this about?

From the moment of our birth our unconscious attention is focused on how to be safe within our social group - from our parents through to our society at large. This focus is perfectly natural, but in our modern world it can often be hijacked so that it becomes a potent source of stress and unhappiness.

The story of *homo sapiens* has been a story of our algorithms evolving to make us more efficient in using our energy to survive. As a relatively frail creature surrounded by competitors red in tooth and claw, an early strategy was to band together, and we've done so with increasing complexity ever since. In our days as hunter gatherers our survival became intimately linked with whoever we became intimately linked with: our parents, partners, and clan or tribe members. The higher we rose within the group, the closer to the carcass we got to sit and the greater the choice of mates. The less we were esteemed the closer to the draughty cave-mouth we slept, and the more we had to make do with the leftovers. That is what I meant when I suggested one of our hard-wired sub-goals was power: the pursuit of influence in its many guises. Being well-thought of became a survival issue for our genes. And so it has continued.

In our modern world there are few physical dangers that create a day-to-day need to respond in all of us. Lions in Piccadilly Circus are a rarity – although sometimes the shoppers might seem just as predatory. While clients will often include obvious examples of our prehistoric conditioning – such as spider and snake phobias - most of the things they complain of will be more of a consequence of the pressures created by being social.

From the moment we're born, one of the primary focuses of the brain is the recognition of others – particularly our parents. Within 40 minutes of being born babies are capable of mimicking the facial movements of others, and can recognise their parents' faces within a week.[49] The hormone oxytocin is released in parent and baby in response to contact, which acts as a bonding mechanism. Nature chucks everything it has at ensuring that the parents connect with their child in order to nurture it, because, if they don't, that's the end of the line for those genes – in cave society there were no social services. Like all brains, a child's is a survival calculator and what is most likely to ensure that child's survival is gaining and sustaining the love of the parents. It's no accident that children are so cute, and manage to dream up another funny little thing just as the last funny little thing was getting a bit boring. They're having you over people! The little brats are manipulating you into loving them for their own ends by a succession of dirty tricks called smiling, laughing, crawling, walking and talking. If they did them all together you'd be bored by them by their first birthday. But don't worry, they tend to give up this subterfuge the minute they hit their teens.

This love-thing works both ways, though. The child is acutely sensitised to the approval, or withdrawal of it, by the parents, and parents use it all the time as a key means of getting compliance. How many of you reward your child's behaviour by giving them a treat of some kind? Of course you do. How many of you punish your child by withdrawing your love, affection or approval? Not so fast...

"It would have been so nice if you'd remembered my birthday..."

"If you loved me you would have..."

"If you loved me you wouldn't..."

And of course, the favourite stealth-weapon..."I'm disappointed..."

> *You say 'disappointed', your child hears, "I'm sure this isn't what I ordered from the stork."*

You say 'disappointed', your child hears, "I'm sure this isn't what I ordered from the stork." In my years as a therapist I have regressed hundreds of people, using the techniques I cover in Part 2.4, to help them with issues of low self- esteem or confidence. On occasion, the sensitising event has been an act of cruelty or abuse on the part of a parent or other person, but the overwhelming majority are interactions that occur in households everywhere, where a parent, whose intention is to teach the child something that will lead to them developing into what the parent thinks is the best kind of adult to survive (i.e., them), says something that the child interprets as meaning they aren't lovable, worthwhile, good enough, or wanted. Gil Boyne, one of the world's greatest ever hypnotherapists and with over fifty years of seeing clients, suggests that the most common neurosis is the belief that we're not lovable, and my experience leans me towards his conclusion. And it's simply because we're primed to look for love - and its absence - as key guidance mechanisms to move us towards safety. But in the way that most families manifest it, and children misunderstand the actions of others, it can become something that leads to the nagging feeling as an adult that, somehow,

> *The most common neurosis is the belief that we're not lovable*

everyone else is better, happier, more attractive, more likely to succeed or be loved. And if that feeling becomes strong enough it prevents us from being in growth.

So, my contention is that most people have a doubt in their mind about their worth that begins in childhood, which can grow into a variety of bigger things years down the line. Depending on the individual experiences we have, it will be expressed in different ways, and in different situations. Some people will strive to achieve but never be satisfied, some will avoid success in case it leads to failure. Some will sweat at the prospect of speaking in front of others, some will find it difficult to sustain relationships for the fear that intimacy will expose their lack of lovability. And the ironic thing is that all such behaviours are being rewarded with dopamine because the behaviours that are the result of such inhibitions are the survival system's best available choice at this time. It is doing the best it can based on the closed-loop information it's using, but it keeps us stuck in protection.

Some would argue that society itself feeds on this neurosis. Ever since the nephew of Sigmund Freud, Edmund Bernays, developed the public relations technique of attaching an emotion to an object in order to sell it, we have been beset by advertisers promising us that we'd be sexier, prettier, more successful, better parents, heroic, more manly or richer, if only we'd buy their product. Apparently, an early success for Bernays was when he was employed by a cake mix company to sell their product in the 1950's. The idea of being able to bake a cake straight from a packet was innovative at the time, and people were slow to adopt it. His suggestion was simply to make it necessary to add an egg. "But Mr Bernays, it was explained, "that's the genius of the idea, the powdered egg is already in the packet." "Yes, but if the housewife adds the egg, she's still a cook," he replied. Sales rocketed, and the 'do something to the ingredients' has been a part of TV meals ever since simply because it rewards the self-image of the user.

Before Bernays, products were sold more for their qualities than their kudos; a shoe was sold on its quality and longevity, not on how cool you were for wearing the same shoes as David Beckham.

Our worth in the eyes of others is judged by the things we own

The consumer society now maintains its purchasing cycle by the insidious suggestion that our worth in the eyes of others is judged by the things we own, the products we use and the places we're seen in. I once had a client who worked for a large computer company. He was seeing me for stress, and one of the things stressing him was that he wanted to change his VW Golf Gti for the latest version. "How old is your car?" I asked. "One year old," he confessed, flushing a little. "So what's so different about the new model?" "Erm...it's got new shaped headlights..." he said, probably hearing the thinness of the argument. The real issue was driving into the staff car park in a car that was 'so last year'. As a young father, the pressure of appearing successful was exceeding his ability to purchase it – hence the stress. Stress is simply the presence of the state of protection in our life.

Steven Sloman, says "A psychologist focuses on human and not material relationships because our emotional health is always a function of our relationships to other people and related only weakly and indirectly to our material possessions."[50] I disagree. In my opinion one is often a symbol of the other. I suspect the builders of the pyramids would agree. And so would a collector of exotic cars, or shoes.

What our society calls stress is actually just a lower-level manifestation of the protection response

Most instances of what our society calls stress is actually just a lower-level manifestation of the protection response. Unfortunately, the ability to live in more densely populated groups (only in the last 8000 years), brought about by the development of agriculture, has greatly outpaced our ability to evolve to suit it. We are far more adapted to the conditions that prevailed for the two million years that preceded it where we lived in groups of between 20 and 150 as hunter- gatherers.

While the last two chapters have identified physical and social survival as the core motivators that drive behaviour, what I'm suggesting is that, while I've divided them into two categories, our survival system doesn't. Survival is survival, so a social threat is treated like a physical one; adrenalin is released, preparing us to run away, freeze or fight. But from what? Other people's opinions in the main. As we grow up, the sensitivity to the approval of our parents migrates onto the opinions of other important adults, like teachers, peers, and, in the bigger picture, the values of society.

Unfortunately, our society has evolved the means of gaining this feeling of approval through the acquisition of possessions, so the threat of not having them, or losing them, creates a response more akin to the threat of an approaching predator than a problem for our intelligence to solve. This confusion of signals lies at the heart of many of our problems; strong emotions make us stupid, so our unconscious response to things that concern us is to hijack our state and propel us to courses of action that are often the opposite of what we, in a more positive state, would choose. All our behaviour has a purpose, but for most of it, that purpose is arrived at by unconscious deliberations we have nothing to do with. We approach many events we perceive as stressful, like job interviews, work and dating as if they're sabre-toothed tigers. Which is, of course, ridiculous, unless you've had my dating history.

What has made social survival such a complicated business for humans has been the arrival of the 'self'. What are simple evolutionary calculations to guide the organism towards social and physical reward and away from social and physical danger get hijacked as the self uses them to 'value' itself. This, I believe, is the root of the damaging invariants many people have about ourselves: "I'm stupid" "I'm not good enough" "I'm not lovable" "I'm not worthwhile" "I don't deserve" "I shouldn't be here", are some of the common self-ideas, which distort, twist, or block the direction our life takes.

There are many social creatures who display behaviours that establish their position within the hierarchy of their group, and increase their chances of mate selection - including, of course, our cousins the chimpanzees. But only with us has the success or failure of these strategies been linked to an emotion about ourselves, because, so far as we can tell, only we have a self to have an emotion about. And in the next chapter I talk about the idea of being ourselves, and its place in our problems. The centre, usually.

How to use this

Over time, two things have been constantly relevant to our survival - the need to keep us from physical harm, and successful social connection.

In the modern western world we feel threatened more often by challenges to our place in society than we do by threats to our physical well-being, but this world is too new for our protection system to have adapted to, so its response to the stresses of modern life is still that of fight or flight.

When we are young, our limited ability to evaluate the meaning of our experiences can lead to errors of understanding that lead to the fight or flight response becoming the invariant response to every connection made in your memoragination, between something in a present situation and the memory of something that caused your protection system to act. The avoidance of such events becomes a goal that your reward system builds into your reality tunnel, so over time your life is guided away from ordinary things you've been unconsciously trained to treat as a threat.

As therapists it is our job to explore such narratives, from original miscalculations, all the way through to their present consequences. But not for the purposes of insight, because our rational understanding of why we do things is usually insufficient to change them. In Part 2.4, particularly, I describe the techniques that don't stop at exploring the narrative, but actively work to reinterpret the meanings about ourselves we pick up in childhood that limit and inhibit us, and enable us to re-write our story.

Is there anybody in here?

What's this about?

The story so far has been one of how a computer has evolved better and better ways of calculating the most efficient actions to take in order to survive. The causative model has proved a great means of predicting outcomes, and our memoragination a means by which patterns of similarity, difference and causation can be stored, accessed and used to create a reality tunnel to guide our actions in the most rewarding (or threat averting) direction. At the pointy end of this evolution, and the thing that has made us so successful as a species, is our great capacity for prediction. The more accurately we can see the future, the less energy we'll waste in pursuit of the wrong goals. In this chapter, I'm going to talk about how the end result of TAOTM pursuing the goal of perfect prediction is our sense of self. Who we feel ourselves to be was just an idea the brain had to help it plan, and then that idea had an idea of its own. And that can be a problem.

Mirror mirror in the brain...

The discovery of *mirror neurons* may turn out to be as defining a moment in history as the apple falling on Newton's head, yet the moment of their being revealed isn't recorded, although the following is the urban myth that fulfils so many of the needs for a good story...

In a laboratory in the Italian city of Parma, a team of neuroscientists led by Giacomo Rizzolatti were investigating an area of the brain labelled F5, part of the neocortex associated with planning, selecting, and executing actions. F5 is packed with clusters of neurons that are responsible for actions by the hand: reaching, gripping, striking, and importantly, bringing objects to the mouth.

The team's work had added a great deal of understanding of the nature of these motor cells by performing experiments on macaque monkeys. One day one of these was wired up, sitting in its chair in the company of one of the researchers, prior to the next experiment. As the monkey waited, the scientist took a bite out of an ice cream. As he did so there was a burst of activity from the machine monitoring the F5 area of the monkey's brain. This was immediately thought strange because the monkey showed no sign of movement. It seemed that the monkey was copying the action of the researcher in its head.

There are other versions of the story, but that's my favourite. Whichever is true, the observation set off a twenty year cascade of investigation into this phenomenon which is still ongoing, and which proved that the monkey had cells in F5 which activated in response to its observation of the action of another creature as if it was performing the action itself. Such cells have since been discovered in humans, and simulate far more than just motor actions. In the words of Marco Iacoboni, a neuroscientist at the forefront of this field, mirror neurons "fire when an individual kicks a soccer ball, sees a ball being kicked, hears a ball being kicked, and even just says or hears the word 'kick'."[51]

One of my most intense emotional experiences when watching someone else, was the rugby player Jonny Wilkinson when he scored the winning drop-goal against Australia, in Sydney, in the last moments of the 2003 Word Cup Final. Even typing these words has raised my emotional state. It's because, I now realise, at the moment of watching, my brain ran a simulation of the kick as if it was my experience and I was rewarded with my approximation of how good Jonny felt as the ball soared between the posts. And because that event was so strongly emotional, thinking about it fires my feelings all over again. Doesn't that make sense of how many of us respond when watching sports?

Now imagine I listen to six clients pour their sad tales out during an average day of therapy, and my mirror neurons cause my body to respond as if their experiences were mine. Is it any wonder that so many therapists and counsellors burn out? This is one of the things that Cognitive Hypnotherapy is designed to protect you from.

Even beyond this, neither monkeys nor humans can look at an object like an apple without firing the motor plans necessary to grab it. Think about that; perception and action are not separated in the brain, they're part of the same thing. What we can do with objects is part of what we perceive about them, and the potential actions for each object we perceive come stored within it. Remember me saying that 80% of the information we use to make sense of the world comes from within us? Every time we look at something we're also unconsciously aware of everything that could be done with it - its potential. The decision our brain makes about the context the object appears in will determine the choice of which action is most appropriate. And if the object is matched with something from within a closed loop (i.e., one containing a strong emotional charge), the range of behavioural choice will be severely limited.

> *Perception and action are not separated in the brain, they're part of the same thing*

New discoveries regarding these amazing neurons are happening all the time, and what is clear is that ours are more evolved than those of any other species so far examined. We have mirror neurons that fire in response to the pantomime of an action, ie performing an action 'as if' the object of that action were present, like swinging a kick at an imaginary ball. And while other creatures have strictly contingent neurons – they fire only when observing a clearly defined action in relation to an object - ours are able to fire in response to much broader imitations of actions. In other words, they allow for creative interpretation of actions that could lead to brand new actions.

In mirror neurons we have a potential source for the causal model: by allowing us to run variations on an action we have the roots of our ability to run counterfactual futures. They let us have new ideas. Mirror neurons may just be the source for much of the creativity that characterises humans.

So, to pause and reflect here for a moment, because I'm getting a bit excited. We have these clever neurons that run simulations of the actions and emotional responses of others. These may be the basis for how we learn as children – and often how we'll continue to learn as adults in many situations. There is compelling evidence that our neurons have evolved to be able to achieve quite generalised patterns of copying – simulations that allow for 'as if' scenarios – i.e. 'what would happen if I did it this way?'[52] Mirror neurons may be how we began to be able to construct the counterfactual futures that enabled us to run different versions of an outcome. And once we started being able to do this, does it seem too far-fetched that the idea occurred at some point to create a simulation of ourselves within such a future to be able to assess it even more efficiently?

Let me give an example: Imagine a pre-conscious human, living within a tribe of hunter gatherers. He does what you and I continue to do every day in the modern world; in the words of Iacoboni, he "reads the world[53]". He searches for patterns of meaning in the activity around him by looking for causal relationships within the actions of his fellow tribes-people. He has for a long time noticed that the most successful hunters get the best looking women, (spot the causal relationship) but he's quite small and can't throw his spear as far or as hard as some of his fellows. One day he's down by the river and he watches some youngsters fooling around in the shallows, ducking each other and splashing about. He notices two boys who are taking turns at hurling themselves out of the water by one of them putting a foot into the cupped hands of the other, who then lifts him up as fast and hard as he can so that he's catapulted backwards. On one occasion the boy being lifted keeps his body stiff as he's rises from the water. Just like a spear. Just like a...The man has an idea. In his mind he becomes the boy doing the lifting, and the other boy becomes a spear: *he puts himself into the simulation*. He rehearses the action in his head...there's something about it...he gets a spear and a shorter length of wood. He makes a hole in the wood so that the butt of the spear fits in it, holds it at the other end and then propels the spear upwards like he'd seen the boy do to his friend. The spear soars into the air far further than he could have thrown it unaided. With practice he learns

> *Mirror neurons may have begun the arms race*

to use the throwing stick so that it flies further and harder than the best hunter in the tribe. The women flock to him and other men notice his success. Mirror neurons may have begun the arms race.

Being able to run a possible future scenario (a counterfactual world) through our own eyes is an advantage, **but**, being able to see **yourself** doing things in the future is an even bigger one. As soon as his rivals see him using the throwing stick, they can run a scenario in their heads of them doing the same in a way that simply isn't possible from a first person perspective. Suddenly, being able to use an object that represents you as the basis for comparison with others, and with alternative 'you's' in the future, conferred a number of survival advantages. Indeed a recent research study found that we are more likely to carry out an action in the future if we picture ourselves doing it, compared to imagining doing it through our own eyes.[54] As well as being able to imagine counterfactual worlds, we became able to imagine counterfactual selves – people we would be in different situations – calm, confident, strong, weak, scared, hurt. How much could that help the reliability of our predictions?

Having a self (i.e. being a something/one that wasn't any other thing or person), and assuming the existence of the 'self's' of others, would also give us a massive advantage when it comes to cooperation. We're not the fastest, strongest, biggest, smallest, most numerous, sneakiest (well, maybe close) or scariest. We live or die as social creatures; it's our intelligence and ability to commune - to be in intimate, accurate communication – that has led to our achievements as a species.

To live with the high level of social interaction we do requires a level of rapport unmatched in the animal world. We are the best imitators on the planet, and borrow everything from each other as a near-invisible form of learning. The simplest of social connections involves an exquisite exchange of near-subliminal, predominantly non-verbal messages which are four times more powerful than words alone.[55] This skill is so taken for granted that it's only its absence that reveals its presence, as in the case of people with autism, and our ability to copy is intrinsic to this level of personal connection. Researchers of rapport have found repeatedly that people unconsciously trust people who are like them,[56] and that people in rapport match and mirror aspects of each other's physiology. Watch two people in enjoyable conversation and you'll soon see them shift positions in response to the movements of the other, use similar gestures, and even adopt similar phraseology. Bizarrely, researchers even found that test subjects rated computers higher for such qualities as cooperation, learning ability, task-achievement, comfort, friendliness, and sympathy when, unbeknownst to them, the computer mimicked the intonation and rhythm of the subject's voice when interacting with them.[57] Mimicry enables close relationships, and also helps us to monitor them.

To be able to copy someone to the level we do, we need to recognise that there's a 'them' to copy (or we'd mimic blindly and start imitating photocopiers and coffee machines – especially those that talk like us), and for there to be a 'them' there has to be a 'me' to compare to.

Having a 'me' also allows the brain to assess our social success in relation to the rest of the tribe, and to see ourselves in different time frames. It transforms the nature of the memoragination by making it personal, and gives us an unrivalled ability to run simulations of our future in order to predict the best course of action. In a very real sense we become a character in a story we tell ourselves, one where our brain can keep refining the narrative, as well as altering the back story to make sense of the present plotlines.

We become a character in a story we tell ourselves

But why me?

I hope I've given you enough reasons for you to see the advantage of the brain being able to create a simulation of the object it occupies and place it within the memoragination, but does that mean we, our subjective experience, needed to appear? Did the simulation need to wake up? Presumably our brains could run a simulation of our physical self simply as another feature of the reality tunnel without needing a sense of a self distinct from our bodies? I think it could, and I think for most of *homo's* time on the planet, it did. Then something happened, probably about 150-200,000 years ago.

I think the relationship between mirror neurons and causal modelling may have been what happened. Our mirror neurons attach actions to objects, ie the existence of this apple contains my intentions towards it. This could be because our brains are tuned to causation; an apple is an opportunity to sate our hunger, just as a group of people are an opportunity to impress and increase our standing in the group. Also, our ability to mirror to subtle levels of abstraction is a use of finely-sliced equivalence; I can watch a seabird tease a winkle from its shell with its beak and have the idea of using my needle to do the same thing i.e., objects and actions can become the cause of new actions.

Once the idea of a self appears in the reality tunnel it becomes another object that has actions attached to it – over a lifetime, a repertoire of what the self is like emerges, and the self becomes a cause of things. This seems so obvious that it is worth thinking of for a moment. Look at any other creature. Animals act and react within the world, but they have no apparent sense of 'agency', of being a creator of the world. This is a momentous difference. The result of a causal model way of representing reality could lead to a new idea - personal agency – a feeling that there's a 'you' that causes things to happen. The existence of our 'I' could just be an emergent property of the sophistication of the causal model, and not something the brain is 'aware' of, beyond its presence as another stream of information to act on. 'I' (and of course I mean 'we'), may be just a good idea.

We're such a good idea

To rewind a little, back to mirror neurons, neuroscientist Dr Susan

Emergent Properties

Emergence is what happens when the whole is smarter than the sum of its parts. It's what happens when you have a network of component parts, which can themselves be very simple and interact in simple ways, and yet somehow out of all this interaction some higher-level structure, action, or intelligence appears without any master planner calling the shots. These kinds of systems tend to evolve from the ground up.

Bees are a great example of this. We think of a Queen Bee in her hive somehow organising the activities of her subjects through a hierarchy of minions. Yet this is not the case. Colonies have this seemingly miraculous ability to pull off complex engineering or resource management feats without an actual leadership dictating what any bee should be doing at any particular time. They just follow a lot of local rules, and through those rules the intelligence of the colony comes into being.

An emergent property is not predictable by examination of the separate parts of that system. For a property to be emergent it has to satisfy two criteria; no part of the system taken in isolation has that property, and the property is not merely a summation (or end result) of properties of parts of the system. In other words if there was a Queen in the colony saying to her dunce subjects "No….left a bit.." the intelligence of the colony would not be emergent, and in the second case the movement of a car is not an emergent property of the car because it is a planned consequence of the properties of all of its parts. An emergent property of a car would be its cultural impact – such as the role of the Mini in 1960's swinging Britain, which was not anticipated by the people who designed it.

Our sense of self could be an emergent property of the complex calculations our causative model is able to make.

Blackmore believes that our wonderful ability to imitate is what makes us different, and this difference is what makes us human.

When you imitate somebody *something* has been passed to you. This *something* can then be passed onto others, potentially for ever. The *something* can have many names, including an instruction, an idea or an action. In the context of Susan Blackmore's work, the name given to it is a *meme*. This word first appeared in 1976, in Richard Dawkins bestselling book *The Selfish Gene*. In that book Dawkins laid out his theory that evolution is best understood in terms of a competition between genes, and he meant them as selfish only in the respect that they act for themselves, their ultimate purpose is their own replication.

Where Dawkins pushed the boundaries was in seeing the principle of *replication* as the defining quality of evolution and the question he asked at the end of the book was, "Are there any other replicators on our planet?" (other than genes). [58] He believed there was another, and he called it a *meme* - a unit of imitation. In his view, just because there appeared to be only one replicator driving life on earth – the gene – it didn't mean there *had* to be. Memetics suggests that there are at least two, that the second one is the meme, and that we are their hosts. And when we talk of memes we basically mean ideas that are transmitted verbally or by repeated action from one mind to another.

There seems to be no reason why not. Evolutionary theory describes how life is shaped by the competition between replicators - something that follows the algorithm of variation (something that changes in the course of its transmission), selection (those changes that bring an advantage to the recipient are likely to be most successful) and retention (a consequence of that success will be their onward transmission). Genes are one example, and a good case can be made for memes being another. For this to be the case the general theory of evolution must apply to both, but how each replicator specifically works may be quite different.

I've provided evidence that imitation improves our ability to survive, and the consequence of that is an inevitable arms race where the brains most capable of imitating survive the best, and the genes responsible are passed on. Throughout our history, as this ability increased and what we imitated became more abstract, the ideas that got transmitted from one person to the other were able to be adapted to more and different

The brain most able to hold the most ideas prospered best

situations; the situation arose whereby the brain able to hold the most ideas prospered best.

This is the point at which, memetic theory suggests, humanity changed from a creature purely driven by the selfish gene, to a creature whose genes had to adapt in response to the thoughts the brain was having. In other words, our mind became a driver for our evolution, where before it had only been our environment. Memeticists, like Blackmore and Daniel Dennett, believe that the reason the brain grew to the size it did (and really in quite an explosive surge) was to make it more capable of passing on ideas, and that the development of language arose from this need too. We talk because it's the most efficient way of passing on ideas (which is why words are such a powerful medium for our therapy), and while that has brought us great survival advantage (i.e., benefit to the gene), it occurred originally for the benefit of the meme and **not** the gene.

> *We could be just another idea the brain is a host for*

Similarly, our memoragination can be seen as a repository of ideas that aid survival, and just as genes learnt to band together for mutual advantage (our bodies can be thought of as a gang of genes that hang out together), so do ideas (or memes). The Algorithms of the Mind (TAOTM) are a system of ideas that aided prediction by finding patterns of invariance. A belief we hold can be seen as a collection of ideas drawn from our experiences that have a strong degree of invariance, and such a collection is described in memetics as a *memeplex*; over a lifetime we would accumulate many thousands of them. If emergence is a continual consequence of complexity, then at a certain point where our brains reached the stage of being able to have the kinds of ideas that separate us from other primates, what might emerge from the interaction of a host of memeplexes is an idea that binds *them* together at a further level of emergence: a self, or, as Susan Blackmore calls it, a *selfplex*.

The idea of a selfplex binds together our experiences and beliefs into a narrative, a story about how this organism called Tom, Dick or Harriet created a life from the things that happened and the choices he or she made. We could be just another idea the brain is a host for, a selfplex, it's just that this particular idea thinks it owns the joint, and what it does and where it goes is down to it alone. We're an idea that thinks it's matter, and that it matters - an illusion, and this is great news, or at least it will be by the time you've got to the end of this part of the book. So from now on when I use the word self, add 'plex' to the end of it to remind you that I'm talking about an idea, not a real thing.

We could be no more than an idea that has an idea of itself being real. And it may be the most successful idea in the history of the world, or ultimately, the way we're going, it could kill us all.

The problem with me

What I am proposing is that within our bodge of a brain are different systems which have evolved at different times in response to the demand to become as efficient at surviving as possible. Amongst these systems is the ancient protection system, evolved to advance the replication of the gene; a fast and dirty gunfighter that throws adrenalin at problems and drives us along a narrow reality tunnel of limited choices and little opportunity for refinement. This is part of a more general unconscious network of systems (that we generally just label the unconscious) that have evolved to go beyond nominal processing and use the idea of a causal network for some sublimely fine observations of similarity, cause and difference. The results of this system we tend to generally label our intuition - knowing without knowing how - possibly what James Clarke Maxwell the brilliant physicist was talking about when he said, "What is done by what is called myself is, I feel, done by something greater than myself in me". Tor Norretranders uses this quote to distinguish between the unconscious 'me' and the conscious 'I'.[59]

This sense of 'I'ness, the conscious, is the new kid on the block. We all know we have one, but it's darned hard to define: that sense we have of experiencing our existence.

I've suggested that this sense of being a 'somebody' is an emergent property of the same causative model that assigned agency to other objects, like "the storm caused the damage", or "that tiger caused that injury". Eventually the meme occurred that there was a 'something' causing the actions of the body we walk around in: an 'I', and at that point 'we' separated from the rest of existence. Ever since, we've had the feeling that there is an 'us' and then there is the rest of the universe.

So we have several systems, all using the causative model, but at different levels of complexity, and all still pursuing the goals and sub-goals we've evolved to follow to enable our genes or memes to survive efficiently. Mainly they operate to mutual advantage, but sometimes an error in understanding communication can cause them to work against each other. John's conscious desire to be found attractive to Bruiser's owner was severely dented by his survival system's choice of action in the face of a 'killer' chihuahua.

84

Having a 'me' takes my concerns about my security within my group to a whole new level of complexity. No longer is it just about simple survival, it's about much finer slices of equivalence - "am I as loved as other people?" - "am I as good?" - "am I fulfilled?" - "do I have as much as others?" Everything we do becomes weighed on the scales of self-worth, and because our 'me' feels responsible for everything we do, it also weighs things it has nothing to do with. So after John has emerged from the shop after the Bruiser incident, his 'I' is likely to weigh his self and find it wanting - "How stupid are you for running away from a little dog like that? What a wimp!"

What he doesn't realise is that his conscious self, capable of clear and rational thought, has been sucked into a nominal reality tunnel by his protection system. In such a closed loop environment all he has available to think with is what is within it, so his conclusions about himself are also nominal. No new understanding or perspective, just a shoot-from-the-hip conclusion - "I must be stupid." And John doesn't even realise how restricted his boundaries are during this process because our sense of reality is always that it is true and complete, not just a momentary snapshot. What is likely to happen as a consequence is that the 'balloon' of this particular tunnel will expand to occupy more of the memoraginaton. Over time, this closed loop becomes the reference for the self in present situations more and more often. As the belief that, "I'm stupid" becomes invariant, it is used to filter an increasing number of situations. Over time John becomes more and more a person who lives in a state of protection, with fewer and fewer opportunities for growth. A simple idea from Dr Leonard Orr captures this perfectly:

Imagine your mind has two parts, the Thinker and the Prover. Your Thinker contains all the conclusions of your lifetime's causal modelling - your beliefs. The job of the Prover is to organise the information flowing through your senses in such a way as to support your Thinker. The adage - which I call Orr's Law – is, "What the Thinker thinks the Prover proves."[60]

"What the Thinker thinks, the Prover proves"

The net result of our mental system is that we become more certain over time. Our Prover gets more rigid in its determination of what supports the Thinker's beliefs. If I can pursue the balloon analogy just one step further, the Prover provides the air that fills the balloon of a closed system. All that fills it will be of a similar substance: everything that entered the Prover's lungs on the in breath is filtered so that when expelled into the balloon it seems like it's all the same thing. If the Thinker thinks itself unloved, whatever evidence there is to the contrary never gets admitted to the balloon until it's been distorted by the Prover to support the invariant.

It's ironic that we have evolved the ability to think logically and apply reason, but use it less and less as we age to deepen our understanding of the world, and more and more rely on the way things have 'always been'.

In a sense our reality tunnel becomes a series of closed balloons rather than a kaleidoscope. As Serge Kahili King points out "the world is what you think it is,"[61] and what you think it is becomes more concrete with every experience that passes. This is the tragedy of having this wonderful consciousness: this 'self', for whom everything is about the 'I', is actually the writer of his own narrative without realising it, but the interaction between protection system and self too often means we just keep reliving old plotlines like a hackneyed soap.

I said long ago that the causative model was the architect of our reality. I said more recently that our 'self' is a part of that same model, so by utilising TAOTM in the ways I'm going to show you we can become the architect of our own reality, the writer of our own tale, the creator of our own 'self'. We make our tunnel a prison or a palace, but most people don't realise we have a choice.

Making our 'self' up

If we let go of the pretensions of consciousness – that we're created specially, we are a soul that is eternal, blah blah blah, and think of ourselves as just another input of information to the brain – part of the brain's environment - it gives us a wonderful freedom: it means we can potentially influence our brain in the way it responds to any other environmental information.

Mind affects matter, because it's the interface between the physical brain and the physical world. Reality is changed into a stream of information by its passage through the senses, and it's from that limited bandwidth of information that the brain constructs its reality tunnel. The world is created within the same 3lbs of grey matter that is the host of the idea that is you, and the brain cannot tell the difference between the world that runs around its synapses, and the you that does the same. To the brain you're another source of information it has to take into account and respond to. And that is how you (I'm just going to say you, and not 'the idea of you', because it would become tiresome) can work to choose your reality, instead of feeling that you're stuck with who you are. If the present idea of you isn't bringing you happiness, isn't keeping you in growth, you can work to intercept and replace it with an idea of you that would.

How can I use this?

Many years ago now I had a client called Chloe, an intelligent, lovely, lively girl of 17 with anorexia. If you look at the history of anorexia you'll find that it's a meme that was first described in 1670, but has only become prevalent since the late sixties. Now, it's become an extremely powerful idea that leads to the death of one in five of its hosts. I introduced Chloe to the idea of memes, and together we developed another idea with which to fight the anorexia: that anorexia was a virus that had infected her brain and was leading her to have thoughts about her body being fat and food being a bad thing. Using a variety of techniques, Chloe became better and better at intercepting these 'virus thoughts' with 'Chloe thoughts'. She's now a talented young Cognitive Hypnotherapist specialising in eating disorders, and a mother of three. Many, if not all, problems can be thought of as memes.

The job of any meme is to be infectious; to be so rewarding that it 'sticks' in the mind and gets passed on to others. The job of therapy is to replace the meme that is having a negative effect with a new idea that proves more rewarding and sticky. All the techniques in Part Two can help to achieve that.

In more general terms, life itself becomes a process of writing the best story about ourselves that we can. If I work to interpret every experience I can as a positive; if I can avoid dwelling on negatives; if I look back in my past for all the evidence of me being loved, and being worthwhile; if I imagine tomorrow and every day afterwards being a positive experience, then my brain has to react to this information, which will cause it to create a reality tunnel within which this perception of reality fits. I will live in growth – which I believe benefits you all the way down to the cellular level, as Appendix three describes. If I act as the man I want to be, the brain has to build a world around me that makes sense of such behaviour. I'm not suggesting this is easy, but it is possible, and in Part 2.7 I describe ways to do this.

You; this idea you have that you exist, could decide who you want to be, and cause your brain to tune itself to create the reality tunnel which supports the you you choose to be. Your brain tunes itself to respond to the environment (i.e. you), so choosing an attitude towards your life will cause your brain to create the model of the world that supports your self-narrative. Whoever you believe yourself to be will be validated by the brain over time, because 'what the Thinker thinks the Prover proves.' You can live as a *growthplex*, or a *protectionplex*.

If our selfplex is the end result of a huge number of experiences that we've woven into a narrative, can science help us in knowing where within this epic we need to re-write key plot points that will change the character that is us in the present?

Thanks to an Italian with an interest in the internet, Kevin Bacon, and a meteorologist, the answer is 'yes'.

Kevin Bacon and the Butterfly

What's this about?

Reality tunnels are created from our stored memories, particularly those deemed relevant to our survival. Our brain is the most complex network of connections in the universe, and in this chapter we explore a model of how complex networks grow and operate that provides a powerful guide to the direction we should take our therapy.

If the negative things we believe about ourselves are the result of the meaning we've taken from significant life events, then changing the meaning of those events, or the structure of the memory of those events, could change the feeling we have about ourselves that is a consequence of them.

If we change the right memories, we change ourselves. In this chapter I suggest how we can know what those 'right' memories are.

A dictionary description of *network* is "a system of interlinking operations". By that definition we are surrounded by them. Social networks like a church group, or rotary, or a football supporter's club, or Facebook, business networks like your team, or your market sector, or your customer base, even the ecosystem which keeps us alive are all examples. In fact, we ourselves can be described as a network of interlinking cells and biological operations that keeps us alive. More particularly, in this chapter I suggest that our memoragination is a network and follows a universal law regarding how complex networks organise themselves that was first discovered by Albert-Laszlo Barabasi[62]. Understanding this law gives us important clues about which memories to target that are the source of present problems.

Barabasi's interest was in discovering more about the properties of complex networks and his research used the world wide web as an example of one. Prior to his work the conventional model of a complex network described a random structure - like putting some dots on a page and drawing lines connecting them at random. You tend to end up with a network where, on average, all the dots - or *nodes* - have the same number of links. By counting the number of nodes with one link, nodes with two links etc and plotting the results on a graph you end up with a bell curve where the mid-point of the curve is the average number of links per node. This is described as a *scale* network.

Barabasi expected to find this arrangement when he looked at the web. He was wrong. Instead is a situation where lots of sites have a few links, a few have a medium number of links, and a very few sites have numerous links. This produced a very different curve on the graph; there was no average scale, instead was what Barabasi called a *scale-free* network.

The dominating feature of this arrangement is that the Web's structure is dominated by a few highly connected sites, which he called *hubs*. Classic examples are Amazon and Ebay. The usefulness of this architecture is that it only takes a few clicks to get from one site to any other, similar to the idea identified by psychologist Stanley Milgram[63] and made popular by John Guare in his play *Six Degrees of Separation*: that to pass a message from one person to any other on the planet only takes an average of six intermediaries.

Utilising this *small world phenomenon*, as it was called, is the Kevin Bacon game.[64] Three college students first demonstrated on the Jon Stewart show that any other actor could be connected to Bacon in fewer than 6 steps. Appearing with him in a film, like Tom Hanks in Apollo 13, gives Hanks a Bacon score of 1. Val Kilmer gets a score of 2 because he connects to Bacon via Tom Cruise, who appeared with Kilmer in *Top Gun*, and Cruise with Bacon in *A Few Good Men*. Even Charlie Chaplin comes in

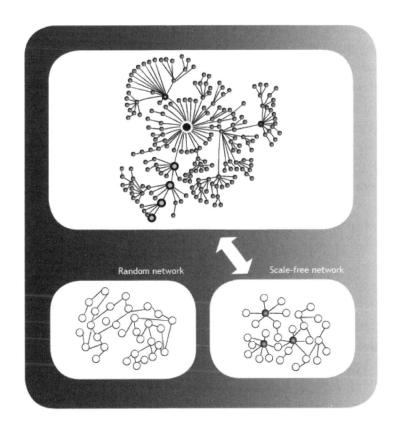

Random network   Scale-free network

with a score of just 3 through him appearing with someone who acted with Robert Wagner who co-starred with Bacon in *Wild Things*.

Barabasi soon discovered this arrangement of highly connected hubs in other networks, from the interaction of proteins to networks of who eats whom in various ecosystems. Even the web of human sexual contacts turns out to be scale-free (a few people have a lot of sex with different people, many have sex with a very few). So Barabasi's work has begun to expose a pattern of organisation that crops up time and time again in the natural word. To quote David Cohen, "Somehow the collective actions of individual agents - be they websites or proteins - generate networks that conform to a single, well-defined mathematical formula."[65] And every agent in all these systems seems to share the same behaviours.

This shouldn't be too surprising. Once evolution hits upon something that works, it tends to appear in more and more places - think fractal geometry that appears everywhere from the design of sea shells to the distribution of rivers' tributaries.

There are two key ingredients Barabasi identified in order for a network to be scale-free (which I've called Barabasis's law):

1. It needs to be growing.

2. The things which comprise the growth must show some form of preference as to what they attach to in the network. So if the network is MP3 owners, it's not a scale-free network if people are buying their model indiscriminately, but it is if a majority are choosing iPods instead of another brand.

An outcome of this form of organisation is that the highly connected hubs tend to become even more connected over time, or, if you like, 'the rich get richer'.

If we return to the Web as an example. When this book is published I will be looking to promote it to as many people as possible who might be interested, and the internet will be one of the key places to do so. I could choose to do it on www.newbookselleronthenet.com which started up last year (it didn't really, I just made it up), or I could go to Amazon. The former will charge me less because they don't have the richness of connections that will bring people to their site when they search for books on therapy. Amazon can charge me a premium because their site grows by hundreds of pages a week and is visited by millions. Their success grows their success, and a major advantage they have is that they were one of the first companies to emerge on the Web, so they've had longer to grow new connections.

> *TAOTM is the brain's equivalent of Google*

Search engines work by looking for this richness. Every connection a site has gives it some 'google juice' which moves it up the rankings. They also use algorithms to sort for relevance, such as how often a keyword is present on a page. I know I've simplified a complex and arcane new science, but I want to highlight these two key features: richness of connection and relevance, for one huge reason. I think that our memoragination is organised like the World Wide Web, and TAOTM is the brain's equivalent of Google.

Thirteen times a second, our brain scans information coming through our senses in order to create a reality tunnel to guide our actions towards safety or reward. Essentially it googles our memoragination, using algorithms of causation, similarity

> *The google-juice of the brain is emotion*

and difference to calculate the likelihood of reward or harm. Whether a pattern of information in your present - which just means an object like a chair, dog or window, or a situation like a group of people, a balcony or a meal - is matched to something from your past strongly enough to lead to a response on your part will come down to the 'google-juice' contained within the memory loop the search has connected it to. And the google-juice of the brain is emotion. The stronger the emotion, whether positive or negative, the more driven we are to act, and what dictates the strength of the emotion is the richness of the connections in a memory loop, and the degree of relevance the meaning in the loop has been given.

If you think back to the story of John I hope you can see how it fits into this theory. His original dog experience of getting bitten was ascribed a high degree of relevance to his survival, because pain will do that (as will fear, withdrawal of love and a range of other strong feelings). The programming error was the rule that nominal processing will tend to make. The best lesson would have been something like, 'that dog was dangerous, avoid it. Other dogs deserve caution." But our survival system likes as few steps in its programs as possible, so 'dogs are dangerous, avoid' was the conclusion stored in this memory. It's lodged in the memoragination as a highly relevant idea because of the fear that is the 'juice' that will drive the response to dogs. It is certainly more relevant than any other dog experience in John's life to that point (if he'd had a friendly pet dog as a comparison then it might have been a different matter), so the next time a dog forms part of his environment and the brain googles for the meaning of it the most relevant match will be the one with the most emotion in it. The present dog situation links to it and the response stored within - run - is activated. In terms of protection, the response leads to a better outcome than being bitten, so the behaviour is rewarded with dopamine and thus reinforced.

Over time, this first event becomes a hub to which all dog events attach (and thus becomes richer), and its relevance remains high because of how reliable it has been in avoiding what has become an invariant - that all dogs are dangerous. The governance of this memory loop by the nominal protection system keeps it a closed one, so no new perspectives on dogs can enter it: the Thinker thinks dogs are dangerous, so the Prover creates a reality tunnel that supports it. And I think this sequence of initial error and reinforcement is the pattern for many, if not most, of the emotional issues clients present with. And all problems at their heart are emotional.

This suggests that the root of most problems is in childhood, and I generally agree, but that doesn't mean that the root of most solutions has to involve dragging the client back into their past. As I explain in Part 2.8, some clients will respond best to work conducted in the past sector of their memoragination, some in the present, some in the future, and most in a mixture of each. And not all problems have their root in childhood. Post Traumatic Stress Disorder (PTSD) is one example of a problem whose key event can occur at any stage in life and leaves the protection system trapped in a closed loop where the event tends to keep bouncing off the walls of the reality tunnel, creating a traumatic prison out of the present for the sufferer.

The fact that hubs will continue to attract connections to new experiences as they occur, also explains an earlier point about how some behaviour patterns become part of the self-concept of the individual and why people become set in their ways. The principle of 'the rich get richer' means that the phobic becomes more phobic and the pessimist becomes more pessimistic. Don't we find that the longer the person has a problem the more they tend to become attached to it, and say things like, "It's just the way I am?" After a period of time the problem has become lodged at the level of identity, where they say something like "It's something I really hate about *myself*" and takes more to shift than where the problem is still viewed as a behaviour, which they verbalise instead as, "It's something I *do* which is really irritating."

> *The longer the person has a problem the more they tend to become attached to it*

Each of us will have a number of such hubs which form the key reference points for how we view the world we live in (and how we judge ourselves). Over time the way we see the world tends to become more and more fixed. New events are interpreted in the light of their connection to the meaning (belief) resident in the hub they connect to, so our behaviour becomes more set and predictable. And for the hubs that contain strong emotion, the behaviour that comes from them will be especially inflexible.

Barabasi found that scale-free networks were robust and vulnerable at the same time. He subjected a scale-free network to two forms of attack. In one, they randomly hit individual nodes, while in the second experiment they only attacked the hubs. Scale networks are very vulnerable to random attacks. As more and more of their nodes are attacked it takes more steps to get from one point in the network to another. Scale-free networks on the other hand, are more robust in such situations. Even with 5% of their nodes taken out, the performance of the network is unaffected. So, returning to Kevin Bacon, potentially you could remove a lot of the minor actors he worked with without it increasing the number of steps it would take to get from him to Patrick Swayze.

However, scale-free networks fare much worse if their hubs are targeted. Once 5% of the hubs are removed the number of steps needed to cross the network doubles. So 'taking out' a few actors of the calibre of Tom Cruise, Mel Gibson or Julia Roberts would quickly bring the network to a halt.

If we assume our memory loops to be scale-free networks, then it suggests that techniques that can effectively change the structure or the meaning of a hub memory will be a powerful means of changing the behaviour that is generated by that memory loop; certainly more effectively than targeting any other memory within the loop, because it is from the hub that all subsequent attachments gain their relevance. This could be the reason why brief techniques based around reprocessing specific key memories can have such a great effect in a short space of time - because a scale-free network is vulnerable to this form of attack, whereas it does not respond to random approaches - which might be what some other, more traditional, regression approaches offer.

But once a memory loop has been created, is there any evidence that changing the hub will change all the other memories that have connected to it since, and would doing so change the behaviour it generates, or indeed, the self who experiences it? Can changing our past change our present? I have one last strand to my argument that suggests that it can.

The Butterfly Effect

On those occasions when I've been on the motorway, alternating between 60mph and zero for no apparent reason, I've often wished I could be in a helicopter watching the traffic acting like one of those slinky springs that used to make their own crazy way down our stairs when I was a child. I find it amazing that a dab on the brakes that drops my speed by 3 mph can set off a chain reaction that causes cars five miles behind me to come to a complete halt 2 minutes later. This is called the Butterfly Effect, named by a brilliant meteorologist called Edward Lorenz.

Back in the 1970's Lorenz developed a computer simulation that modelled weather patterns. By keying in data representing wind direction, tides, rainfall etc, he could watch their interaction in his virtual world develop. As would be expected in a Newtonian world of cause and effect, using the same data produced the same weather systems.

One day something curious happened. To save time on a particular experiment he took the data from a previous run, and began a new run halfway through. He left the computer running and returned several hours later to find something inexplicable –

the results were completely different to the earlier weather run using the same data. Eventually he found out why. The original data had been entered to six decimal places (.606832). When he copied it for his new experiment the computer only recorded the data to three decimal places (.606).[66]

Within the context of the weather model, this difference amounted to a belch in a hurricane. According to accepted wisdom, and perhaps even common sense, this shouldn't make any difference. To quote a prominent theoretician, "The basic idea of Western science is that you don't have to take into account the falling of a leaf on some planet in another galaxy when you're trying to account for the motion of a billiard ball on a pool table on earth."[67]

Lorenz proved different: small differences can make a massive difference further down the line.

This phenomenon was popularised by the analogy that a butterfly flapping its wings in the Amazon could result in a thunderstorm in Australia – hence the Butterfly Effect. It affects any complex, dynamic system. That is where this element of Chaos Theory supports Barabasi's findings and can serve to guide our therapy. The brain has more neurons than there are stars in the universe; there is nothing more complex. The brain makes millions of calculations every second; there is nothing more dynamic. The brain uses memory to make sense of the information it is receiving from the senses every waking moment, so events in our life that are given meaning at four years old can guide our responses to events when we are ten, which can then guide our responses when we are forty. A butterfly event as a toddler may culminate in the storm of a mid-life crisis, depending on the TAOTM connections linking past to present.

A butterfly effect as a toddler may culminate in the storm of a midlife crisis

The technical term for the Butterfly Effect fits perfectly into this picture. That term is 'sensitivity to initial conditions'. In the TV programme 'Child of our Time' Professor Robert Winston said that events in the womb, including traumatic incidents such as car accidents, anxiety of the mother, or the experience of birth, can all affect the personality of the child.[68] For example, children delivered by caesarean section are likely to be bolder than those born naturally. Are extroverts the product of an easier birth? It would appear so.

All childhoods are going to contain key 'Butterfly' events, what in complexity theory are called *'points of instability'* – critical moments where a small push can have large consequences, as with a ball balanced at the top of a hill. In personality terms they are likely to be events that trigger a large emotional response (or SEE, as we've termed it). Rapturous applause for a precocious talent in a school play may metamorphose into an Oscar winner twenty years later (growth). Tripping over your tutu in front of the same audience may cause a lifetime of performance anxiety and low self-esteem (protection). But only may. An individual's response to an event can never be predicted with certainty, especially the young. One child who trips up laughs with the audience, another runs from the stage. It is never the event; we know by now (by which I mean I've said it a lot), it is the individual's perception of the event that matters. That is why it is vital for the therapist to not superimpose their response to an event onto the client – as in "that must have been terrible for you". Your client may have been the child who laughed.

> *All of us are a version of ourselves that has evolved in response to our environment*

To understand this range of possibilities within us, imagine taking a child at birth and cloning it one hundred times. Place each child in a different environment and re-visit thirty years later to view the consequences of the Butterfly Effect. It is likely that you will find a huge variation in the potential they have fulfilled. One may be a brain surgeon, another a bank robber. All of us are a version of ourselves that has evolved in response to our environment. If our past had been different so would we be - often markedly so. Imagine that we are born as a golden seed bursting with infinite potential. As we grow, our interaction with others, our triumphs, traumatic events, and the beliefs we are fed, distort us into the form reflected in the mirror, a form that in most cases has been separated from aspects of its original potential. That is why, in Cognitive Hypnotherapy, we say that people are doing the best they can with the resources they have available (which itself came from NLP), but they always have more than they think - because in relation to their problem they are stuck within a nominal closed loop. In a sense, the purpose of the interventions described in this book is to undo the power of the negative Butterfly events, and by doing so, the personality can be induced to grow in a more productive way. In computer-speak it's a little bit like restoring the system to a previous point, only bringing to that point more than it could have had to begin with.

How can I use this?

Reduced to the essential elements, most regression (context) interventions described in this book work in the following way: the client is taken back to the Butterfly event and assisted to bring new meaning to it. This is achieved by discharging the negative emotion attached to it, by changing the submodalities, or by cognitively reframing the old perception. The result of doing this successfully can be a sudden, and often dramatic, change of behaviour and a growing sense of difference in the self.

But why should going over old territory matter? Surely what is done is done? Not in a reality tunnel model such as I have described; a complex, dynamic system that follows Barabasi's Law. Within the tunnel all events in our life are potentially present at all moments; the past is as alive to the brain as our present. They are all part of the memory loops that comprises our selfplex. What is understood by us at this moment, and what is anticipated as a consequence of it, depends on what was understood before. Our memories are alive within the system and continue to exert influence over the present, they are not filed away in a musty cabinet.

That is how working with memories can bring benefit. Take a client back to the Butterfly event connected to the problem, stuck as it is within a closed loop, and change the way it flaps (the way they perceive it). Do more, guide the client in choosing the way the butterfly flaps for them to get the most benefit – make it an open loop. In this way, the effect of that new perception ripples from that hub throughout the scale-free network of that particular reality tunnel and the personality it creates. If the past is changed in your memoragination, it changes your perception of yourself in the present, and the future. An effective intervention that targets a Butterfly event can begin to nudge the brain towards a selfplex that embraces growth, and away from one that lives in protection.

Taking John to his memory of being bitten and finding a way to change the perception of its meaning, will mean that it ceases to be an SEE hub. The consequence of this is that if there is no 'fear butterfly' in the past, there is no reason for an 'anxiety storm' in the present. That is the therapeutic change; and the continuing effect of changing this loop is that it can be used to begin to infer in John a growing sense of confidence, which I'll explain more about in Part 2.7.

So now we come to the crux of our interest in this as therapists. If we are just an idea, an idea that makes a story out of the experiences of an individual organism, and that idea shapes its interpretation of its self using a causal model that the brain uses to create a reality tunnel, then it opens up a host of possibilities for personal change. Our brain is plastic, it is changing all the time in order to update its 'prediction map' of memories (past and present), and yet some hub memories that lead to problems seem frozen within the memoragination. Can science point us towards how best to utilise this plasticity to open up these closed loops and enable the story of me to be a happy one? Can we deliberately focus on a specific part of our memoragination and re-engineer it in a way that will suit our purpose? Can we re-write our remembered reality?

Do you think I'd finish a chapter with that question if I thought the answer was no?

Things aren't what they used to be

What's this about?

So far, I have suggested that our memoragination contains two types of memories: ones which are 'kaleidoscopic' - open to new information and perceptions which can change the meaning of them. These form the basis for our creativity, ideas within them are able to connect to ideas within other stored experiences that enrich and deepen our understanding of the world. The second are 'balloon' memories - experiences whose strong emotional content cause them to be closed to information and perspectives that don't share the same emotional thread. These memories tend to be the ones from which our problems stem (predominantly), childhood butterflies whose emotional vibrations create storms of unhappiness in our adult lives. Our brains use emotions to guide our belief in the truth of something, so memories brimful of the certainty that comes from fear, or anger, or panic or despair become powerful predictors of a world full of more of it. Between the TAOTM calculations of the survival system and the self, a world is created and reinforced that leaves us lonely, desperate, anxious and a thousand variations of miserable. But there is hope. The brain is plastic. Research has led us to an understanding of how memories get updated - whether simply to become more of what they already mean, or to transform into something else. In this chapter I explore that research and its implications for personal change.

When our brains record an experience it is captured by the firing of a particular arrangement of neurons (nerve cells) which leave them connected and primed to fire again to re-create that ' just happened' moment. This short-term memory trace lasts just a few seconds. To be turned into something more permanent, the synapses that connect the arrangement of neurons that equal the memory swell with more receptors and neurotransmitters and after a few hours the brain cells themselves actually grow, sprouting new and thicker connections to make the memory trace permanent. Proteins are produced by a range of genes to facilitate this process. This is a very simplified account of something termed *consolidation*. What renders this process even more remarkable is that this memory pattern then migrates.

Initially, the building of this brain pattern occurs deep in the brain in places like the hippocampus, but over the course of weeks, and even years, it moves to more general areas of the cortex - a bit like moving something from your RAM to your hard-drive. Until recently it was felt that this was the end of the story, the memory stays in the backwaters of the mind gathering dust but essentially remaining the same. A single experiment blew this idea away.

To study the process of consolidation, researchers interfered with the steps involved in fixing a memory in order to test their influence on long-term recall. When they did so Joseph LeDoux and Karim Nader discovered something puzzling.

LeDoux and Nader trained rats to associate a darkened box with an electric shock to their paws. The rats learned that the box was to be avoided and froze whenever they were put into it. If, a few days after this conditioning, the animals were given a drug to prevent protein synthesis before being reminded of the box it made no difference to their ability to remember it as a bad place. The memory seemed fixed and safely stored. But if the rat had a brief reminder of the box just before the drug was administered, the rat lost its conditioning - it forgot it was supposed to be scared. The memory had somehow been erased. The pair labelled this *reconsolidation*.[69] Intrigued, they went further. Traditional consolidation theory suggests that memories are fixed locally by protein changes within a few hours of the event and then filed to long-term storage in the cortex after about a month. After conditioning rats in the same way as before they left them for 45 days, by which time the memory should have been fixed and immune to interference.

The rat forgot it was supposed to be scared

As before, the rats given no reminder of the box before being injected, or who had their hippocampus destroyed, kept their conditioned response to the box.

But the rats that were given a reminder of the box before being given the drug did develop amnesia. Destroying the hippocampus after the reminder also took away their fear of the box. The consolidated memory - which conventional wisdom said was permanent and stable - had been removed by the action of recalling it. In Nader's words, "The dogma was that once a memory trace had been consolidated, it is permanent. But here it is labile - subject to interference in exactly the same way as a brand new experience. We were showing memory to be something incredibly dynamic."[70]

We were showing memory to be something incredibly dynamic

It appears that memory moves from the hippocampus to the cortex during consolidation, but is returned to the hippocampus for reconsolidation by the act of recall. Every time a memory is recalled, the proteins that strengthen the synaptic connections between the cells are broken down and have to be remade. Like an open Word document, while the memory is being recalled, it can be re-written.

This dynamism would be unnecessary if the brain just wanted a photograph album, but it fits perfectly into our model of memories existing to make sense of the present. The ability to distort some memories while generalising about, or even deleting others, serves to improve the mind's recognition and understanding of the world in order to prosper within it. If a memory becomes plastic every time it is recalled then it can be re-filed in a usefully updated way (or, in the case of one containing a negative SEE, re-filed in an even stronger form). The brain makes choices about whether to merge old and new, or to reinforce their differences. The story of ourselves is being constantly revised and re-written.

Some previous findings in therapy support this new model. Back in the '60s it was noted that electro-convulsive shock treatment given to conscious psychiatric patients could produce amnesia of any recently recalled memories, but not memories left dormant. In the '70s Canadian psychiatrist Richard Rubin used this to cure Obsessive Compulsive Disorder (OCD) by getting the patient to focus on their obsession before administering the shocks[71]. Before you start wiring up your recliner, there are other methods that may be using reconsolidation. Stanislav Grof of Maryland University investigated the clinical use of LSD back in the '50s and found that the hallucinogenic experience often changed the patients' perception of memories and dramatically reduced treatment time.[72] More recently an African herb with similar properties has been used successfully with heroin addicts, reportedly by changing the memories connected to their addiction and releasing them from their need.[73]

I'm not advocating a trip to your local dealer, because in the USA one of the best-documented forms of effective therapy for Post Traumatic Stress Disorder (PTSD) is Eye Movement Desensitisation and Reprocessing (EMDR), where the sufferer recalls a traumatic memory while following the path of the therapist's finger through their visual field. Without doubt it can be highly successful. Within the framework of reconsolidation theory it may be that recalling the memory and moving the eyes while doing so causes the memory to be re-stored using different submodalities, which change the meaning of it. This is similar in principle to other interventions described in Part 2.5, such as the Swish Pattern, Spinning, and Rewind. So, there already exist non-invasive and non-drug-based approaches whose success can be understood in terms of reconsolidation theory.

Research by psychologists such as Alison Gopnik show that children are learning about their environment from the moment of their arrival (and probably before). Babies can mimic facial expressions when only 42 minutes old - they are, quite literally, learning machines.[74] We've already covered how brains are scientists, learning by creating models of how things work, testing them, and then updating them as they gain new information. This fits well within the model of reconsolidation, and is obviously useful for our survival. For example, as a child I was told not to go near the fire because it would burn me. Having no model for what burning actually was in terms of its effect on me I touched the hearth and burnt my fingers. My information was updated and I learnt to avoid getting burnt - I didn't have to keep testing to see if hot things still burnt because that belief became invariant. As I look back at memories involving heat they are filtered through the belief that has emerged as a result of them – the memories create the belief that then can adapt and update the memories that created it. It is the meaning of the memory that is evolutionarily necessary, not the accuracy of the recording of the event itself - how I remember the look of the hearth may be largely irrelevant.

> *It is the meaning of the memory that is evolutionarily necessary, not the accuracy of the recording itself*

This structure is fine when the child-as-a-young-scientist makes the right connections, and creates a useful belief. The problem arises when immature inference leads to inaccurate TAOTM nominal conclusions - as in the case of John. Once an invariant belief is formed, recollection of any memory connected to this belief is likely to be strengthened because of the belief it is viewed through (hence what the Thinker...). It becomes a self-supporting belief system, from which grows a self-fulfilling prophecy and the world becomes more and more they way we expect. While the evolutionary purpose of reconsolidation is to keep us safe, its drawback is that mistakes of interpretation made when young flow down the years and tend to become stronger and more resistant to change as we age. What we can do, and what we can't, becomes set in stone.

In brief then, reconsolidation theory suggests that when memories are recalled they become vulnerable to change, and if I'm right in suggesting that certain key, closed, memories are the basis for the reality tunnels that are created when we begin to experience a problem, then we have a model that guides the way we work with our clients' thoughts of their past:

- A negative hub memory could be weakened by changing its submodalities - so it has less (or no) effect on the belief network to which it's connected.
- A negative hub memory could be transformed by having the meaning of it reframed – and by doing so transform the belief that derives from it.
- A positive memory could be strengthened in its meaning – it becomes more of what it was and becomes a hub the brain uses to anticipate future events.

Recent studies of counselling styles that rely on going over past events and talking about the feelings relating to them have shown that they tend to deepen the client's experience of the problem;[75] LeDoux and Nader have shown why. The logical conclusion to be drawn from reconsolidation theory is that the only purpose of talking about any aspect of a client's past experience is to change either its meaning or its coding so that it creates a positive change in the belief system responsible for the client's problem. Simply recalling it and crying about it may only serve to increase it.

This line of thinking is a real motivation for me. How many ways can we find to give a client's mind a new experience of their memories which would cause a reassessment of their future? What techniques can we discover or refine in the light of this understanding of our neurology that can achieve one of the three possibilities of memory change I mentioned just now? The Context, Structure and Consequence

If our past is just a story that we create to confirm our beliefs, which are themselves the emergent consequence of memory loops, then therapy becomes a medium by which clients can create whatever story of their past forms the basis for their most productive future.

interventions described in Part Two are all guided by this work of LeDoux and Nader.

If our past is just a story that we create to confirm our beliefs, which are themselves the emergent consequence of memory loops, then therapy becomes a medium by which clients can create whatever story of their past forms the basis for their most productive future. By changing our memories we can change our beliefs. We are just a story we tell ourselves about ourselves, and that story is constantly being rewritten. Now we have clear scientific indicators of what we can do to most influence the plot.

How can I use this?

Our reality tunnel is created from our stored memories: what you see around you at this present moment is dependent on the meaning given to things in your past.

Our ideas about ourself are a consequence of the meanings given to events that have occurred to us, and our reality tunnel is created in response to these beliefs.

Reconsolidation theory demonstrates that every time we recall an event it becomes unstable and available for re-evaluation or re-structuring. Old memories can be rewritten.

If the negative things we believe about ourselves are the result of the meaning we've taken from significant life events, then changing the meaning of those events, or the structure of the memory of those events, could change the feeling we have about ourselves that was a consequence of them.

If we change the right memories, we change our very selves.

Conclusion: The story so far

In this part of the book I have sought to create a model of the way our subjective experience of the world emerges from the brain's striving to stay alive; how our sense of self is the end-result of one organism's route to survival.

I titled this part of the book, *a strong theory, weakly held*, because I don't pretend to have come up with something that is true, just something that is useful and plausible, and in time it will be amended and improved upon to become something that is even stronger, but still weakly held. I went looking within science for evidence to support and guide our therapy, and this is what I have for now. And if you've followed my argument you'll realise that what I've described doesn't have to be true, it just has to be sufficiently plausible to you or your clients for it to have the effect of feeling true, and being the cause of change.

What I am suggesting is that the *you* reading this book is an idea that sees itself, that has emerged from your brain's memoragination as the end result of the causal model it uses to predict the meaning of events. *You* is treated by your brain as another piece of information from the environment for it to respond to - all the way down to the cellular level. Indeed, in Appendix three I go one step further and suggest how this model suggest the means by which our thoughts can affect our physical health.

Almost like another sensory channel, the ideas we have about the world have a direct route into the brains calculations, and through them, into the body itself.

Almost like another sensory channel, the ideas we have about the world have a direct route into the brains calculations, and through them, into the body itself.

What is experienced by you as reality is just a tunnel created from your memoragination to guide you to the next best action you could take in the most efficient way. There is no separation between *you* and the world, because they are both the same thing, just an illusion created by our brain. And because our brain cannot help but respond to our thoughts, it means we have the ability to create our own reality; to create the best possible world to live in, and the best possible person we can imagine being.

Sir Isaac Newton was one of the world's greatest scientists, and yet most of his published works relate to alchemy. Most people think of alchemy as being concerned with the transmutation of one substance to another, like lead into gold, and the search for the philosopher's stone, which would confer immortality upon the holder. A strange fancy for one of the best thinkers of any age, you might think. But actually, at its core, alchemy is about personal transformation.

The idea of changing lead to gold was simply a metaphor for the personal change alchemists believed we are all capable of. When Hermes Trismegistus wrote "Know ye not that ye are gods?[76]" he wasn't inflating humanity any more than Budhha was when he said "You are god yourself[77]". I think their point was simple. We are not the *created*

We are not the created in our world, we are the creators of our world

in our world, we are the *creators* of our world. Holding the former perspective keeps us slaves to our environment, continually having to look outside ourselves for the agent that will bring us the effects we're after. Holding yourself as the creator means that everything you need is on the inside. You become the cause, and the world around you becomes the effect. You are the active agent, yours is the control over your destiny. That is what I think this model can provide as a destination to aim for. And in the next part I offer the best techniques I know to effect this transformation and help you and your clients in the lifetime journey for agency in pursuit of growth.

part 2

The Philosophy and Practice
of Cognitive Hypnotherapy

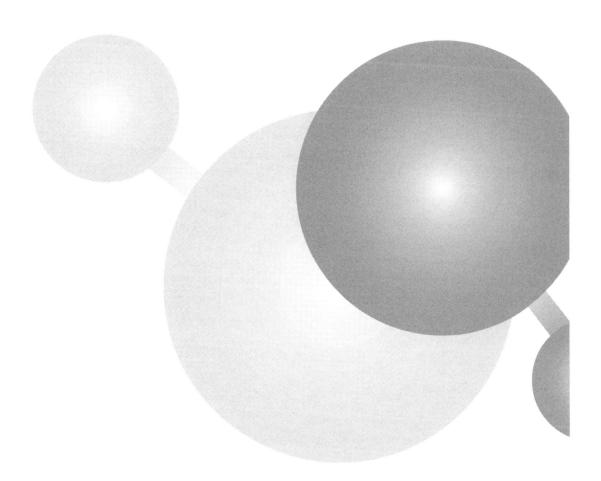

The Practice of Therapy:
The Way of the Intercepting Idea

In Part One I developed a theory of mind that suggests that all our behaviour is the result of calculations that have evolved to predict reward or the avoidance of threat. Within that definition, all behaviour has a positive intention. Negative behaviours and beliefs that limit us are the result of a learning system that seeks certainty, and in survival situations the 'fast and dirty' use of nominal processing can end in certain situations becoming groundhog days, where no new learning is possible, just a repetition of past mistakes which over time can cause them to become the defining theme of an entire life.

In this part of the book I describe over a dozen techniques that I've found to be a powerful means of helping a client to access the closed loops that fuel people's problems and open them to new information and perspectives, or code the meaning of the information in the loop in such a way that the pattern changes and the problem disappears.

What I don't want this part of the book to be, however, is a bag of tricks to throw randomly at a client. It is going to describe a model that can guide your choices, and help you and the client construct a unique map from their first session through to their resolution. Underlying that model and map is a philosophy of uncertainty that I want to begin with, and its inspiration comes from an unlikely source.

I was at my mother's 70th birthday, sitting next to my brother Peter and catching up. He's interested in my field but has had no real contact with it , so I was talking to him about the principles of Cognitive Hypnotherapy (CH) that make it different to other forms of therapy. We share an interest in martial arts, and at a certain point in my description he exclaimed, "So it's therapy JKD!"

JKD stands for Jeet Kune Do, or 'Way of the Intercepting Fist', Bruce Lee's approach to martial arts. I deliberately say approach, rather than style, because in many ways JKD is more of a way of thinking than it is a way of doing.

This led to a cascade of thoughts which made more and more connections between what I had been trying to achieve in defining Cognitive Hypnotherapy, and Lee's work in defining JKD, and it became apparent to me that by adopting the metaphor of therapy as a martial art, I could cut to the heart of my message.

However, I want to make clear several things from the outset. By describing it in this way I am not suggesting CH as a muscular, testosterone fuelled, aggressive approach. In many ways I mean the opposite. I propose a fluid, flexible utilisation of the client's way of thinking:

(All Bruce Lee quotes taken from *Striking Thoughts* by John Little[78])

"Don't get set into one form, adapt it and build your own, and let it grow, be like water. Be formless... shapeless, like water. If you put water into a cup, it becomes the cup. You put water into a bottle; it becomes the bottle. You put it into a teapot; it becomes the teapot. Water can flow, and it can crash. Be like water, my friend..." BL

The focus of our effort is the pattern of subjective experiences that drive the client's perception in creating a limiting belief or behaviour; what we in Cognitive Hypnotherapy describe as a *problem pattern*. The role of the therapist is loosely that of a trainer, teaching the client how to better utilise their thoughts.

"Unfortunately, in boxing people are now only allowed to punch. In Judo, people are only allowed to throw. I do not despise these kinds of martial arts. What I mean is, we now find rigid forms which create differences among clans, and the world of martial art is shattered as a result. I think the high state of martial art, in application, must have no absolute form. And, to tackle pattern A with pattern B may not be absolutely correct." BL

Martial arts is an umbrella for a myriad of approaches, each of which tends to be organised around a central proposition about what is the best approach to combat. For example, *Tae Kwon Do* tends to emphasise kicking, *Western Boxing*, hand techniques, *Aikido*, locks and grappling. This means that any response to an attack is filtered by this proposition, not necessarily by the best available choice out of all available choices – so to beat someone using Tae Kwon Do it helps if you fight someone suited to that kind of approach. But what happens if they're not? Potentially, you lose.

The world of therapy has been very similar. Each approach, whether it be Freudian, or Behaviourism, Gestalt, or Cognitive Behavioural Therapy (CBT), develops from a central proposition about human functioning which guides the interaction between therapist and client. It also limits the choices available, because after a while barriers are erected around each approach, and dogmation is the result (I just made that word up by putting stagnation and dogma together. I hope the Oxford Dictionary pick it up).

"The weakness is, when clans are formed, the people of a clan will hold their kind of martial art as the only truth and do not dare to reform or improve it. Thus they are confined in their own tiny little world. Their students become machines which imitate martial art forms." BL

If a Freudian or Gestalt or CBT world-view doesn't resonate with the client's model of the world, what is the therapist able to do? Try more of what isn't working? Surely therapy should adapt to the client, not expect the client to adapt to the therapy, any more than a judoka should say before a fight, "I'm afraid many of my moves work best if you're wearing a jacket, would you mind putting one on before we start?"

Lee's approach was to step outside these constraints, and use a simpler proposition:

*"Use only that which works, and take it from any place you can find it."*BL

He studied a wide range of martial arts and began to apply them to his combat – but didn't synthesise them into a new 'style'. Each technique comes from where it came from – it's the context of its application that makes it JKD. So to block a punch with your own might come from the philosophy of Wing Chun; to evade an attack by circular movement from Hapkido, but to have both available, and to choose which is the simplest and most effective in the context of the opponent in that moment – that is JKD. That is also how I envisage CH; a way of thinking that takes anything that works and applies it in the context that is right for the client, at the moment it is right for the client. In that respect it is not a 'style' of therapy, more a style of thinking to guide therapy.

*"I have not invented a 'new style,' composite, modified or otherwise that is set within a distinct form as apart from 'this' method or 'that' method. On the contrary, I hope to free my followers from clinging to styles, patterns, or moulds. Remember that Jeet Kune Do is merely a name used, a mirror in which to see 'ourselves'. . . Jeet Kune Do is not an organised institution that one can be a member of. Either you understand or you don't, and that is that."*BL

When fighting an opponent there are basic elements that guide the actions you take. In nearly all situations they will have arms and legs. Their height and weight will always be a factor. In therapy it is the same for a client's problem if you imagine their issue as a pattern of information running in the brain; it also contains basic elements that organise its function. In CH we recognise a problem as a pattern made of four categories, or quadrants, of information; *context, structure, process* and *consequence*. An organising proposition of ours is that when a therapy (of any kind) works, it is because it has had a critical effect within one of these quadrants and changed the pattern. Most therapeutic approaches focus on one quadrant more than the others (or don't even recognise the existence, or the importance, of the others). Every technique used in CH is aimed at changing some element of a quadrant, just as any strike or hold is aimed at a particular part of the body.

The content of each client's quadrants, and the relative importance of each in maintaining a problem's integrity, is different for each person. This explains why people with the same label for their problem, such as a dog phobia, anxiety attacks, or low self-esteem don't respond in the same way to the same approach; all will need attention paid to different aspects of each quadrant for their problem to change, and exactly where this is needed is often only apparent by experimentation. This is where the 'therapist as water' comes into his or her own. A technique that doesn't work is simply information about where else to focus attention, just as a block to a head punch might suggest a switch to a kick somewhere less well defended.

 *"True refinement seeks simplicity"*BL

In CH we adopt the same stance as a JKD practitioner; we take the simplest technique from whatever form of therapy is suited to the particular part of the *problem pattern* that is the focus of our attention at that particular moment.

When learning a martial art JKD suggests there are three stages of cultivation. The first is the *primitive stage*, where the student is untutored, ignorant, but still possessing those attributes that make him or her capable of some level of attack and defence in a reflexive, intuitive way. In therapy training it is the same; people begin ignorant of the techniques and principles, but still equipped with the human skills essential to its effectiveness – rapport, engagement, patience – the qualities that have made a good talk with a friend so beneficial for the millennia we managed to get along without therapists.

The next stage is the *stage of art*, where they are taught the various forms of striking, blocking, kicking etc. A scientific understanding of technique is gained, but at the expense of the natural 'self' and the flow that comes from intuition. Movements are often conscious, and thus restricted. Again, it is the same during the development of a therapist; techniques are learnt and adhered to, often at the expense of flexibility. True engagement is lost owing to the conscious awareness of the 'process to be followed'.

Finally is the *stage of artlessness*, when a maturity emerges and conscious awareness of the techniques and the choice behind them is lost. It is no longer a case of "I punch", but of "it punches". With therapists too, this stage can emerge with experience and good mentoring, where the skills and techniques become assimilated into an informed intuition – what in JKD they call *cultivated ignorance*.

In my opinion, too many therapists remain stuck at the second stage; technically competent but missing the ability to be fluid. If they are within a certain discipline, such as counselling, an adherence to the orthodoxy is demanded so this stuckness becomes something that is actually aimed for. And in many cases, owing to poor training in any therapy, some are stuck somewhere between the first and second stage, where they rely on their uninformed intuition and a smattering of techniques without an understanding of when and why to apply them. They often describe themselves as eclectic, but in reality tend to just hit and hope.

Bruce Lee recognised that any technique works because of the principles that underpin it and that once these principles are understood the techniques themselves disappear. So it is with CH; every intervention you learn has a series of steps to follow, but it is the principles that drive these steps that cause them to create change. Many different steps can follow from the same principle, just as many different forms of attack stem from the principle of attacking the centre line of an opponent. Once you understand which change principle applies at a particular moment when working within a problem pattern, then the technique it belongs to becomes irrelevant, and all that is left is the change that occurs.

I remember when I was young and starting to learn Karate, one of the things that put me off was the boredom of repeatedly punching, kicking and blocking in a seemingly robotic way. What I didn't realise then was that particular kicks or punches may not have value as combat moves in themselves, or that the forms beginners learn in order to master the movements may never find application in a real situation, but the value is derived from the principles contained within the movement. Once these are ingrained within the muscles, a spontaneous, creative response to an opponent is possible.

This is not quite the same with CH; all the techniques and language forms work, and often they work in their standard delivery, but for that they depend on the client following the steps. Not all can, or will, and it is then that the fluidity of this approach comes into its own. In situations where the client is viewed as having interfered with the progress of an intervention by not being able to follow the steps, or by being seemingly obstructive, it's often labelled as resistance and is frequently seen as a negative facet of therapy. In CH it's seen as an indicator that the therapy has touched somewhere relevant, and it's a diversion sign, not a stop sign. All that's probably indicated is a shift within the problem pattern by using a different technique aimed at another quadrant.

What I want to provide in this part of the book is a number of techniques that are used by Cognitive Hypnotherapists, but more importantly I want to describe the principles that make them effective, and the mindset of *the intercepting idea* that will help you learn how to flow from one principle to another in response to a client, making you fluid and without boundaries. I want you to be able to look at any other talking therapy approach and be able to take from it what works and incorporate it into the Cognitive Hypnotherapy model. In so doing we can create a home for therapy which is open to everything that works, and to everybody who wants to learn it.

 *"Sculptors do not create by adding more and more clay, they do so by stripping away all that is not essential to the art."*BL

So it is with Cognitive Hypnotherapy:

 "True refinement seeks simplicity." He then went on to add: *"And within simplicity lies brilliance."* BL

Welcome to the Way of The Intercepting Idea.

Just as Bruce Lee looked to trap the underlying principles of combat in order to use them, but without seeking to cage them, so I'm striving to arrive at a set of principles that can guide our actions without limiting them. So it's important to remember that, for as much as you can believe in a principle, there are always times when it doesn't apply. Use what works in the moment, not what you think ought to work. I've found that believing nothing to be true really sets you free, because then everything need only be useful. I begin to lay the foundations of a mindset for your therapy by introducing a single concept and ten guiding ideas before moving on to the structure for change-work itself.

The concept of inception

The film Inception has Leonardo DiCaprio playing the role of Cobb, a man who heads a team of industrial spies who invade the dreams of their targets in order to trick them into revealing their secrets. The plot of the film follows them trying to achieve something different. Instead of trying to steal something, their client wants them to plant an idea into the mind of his enemy so that he believes the idea is his own.

I got goosebumps when I watched it, because that's exactly how I see the role of the therapist. As Cobb says: "What's the most resilient parasite? An Idea. A single idea from the human mind can build cities. An idea can transform the world and rewrite all the rules."[79] As you read in Part One, we ourselves may only be an idea that is the sum total of all the ideas we hold about the world. Those ideas may have led us to protection, or growth, and more usually a mixture of both. I think that therapy is the process of helping your client remain in growth during the periods when they used to be triggered into protection and, at a higher level, the goal of personal development is that of learning how to remain in growth regardless of our situation. The way we can help clients achieve that is through inception – Cobb: "It's called inception. One simple idea that changed everything."[80] If we can cause the brain of our client to accept an idea that counteracts the belief that holds them in protection, and which they feel is their own idea, then it creates the conditions by which the perceptions about themselves and the world have to realign to support the truth of the new idea. Our role as therapist is an *inceptor* (that may be another word I just invented!), someone who helps the client drop the butterfly of a new idea into their memoragination, from where it can spread all the way up to the selfplex, eradicating the reality tunnels that created the need for protection, and creating the loops that support growth.

Perhaps Cognitive Hypnotherapy is more truly the Way of The *Incepting* Idea. Throughout this part of the book I'll be suggesting how this can be achieved.

First idea: Have strong opinions, weakly held.

I have been strongly influenced by this simple saying, attributed to Paul Saffo, head of Palo Alto's Institute for the Future[81]. In fact, I like it so much I paraphrased it for the title of Part One.

By this stage you're familiar with the idea that the brain seeks certainty, and that much of the workings of the brain are dedicated to finding it with the greatest degree of accuracy possible. The downside of this is the attraction we feel for people who sound sure of themselves, and for things that seem certain when they're not. It often leads to strife when such certainties collide, or where people feel the need to defend their 'truth' against something as scary as a new idea. To maintain a position of uncertainty in a world seeking the comfort of its opposite is difficult, but, I think, necessary if therapy is to evolve.

The principle of permanent revolution lies at the heart of Cognitive Hypnotherapy, and a mindset of permanent uncertainty is required for that to be the case. Any model is open to adaptation or be superseded the minute something else is shown to work better. The only way for its practitioners to avoid being part of yet another therapy dogma is for them to embrace uncertainty as a position of strength, not of weakness. As Bruce Lee suggested for JKD, "Have *No Way* as *Way*".

Second idea: Orr's law

Orr's law has been a part of my armoury ever since I was introduced to it by Robert Anton Wilson in his excellent book *Prometheus Rising*[82]. If you read Part One you're already familiar with it. It asks you simply to conceptualise the mind as having two elements, the Thinker and the Prover. The principle is, 'what the Thinker thinks the Prover proves'. This is all about the power our beliefs have to create the world around us. Leonard Orr suggested that our brain filters information to maintain our beliefs about the way the world works; so what you think to be true your prover will prove to be true. If you think you're worthless.....if you think you're loveable...etc. A phenomenally powerful tool to view your experiences through, and which, unconsciously, can turn your world into a limited, miserable certainty.

Third idea: All behaviour has a purpose

This is probably the defining principle which guides me in every session. It usually arises as the thought "what's that about?" in response to something the client has said or done. By assuming that there is an underlying motivation for doing something that is against the client's conscious wishes, we are released from the Freudian idea of a naughty *id* lurking within and desperately writhing to get out, and able to embrace the idea that limiting behaviours are being driven by the brain for a positive intention. One of the key skills as a therapist is to avoid being sucked into the client's story and emotionally responding to it, and I've found that by maintaining this questioning approach, everything that's recounted to me is just information. By remaining cognitively engaged, my limbic system is deprived of the chance of mistaking the client's story as being about me.

Fourth idea: There is no resistance, only information

If the first question I ask in any situation is "what's that about?", the second is "how can I use it?" There will always be situations where clients are unable or unwilling to follow the process you're using. They might not be able to find a relevant memory, or visualise, or pass learning down, or release an emotion, or get above their timeline. These are not signs the intervention has failed, just that they've come to a road sign. Many therapists take it to be a Stop sign; I take it to be a diversion. If a client can't do something, I ask myself "what's that about?" and ask questions to find the answer, and when I have the answer I ask myself "how can I use it?" to get the client moving again. Everything the client does or says, or doesn't do or can't say is information that is potentially useful. In the words of the classic NLP presupposition, "there is no failure, only feedback". What is often termed resistance by the client, or as secondary gain, is often a sign that you are in the right place: the resistance or secondary gain – at that moment – *is* the problem. Find a way to move around it, below it, above it, or move it out of the way, and you'll find beyond it the very thing you were after. In Part 2.8 I go into more detail about how every challenge a client creates during a technique is an opportunity to switch techniques.

Fifth idea: People have everything they need to help themselves

It is not the job of the therapist to 'fix' their clients, because they are not broken. I think a mindset has developed over the years among many within the therapeutic community that their clients are vulnerable and weak, victims of their problem. It has led to a great deal of emphasis on the setting of boundaries between client and therapist, over-supervision of the therapist or counsellor and a culture of client 'holding' and negotiation of 'endings'. Frankly, I have little time for any of it, because what I'm interested in is an authentic relationship with someone where we both pool what we have in the service of the client's goal.

I believe people are strong and resilient, even when life has convinced them otherwise, and I continue to believe that until they share that belief with me. Some clients will live in a reality tunnel which creates a personality which is fragile and they can take a lot of gentle care to begin any kind of movement, but their delicacy is still only the result of their belief systems. Their strength lies within; it's just untapped – after all, they own genes which have survived every survival challenge thrown at them over millennia.

Sometimes you have to slice progress thinly to pace the speed at which someone is prepared to change - sometimes not sliding back is the only progress that's possible - but overall the journey is towards their goal, and part of that will be the realisation that they have what they need within them for the journey.

In Cognitive Hypnotherapy we avoid being the source of the client's solution. Mirror neurons mean that whenever a therapist hears a client's story their brain cannot help but run a simulation of it – and look for solutions. It is the easiest thing in the world to mistake such a solution for an insight – it isn't; it's an 'outsight' – it is coming from your model of the world interpreting the client's model of the world. In the spirit of Milton Erickson I believe that clients should be helped to find their own answers from within themselves – because they are always there. This is what I mean by inception: letting the client believe they created themselves, not that you did.

Sixth idea: Internal v external locus of control

One of the joys of my life is working in a garden office. As I type this I can look out of the window to my left and look at the bird feeders that are a few feet away. All day long I'm happily distracted by a great variety of birds coming to feed. Spring is particularly fun because the babies have fledged and clumsily follow their parents around, performing a variety of wing flutters and squawks to get the parents to continue to feed them, even when the seed is only inches from their beaks. This is an *external locus of control (ELOC)*, and you may begin to notice how many adults continue to look to the outside for a solution to their needs. "Something should be done about it" is a typical 'ELOC' phrase. Most clients will arrive with this orientation, looking for you, the therapist, to solve their issue. Many of them simply want to lie back in your chair while you magically click your fingers so they can awake a little later with their problem removed. Some will believe in your ability so much that it might even work, but for most their issue will only be improved when their orientation does, because being at the mercy of what the world throws at you is part of most problems.

When you look around at many modern parents you can see its beginnings. People are often so busy that they think being good parents is solving their children's problems. Modern schools seek to protect children from the hurt of failure by making school sports days full of events where everybody wins. The former is preventing the child from learning how to problem solve: they learn that if they take their problem to an adult it will be solved for them. In the latter case children don't learn resilience: the internal strength that comes from striving and failing and striving again. We're left with adults who continue to flap their wings whenever life gets tough and hope that someone passing can help, not realising that what they're getting from someone else also comes from within that person. Success in life comes to those who take action - those who say, "Something should be done here by me" - who are agents acting on life, not letting life act on them.

My point is that life happens, but, as Victor Frankl so wonderfully pointed out, "Everything can be taken from a man but one thing, to choose one's attitude in any given set of circumstances; to choose one's own way."[83] The ultimate freedom we have in life is the meaning we give to what happens to us. The more we feel in control of our choices, the better we'll feel about them. And we always have a choice.

From a personal point of view, if you take nothing else from this book other than the resolution to develop an internal locus of control, to ask yourself in all situations, "what can I do here to bring the best result?", it will change your life. If the answer is 'nothing', then sit and wait until you can, and then take action, and keep taking it until you get to where you want to be. And that is your task with your client, to help them infect themselves with the meme of ILOC (internal locus of control); to help them realise that they have all the internal potential they need for their journey, they just have to start exercising it - whatever life throws at them. Growth begins from within.

Seventh idea: There is no failure, only feedback

This is a classic presupposition from NLP, and living to it can also change your life. Imagine how different your life would be if you never saw the possibility of failing at anything. We live in a blame culture, where any mistake begins a search for someone to be at fault. We have the ridiculous situation of senior politicians having to resign for a mistake within their department that they couldn't have known about. As a society, we become paralysed at the prospect of having the finger of blame pointed at us, and our fixation with Health and Safety gives us a never ending stream of opportunities for something to be someone else's fault.

In Cognitive Hypnotherapy we swim against this stream. Vigorously. When something goes wrong or doesn't work, the only thing of interest is 'what can we learn from that?' Bruce Lee said, "The man who never makes a mistake never makes anything." The trick is to learn from it so you don't repeat it. And even if you do, it's still just a sign that the learning isn't complete.

As a therapist, if you maintain this mind-set then your emotional state will not be a barometer for the progress of your clients, or lack of it, and you will be much less likely to burn out from your work. This idea will turn you into a curious learning machine - unafraid, adventurous and flexible.

The official term in psychology is priming, which describes when an earlier stimulus influences response to a later stimulus. I think this, more than anything else, is the reason why hypnotic suggestion works. If you have ever been trying for a family did you notice how suddenly everybody seemed to be pregnant, and babies were everywhere? Or when you were thinking of changing your car for another model and you spotted examples of it at every junction? That's priming: what is on your mind, or has been recently or powerfully, is given a higher relevancy score than it might otherwise have and it affects what your brain filters from your environment.

Over the course of your life your brain becomes tuned to certain themes of information that can be present in your environment, like dogs in the case of John (from Part One). His brain has been primed to find dogs relevant for so long that they become a running background theme in his model of the world, and their appearance is given a much higher relevance than they actually need, so we could say that client's problems are the result of priming-over-time. The techniques in this part of the book that work directly on the client's perception of a memory - one that is acting as a stimulus that influences a later stimulus (like John getting bitten when he was five) - work because, by changing the meaning of that memory or ridding it of its powerful emotional charge, they remove it as a priming stimulus.

When making a hypnotic suggestion, the therapist is planting in the unconscious of the client an idea that acts as a stimulus that influences their response to a later stimulus. So, for example, if I include within my suggestions to John "and you might be surprised the next time you see a dog how differently you feel", then I am priming him to find a difference in his feelings, rather than his brain seeking confirmation of his default response of panic.

During the course of our life we all build up a great range of 'priming potentials' - which we describe as memory loops - which tune the brain to interpret the world in a particular way. The treatment process of **Cognitive Hypnotherapy as a whole works to 'de-prime' connections between past and present stimuli that lead to negative outcomes and a state of protection, and to prime new connections that lead to a more positive interpretation of the world – a state of growth.**

In Part 1.2 I described trance phenomena as being the means by which the brain creates our reality tunnel. When I talk of trance I'm talking of mental states each and every one of us goes into and out of throughout our waking day. In that regard I'm not much of a hypnotherapist, because I don't actually believe in 'hypnosis'.

I imagine mental states being like radio stations, operating at a range of frequencies. Your selfplex operates as one 'station', daydreaming as another, you going into a 'smoking' trance as another. Every state you experience as a problem, and where you have no active control over its outcome, is a radio station. The purpose of Cognitive Hypnotherapy is to retune your radio, so those stations are no longer on the dial, and you can choose which ones you want to access - like the 'easy living' station, the 'confident, competent' person channel, or radio 'I love myself'. These are the *solution state* channels Wordweaving™ is designed to prime the client to become more and more expert at receiving.

Different problem stations will utilise different trance phenomena to create the reality tunnel that supports the actions it wants you to take, and everyone has varying abilities in which trance phenomena they can access, and how strongly. The person who is selected by a stage hypnotist to come up on stage and dance like a chicken or see the audience as naked comes from the group of people with the widest and strongest natural disposition to access these phenomena, the 10% of the population labelled somnabulists. This variation of ability, in my opinion, led hypnotherapy to a limiting conclusion - that whether hypnotherapy works on a client or not is dependent on the client's ability to go deeply into 'hypnosis', i.e. to exhibit the ability to utilise these trance phenomena strongly in response to the suggestions of the therapist. The therapist operates as the person 'doing' the hypnosis, but it was down to the client as to whether it worked or not. This hardly seems fair when they're the ones who are paying.

If instead we recognise that trance phenomena are used strongly enough by any client who has a problem - because the problem depends on trance for it to happen – then every client can be 'hypnotised' sufficiently to be helped. If the trance is enough to cause the problem, it's strong enough to resolve it.

We don't need to turn the client's radio dial round to 'somnabulist', only to a wavelength similar to that experienced when they are 'doing their problem', which is usually one of slightly altered wakefulness.

Trance states are part of every problem, and need to be part of every resolution. The good news is that, for the techniques that work, they already are. Ask someone to remember a time when they felt anxious and they have to age regress to answer. Ask them where in their body they feel the urge to have a smoke, and that's sensory distortion. Every technique that works, from any branch of psychotherapy, counselling or coaching, utilises trance, whether they acknowledge it or not. This is why in Cognitive Hypnotherapy we often don't use a trance induction (the traditional process of taking someone into a trance, i.e. "you're sinking deeper and deeper"), because the trance is contained within the technique itself, and relaxation - which is the state most often induced as a prelude to the commencement of an intervention - is often not the most helpful state for the client to be in if you want to access their negative loops. If we go back to idea eight - priming - if you've spent twenty minutes priming the client with relaxing imagery, how easy is it going to be to bring to mind the thoughts and feelings they want to be rid of? There is a time for this kind of induction - because the client expects it because you're a hypnotherapist or because relaxation is something you want to utilise, but aside from these considerations, I haven't used a formal induction on a client prior to an intervention in the last five years at least.

Once you recognise that trance emerges in our lives on a regular basis - we're in what I'm defining as a trance more often than we're not - then it's your job to utilise them as they appear. Even the client who sits in front of me, fingers white with tension on the chair arms and says, "You're not going to be able to hypnotise me", with a look of pride in their face, has already done the job for me - they're in a 'I can't be hypnotised' trance, and all that is in *my* head is "how can I use that?"

Every technique in this book has trance phenomena within it, see if you can spot them. Hypnotic suggestion is, I believe, a very powerful way to utilise trance phenomena to prime the client's brain for evidence of improvement. In Appendix One I give a synopsis of my method of creating such suggestions based on the client's model of the world, Wordweaving™. At various points throughout the rest of the book I mention the use of Wordweaving™ as a complement to the techniques you use, but I appreciate that some of you may not yet have learnt how to use it - or choose not to. In that situation, substitute the word 'Wordweaving™' with 'your suggestions' (still meaning them to be based on the information your client provides, rather than your own ideas about what they need).

Tenth idea: Problems are created by TAOTM... so must the solutions be

Our reality, for better or worse, is created by the causal connections our brain makes between our past and our future, and the projected future it anticipates as a consequence. Our whole universe feels as if it's based on one thing being the cause of another.

If you, or your client, feel unloved, or unworthy, stupid, clumsy or ugly. If you or they overeat despite the desire to slim, smoke, despite wanting to stop, remain stuck in a life that is less than it could be, it's all because the brain is comparing what's around you with an interpretation from your history that is based on cause and effect, similarity or difference.

This constant shuttle between past, present and future within our memoragination is so seamless that it's invisible, which makes a therapist's utilisation of TAOTM so powerful. You can create change as invisibly and easily as our clients' brains create misery.

In the chapters ahead are a great many techniques. Used alone they can create a change in the client, but using them within a TAOTM framework, as I describe in Part 2.8, can embed that change within their memoragination so that it becomes permanent.

Before we begin I need to make a point about the use of what you're about to read. Clearly I'm going to be describing a model I encourage you to use, but only within the limits of your experience and training. I've included the techniques I have for existing practitioners to compare with their own use of them, or to add to their toolkit if appropriate. However, use of them is the individual responsibility of the practitioner, and such use should only be after relevent training and with qualified supervision. As I'm sure you'd expect me to say, I can't accept any responsibility for their use.

A framework for change

For any therapeutic approach to work, it must have something within its system that causes it to have a consistent effect, some set of underlying principles. Cognitive Hypnotherapy is a model that seeks to organise the principles contained in all effective therapies within a single organising framework to enable the therapist to be 'water', continually able to adapt their approach in response to the information they gain from a client, rather than being limited to forcing a client into the constraints of a single school of thought. It focuses the therapist's attention on two of the client's key thought patterns. The first is the bundle of information we call the Problem Pattern, the second is the Solution State.

The Problem Pattern

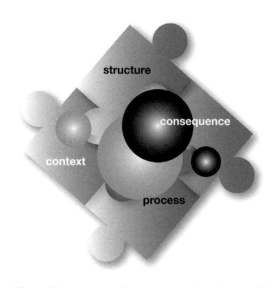

This is the client's unique experience of their difficulty. Cognitive Hypnotherapists do not diagnose, so finding a label that fits the client's description of their problem isn't considered important – ask five people suffering from anxiety or PTSD, or five people who smoke, and you'll get five different versions of the problem pattern that drives their issue. If a client says "I have anxiety", or "I have low self-esteem", our response is (in essence) "How do you do that?"

The problem pattern identified in each client can be thought of as being made up of four quadrants, and our questions to elicit the unique way they 'do' their issue are aimed within one or other of these quadrants; every technique or intervention used is identified as belonging to one of them - in that it is within a particular quadrant that the technique has its effect. The four are:

Context

As I stated earlier, one of the key ideas in Cognitive Hypnotherapy is "all behaviour has a purpose". If we consider ourselves as just another organism on the planet vying for limited resources, every expenditure of energy has to be measured against the benefit it's

likely to bring – and ultimately its contribution to our survival. So not only do we believe that the issues that people bring are serving a purpose, but that that purpose has a positive intention for that person. From an evolutionary point of view, investing energy in a behaviour that causes us harm isn't something that would be done deliberately, so the problems people bring to therapy are the result of an error somewhere in the calculations of the mind.

The context of a problem describes the boundaries within which the problem exists, and its reason for existing. In other words, it explores the connections that TAOTM has led the brain to make between different sets of information, usually one set from the present environment and one from the remembered past. It's probably easiest to explain with an example: if someone has a fear of spiders, it means that every time the brain receives information from the environment that 'equals' spider, the brain responds with a behaviour designed to protect from that information – usually the protection response, which means that the person will either flee from the spider or bash it with something heavy. However, for some people, the information that is the trigger for the response might only be whatever equals 'big spider', or 'small spider', or 'spiders with gangly legs'. Also, for some people the pattern might extend to 'spider-like creatures'. In other words there is a boundary of recognition, within which the brain triggers a response, and beyond which it doesn't.

The reason for the response exists in the past. The brain has learnt that spiders are dangerous and need to be responded to as a consequence of some defining event in the past. The same can be said to be true for just about all presenting issues: none are independent of a context. If someone lacks confidence there will be situations where that is true, and where it isn't, and times when it's worse than others. The same algorithms are working in the background creating causal connections, whatever the issue. Techniques that can reorganise this causal link so that it ceases to be a problem are explained in Part 2.4.

Structure

Everybody knows they think, but most of us don't think about how we think. Hands up those of you who think in colour? Whatever the answer, I bet many of you had to think about it. Our thoughts are so automatic we get a feeling of them being provided for us without being aware of their makeup, and probably the thing that causes the most difficulty in human relationships is the

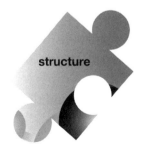

structure

mistaken belief that we all think the same way. We actually don't – often by a wide margin. In Part 1.2 I described the different trance phenomena and introduced submodalities. These are what we are exploring when we are mapping the structure of a client's problem pattern: what are the qualities of their reality tunnel at these moments? Are the thoughts running through their heads in colour or black and white? Where is the feeling that comes with it? Are there any sounds? The more clearly we can understand the way that a client's problem is constructed, the more accurate an intervention based on changing that construction will be. Techniques that can be described as structure interventions include the Swish Pattern and Spinning, and are explained in Part 2.5.

Process

In *Indiana Jones the Temple of Doom* there's an iconic scene where Indy is faced by a native wielding a sword. The swordsman goes through an elaborate show of twirling it around his head, a display calculated to scare anyone prior to him launching an attack. It looks like the end for Indy, until he pulls his pistol and casually shoots the swordsman. Threat over. In therapy that's called a *pattern interrupt*.

Suppose the swordsman went through the same routine prior to every attack? If that routine got interrupted, or adapted, it could fundamentally change the end result. Swap the sword for a lettuce, for example. Or follow Indy's example and shoot him before he gets to the slicing part.

A process is any sequence of actions directed to some end. Swapping metaphors mid-crocodile; a recipe is a process. And if you change the steps of a recipe, or interrupt them, you get something coming out of the oven that is different from what you intended.

Problems are a process too. They have a beginning – something triggers them, and they proceed to an end point. No problem experienced by a client is continual – although it can often feel that way, largely as the result of trance phenomena creating that perception. In Part 2.6 I describe the model for mapping the process of a problem, and describe techniques to interrupt, modify or negate it.

Consequence

From reading Part One you will know that I think the brain can be thought of as a reward calculator. Every moment of the day the brain is reviewing the current situation, interpreting it on the basis of matches it makes (or doesn't make) with past situations, and running simulations of possible future actions and their consequences. All in less than half a second, even on a bad day.

We have a memoragination, a system comprising millions of memory loops organised around particular contexts and each with a particular meaning. Memories can belong to more than one network: our brain isn't like a filing cabinet, it's a matrix of potential connections linked by perceived similarities, differences and causes.

If the memory loop activated by a current situation creates the anticipation of a negative future consequence, then our survival system responds by releasing a quantity of adrenalin – i.e. the protection response. The more strongly negative the future appears, the larger the dose. The flash of this anticipated future is so fast we're usually unaware of it, all we're aware of is our bodily response. This might be labelled by us as stress, or anxiety, perhaps fear, and our behaviour will seek to move us away from what our brain has decided is going to be a bad experience.

If the memory loop activated by a current situation creates the anticipation of a positive future, one that carries a reward, then dopamine is released and we feel motivated towards that goal. In that respect Freud was right: organisms move towards reward and away from pain.

Because of these future simulations and our physical responses to them, the adage that 'we get the life we imagine' is truer than might be thought. If you are about to go into an important meeting and your brain has run a simulation that predicts it going badly, the fight or flight response your body responds with is likely to reduce your conscious capacity to speak and think clearly. In those circumstances it's likely to go as badly as was anticipated. It explains why 'self-fulfilling prophecy' is a common phrase in our language.

Identifying the perceived negative consequence in a client's problem reality tunnel enables us to begin to prime their unconscious towards what would be its opposite: their solution state.

Solution state

It's fundamental to the success of therapy, for most clients, for us to have an understanding of the consequential thoughts that direct their problem behaviour. It is just as important to have a clear idea of what the client's evidence would be for a future that would be free of their problem. By getting their brain to anticipate **that** kind of consequence, the positive kind, we can create self-fulfilling prophecies that work on the side of the angels. It isn't enough for the client to no longer foresee their problem (although it's a step in the right direction), you need to work together to re-tune their brain to foresee whatever takes them towards their better world. How to do this is explained in Part 2.7.

Over the last fifteen years it has become fashionable to partition therapies into two camps, problem focused and solution focused, with the latter being currently more fashionable. As with most either/or situations, in CH we avoid this categorisation. Our memoragination uses the past, present and future, therefore so do we. Cognitive Hypnotherapy focuses on both the problem and the solution, with whatever bias obtains the optimum positive response from the client.

The goal of therapy: from problem toward solution

I remember once meeting a Transpersonal Therapist at a seminar. We were talking about the process of therapy and I said something about the client reaching their goal and therapy ending. She gave me a look and said, "But of course, therapy never really ends, does it? It just moves to another level."

I think that everybody needs therapy, but most people don't need very much, so it definitely should have an end. The point of therapy is to enrich life, not to be a substitute for it.

> *The point of therapy is to enrich life, not to be a substitute for it*

Cognitive Hypnotherapy is predicated as a brief approach, which means that it takes as long as it takes, but the guiding assumption is that most problems begin in an event that may only take a few seconds, so potentially, any change can occur within that same time frame. The art is in helping the client create those few seconds which will change them for the better, as soon as possible. A simple phobia may only take twenty minutes to negate, an eating disorder may take twenty months, but that timescale can be reversed for either condition. It depends on the client.

> *Problems begin in an event that may only take a few seconds, so potentially any change can occur within that same time frame*

Pacing

Instant change is possible from the brain's point of view, and we should always hold that possibility in our mind; if you pick up something that is burning hot you won't need a reminder not to do it again in the future. What can prevent such change from happening in a session are beliefs about the difficulty of change, or the time change takes. If these are limiting factors they are another facet of your work together - to change them, or to utilise them. And they should only belong to the client: progress should never be slow because the therapist believes it needs to be so.

The slowness of change in some clients used to irk me, and I know that sometimes it can knock the confidence of those I've trained. They know that X technique can work really well and yet the client remains unchanged, even when Y and Z technique are thrown at them too, and so they start to doubt themselves. Cue the moment for a metaphor:

> *Cut at the speed of the bread, not the speed of the knife*

I mentioned earlier in the book about how I severed my thumb tendon with a knife. As you might expect, Rebecca has been reluctant to let me loose with anything sharp ever since. Honestly, one small slip...Anyway, she found it easy not to have me slice the bread because I was rubbish at it. More often than not I'd end up with a pile of crumbs and either a wedge shaped door-stop or a sliver. Meanwhile, Little Miss Perfect would cut slice after slice the same size. It was a bit galling, to be honest. Then one day I had a go when she wasn't looking, and I finally got it. All these years I had been trying to bend the bread to my will: a typical boy, I had a sharp knife so I felt I should be at liberty to cut at the speed my manly strength allowed me. This time, I felt the resistance of the bread and adjusted to it. In other words, I cut at the speed of the bread, not the speed of the knife. And so it is with clients: you help them to change at the speed they are comfortable with, not the speed you know has been possible using that technique with others.

As clients gain in confidence as they witness personal change, their expectations will almost certainly shift and allow the pace to accelerate, but I realise now that in my early days I scared away more than one client by panicking them about how quickly the pattern of their life was changing. As I've said before, the brain is often more comfortable with predictable misery than uncertain happiness, so pace it while the reward system adjusts.

So, in my opinion, therapy should always have an end-point to prevent it from becoming part of the fabric of the client's life. I often say that once they start looking forward to seeing me, we're nearly done. You should always have a clear idea of what you're wanting to achieve, not necessarily in regard to the detail of each session - I'm a great believer in Gil Boyne's assertion that you should 'work with what emerges' - but overall in terms of what the client first came for. In other words, you should be clear about your goal - their solution state.

Quite simply, the goal of therapy is to move your client beyond the life their problem pattern has created, and towards the life having their solution state would bring. Success won't always be getting them all the way towards their ideal outcome, but it *will* always be a shift in the reality tunnel the problem pattern used to construct to guide them.

In reality, apart from the one-to-two session clients who walk away without anxiety or their phobia, or who have quit smoking or stopped biting their nails, most clients will stop seeing you

Cognitive Hypnotherapy is about empowerment, the belief that they have within them what they need

before they have reached their goal, usually when they're about 60-70% better. This is a sign of success. Cognitive Hypnotherapy is about empowerment; the belief that they have within them what they need to succeed, that they don't need to come to see you every week to give them a 'top up', or hold their hand every step of the way. Once progress is being felt, my suggestions begin to incorporate the idea of the inevitability of their continuing movement towards their solution state. But that's for a little later. Let's get onto the specifics of changing the problem pattern.

Helen's Story

This is my third book. My first, *Wordweaving: The Science of Suggestion* presents a model of hypnotic language that uses the client's own words in a way that enables the therapist to creatively prime them towards their solution state from within the client's reality tunnel. It effectively frees the user from the one-size-fits-all scripts that tend to predominate in traditional hypnotherapy. The second book, *The Question is the Answer* was written for my students to give them the questioning tools to identify the important information contained within each client's problem pattern and solution state, and provide a model that maps the progress of therapy from first session to a successful conclusion. This book takes the information you gain from those questioning tools and provides the techniques you can choose to do something with that information, and how to adjust them to fit the direction of your treatment.

In *The Question is the Answer,* I use a fictional client called Helen as a means of bringing to life the problem pattern and solution state question sequences. I am going to continue to use Helen as an example as I take you through the different techniques I describe, so you can see how they develop within a therapeutic conversation, and how one technique can morph into another. Here is a transcript of our initial conversation, where I identify relevant information from each quadrant of her problem state. I have pretended that each quadrant is addressed in sequence, but in reality it will flow between them in the manner of a normal conversation. It's beyond the scope of this book to repeat my analysis of what she tells me that leads to my decision about which quadrant to focus on, I recommend you buy the book for that; the purpose of this information is to bring the techniques to life.

"Hi Helen, what can I help you with?"

"It's everything really. I just seem to get stuck with everything."

Context

T: Can you give me some examples?
H: Well, at work I know I'm capable of more but something just holds me back. I've got an exam coming up and I panic every time I think about it.

T: Have you always felt this way?

H: Pretty much. I scraped through at school even though I should have done better. I always get this feeling that people think I'm stupid.

T: Can you remember a specific time recently when you got this feeling?

H: ….Yes, I had to give a presentation to my boss and some of my colleagues. It wasn't even about anything important.

T: And what happened?

Structure (trance phenomena)

H: When I stood up my mind went blank and I thought I was going to pass out. I just wanted to run out of the room I was so scared.

Consequence

H: Now every time I think about doing something like it I feel sick.

Structure

T: And as you remember being so scared, if you could point in your body to where you get that feeling, where would you point?

H: (Indicates chest) Here, and my face feels really hot.

Context

T: Right, so as you feel that feeling, are there other times when you get that feeling?

H:……….Yes, every time I took my driving test …..meeting new people….

T: Good. And are there ever times when you're with people and this doesn't happen?

H: Oh yes, when I'm with my friends I'm happy to speak up – in fact they can't believe I have this problem. Also I play netball and I shout my head off on the court.

T: What's different?

H: I don't know……..I guess my friends don't judge me………and I know I'm good at netball.

T: Are you ever comfortable with people who you feel are judging you?

H:…………..No…I can't think of any.

T: Does this have an effect on relationships?

H: Oh totally! I hate dating because I get in such a state, worrying about saying the right thing, whether they'll like me. It's a complete nightmare.

T: Are you in a relationship right now?

H: Yes , Mark. We've been going out for about a year.

T: Do you get that feeling with him?

H: Not any more. I did the first couple of months but it's easier now.

T: What made it easier?

H: Well, he's just very sweet and patient and I kind of relax with him.

Structure

T: When you think back to that time when you gave that talk at work, when you think of doing something like it again, do you get an image?

H:.........Yes, I see myself making a pigs ear of it again.

T: And is that picture close or far away?

H: I hadn't really thought of it.........er it's really close, in my face.

T: And is it black and white or colour?

H: It's colour.

T: And as you look at that picture are you in it or looking at it through your own eyes?

H: Through my own eyes.

T: And can you describe the feeling of passing out?

H: Errm...well my breathing got really tight...

T: And as you remember being so scared, if you could point in your body to where you get that feeling, where would you point?

H: (Indicates chest) Here, and my face feels really hot.

T: And if that feeling had a shape, what shape would it be?

H: Oh, a kind of band around my chest.

T: Is that a wide or a narrow band?

H: It's wide.

T: Does it have a feeling to it?

H: Yes it's really tight.

T: On a scale of 0-10, where 10 is the worst, how strong was that feeling?

H: Easily a 10.

T: How is the relaxed feeling you get from Mark different from the tight feeling in your chest?

H: It's lower down, like a warmth in my stomach.

T: Anything else?

H: Well, it's just a slower feeling - I know that sounds silly, but when I'm scared the feeling in my chest is really fast.

140

Process

T: Good, so what was it that triggered your mind going blank? Take me back to that moment.

H: Let's think...I was shuffling my papers trying to stay calm and then my boss announced my name and what my presentation was about. So I stood up and looked around and everyone was looking at me. I remember thinking "Oh God", and I froze. I must have looked like a rabbit caught in headlights.

T: And as you froze what were you feeling?

H: Absolutely terrified, I really thought I would pass out.

T: So you 'saw all of their eyes on you' and you felt terrified...what did you do?

H: I tried to talk but it was pretty obvious to everyone that I wasn't right, so I apologised and said I felt ill and went off to the toilet.

T: How quickly did you feel better?

H: Well, I felt absolutely sick in the loo, but then Tricia came and said the meeting was over and they'd rescheduled my input and I felt instant relief.

T: And what did you think about what had happened afterwards?

H: I really beat myself up. They must have thought me so stupid; no way would they have believed I was ill.

That is enough of the problem pattern for our purposes. I also elicited Helen's solution state using the magic wand question.

Solution state

T: "If I could wave a magic wand and you had what you wanted from coming here today how would you know? What would be different?

H: Well, I'd be with someone – or a bunch of people like that time with my boss, and I'd feel confident.

T: And how would you know you were feeling confident?

H: For a start my hands wouldn't be sweaty, my face wouldn't be hot and I wouldn't feel I was going to be sick or faint.

Notice how she's focusing on kinaesthetic submodalities. Also, Helen's telling me what she doesn't want to feel – which is valuable, but it's easier to move her attention onto something else she can notice, rather than create a non-awareness of the negative pattern. So I continue to question:

Solution state

T: What would you feel instead?

H: Oh.......I hadn't thought of that, I've felt this way for so long.

T: Sure. How about those times when you are confident with people? Would how you feel then be a good way to feel in the situation we're talking about?

H: Oh yes, of course. When I'm with my friends I feel....relaxed.

T: How does 'relaxed' feel?

H: Nice. It's like when I feel warm and cosy...safe.

T: How's your breathing? Do you breathe in the same way?

H: Uhhm...no. When I'm panicking my breathing is short and high in my chest, almost like I'm panting. When I'm relaxed my breathing is slower and kind of sits in my stomach. Funny...I hadn't thought of that.

T: Excellent. How else would you like to feel?

H: Well, when I'm playing netball I feel in control of what I'm doing, and that makes me feel confident. Both of those feelings are really important.

T: Brilliant. Anything else?

H:....No....I think that's the main things that come to mind.

With this information I'm equipped to begin to work on changing the problem pattern with a range of choices about which techniques to use to focus on particular quadrants. I begin with context.

Context Interventions –
The Past Participant

What's this about?

Most of the problems our clients experience are the result of a memory loop being closed to new information. In this chapter, I describe techniques that work by opening the loop up to new perspectives that can enrich the meaning and liberate the client from the stagnant repetition that is the hallmark of most issues.

By enabling our closed loop past to be reinterpreted through higher levels of mental processing in particular ways the TAOTM connections that link past to present can be reformed. What was the root of the problem becomes the root of the resolution.

A man is driving fast along a country lane one day in his open-topped car. As he approaches a corner a car emerges from it on the wrong side of the road and only narrowly misses him. As it flashes past him a woman leans out of the driver's window and shouts "PIG!!" "Bloomin' cheek", he thinks, "It was her fault we nearly crashed," and he turns in his seat and shouts back "BITCH!" and drives around the corner and...hits the pig. Context is everything.

Every client needs to be assessed as an individual, so the urge to attach a label should be resisted. For every client the possibility exists for their problem pattern to be changed within one, or all, of the pattern's quadrants, depending on the information you've ascertained from them. In my experience, context interventions are the most commonly used first step, because no problem is independent of context and the techniques work well on the majority of people, but that just means more than 50%, and there are also those who aren't good at introspection, don't access memories well or don't use a change in their feelings about them as evidence for their improvement, so don't mistake context interventions not rocking their world as evidence of resistance. Sometimes it's just difference.

Context interventions work by accessing the memoragination and enabling our view of the past to be changed. Isn't that impossible? The past happened, how can our view of it be changed? Well, it happened, but it probably didn't happen exactly the way you remember it, and I said change our 'view' of the past, not the past itself. And besides, the past isn't happening now any more than your future is – except in your head. Our past is just electricity and chemicals firing somewhere in the brain, existing as memories simply to guide our present actions; a repository of useful experiences upon which to build models of present and future activity, and as such are constantly being adapted in the light of ongoing learning, so why not utilise the ongoing learning process?

Those who don't change their history are doomed to repeat it

After all, those who don't change their history are doomed to repeat it.

I've suggested that a feedback loop exists, our memoragination, whereby our memories create our perceptions in the present, which then influence our perceptions of the past. For example, if a client has several experiences in her childhood which lead her to believe she's not loved, then this is likely to influence her behaviour as an adult – remember 'what the thinker thinks'? Let's suppose that this belief leads her to anticipate being rejected in relationships, which then creates behaviour that pushes people away. Her feelings of pain and rejection get stronger and stronger and the reality tunnel she lives in becomes a closed loop, so when she looks back on her memories in relation to this context, her Prover will only bring up memories that confirm her thought. The older she gets, the more invariant her belief about these memories becomes, and she creates a life surrounded by loneliness that has 'always been that way'. i.e she's stuck in protection.

Do you remember I quoted Ernest Rossi's point that you can't recall a memory without changing it, because it's always interpreted through the lens of your present feelings, and how Joseph LeDoux's research into Reconsolidation Theory demonstrates that memories become unstable and changeable *whenever* they're recalled? This makes the way therapy is conducted crucial. Probably more damage has been caused by the inappropriate handling of memories than any other therapeutic intervention. The only purpose of talking about the past is to change it or use it. The act of changing a memory is an act of inception – the beginning of something new.

> *The only purpose of talking about the past is to change or use it*

It may be why evidence has emerged that some talking therapy or counselling approaches – "so how are you feeling about that" – actually do more harm than good,[84] by firing further negative emotions into the recollection of an event, so when it is sent back to the cortex for reconsolidation the feeling is actually stronger than before.

So, if memories are a key part of how we experience a problem — they're really the 'why' it happens — and they can be rendered unstable, what can be done to change them in a positive way, rather than making things worse? In this chapter I focus on the use of regression as a means of achieving this, and within this approach there are two main schools of thought from which come a number of different possibilities and several shared principles.

Associated or dissociated?

Association is where you experience something from a first person perspective – through your own eyes. Dissociated is where you watch yourself having an experience, as you would when watching a home movie.

Both of these perspectives are available to most of us when thinking of a memory, but you will find that some people have difficulty in either separating themselves from their experience, or in involving themselves. The following can be a guide for which approach to take.

My first exposure to regression was during my NLP training, where I was taught a version using a time line. This involves visualising your life (past, present and future) as a line, usually on the floor, and you floating above it. This, as you can picture, is a dissociated approach - I was looking down at myself living my life. For many years this was my 'way' of doing regression. And it was, overall, very effective. But not with everyone. Back in those days I assumed it was the client's fault – 'resistance' probably. And then I went to see the late, great, Gil Boyne in action. Gil believed that for change to occur people should be fully associated. His approach is called Transforming Therapy,[85] because the aim is to take the negative emotion that has been fully manifested in the client, and transform it into a positive emotion – usually love. His approach was almost completely opposite to my own – and very obviously worked. I was fascinated and learnt several big lessons: to look in the opposite direction of what you think is true - it's often where new learning is hiding, and that there is no single way of working with a client, even when using the same approach.

> *Look in the opposite direction of what you think is true – it's often where new learning is hiding*

This is a simplification but, basically, dissociative techniques predominantly focus on giving a different meaning to an old event, known as reframing, so the emphasis is on the change of thought that leads to a change of feeling. Using the language I've been developing so far, it involves opening up a closed loop by adding new perspectives that enrich it. By turning it into an open loop the negative feedback that has maintained the problem is broken and new behavioural options can develop.

With associative approaches, the tendency is to focus on the emotions present in a memory by taking the feelings and changing or transforming them in some way – although reframing might form part of the means by which this is achieved. If, as a result of your work, the client's problem memory loop is no longer held together by the negative emotion that TAOTM used to match it to present experiences, then the loop itself will cease to exist, and so will the problem. Both approaches have the same effect - the opening up of a portion of our past so it can be updated with more useful understandings - they just achieve it from different directions.

Since learning from Gil I have incorporated both approaches into my work, and have let the client guide me as to which is likely to work – and of course it's not entirely an either/or choice; it's perfectly possible to switch between them as the need arises, as I'm going to be showing you. I'm going to start with dissociated approaches and then associated, highlighting the similarities and differences between them and how they can be folded into each other.

Creating the time machine

While quantum physics might tell us differently, we all recognise time as something that passes; our lives have a past, a present and a future and our perception of our life is of a seamless succession of moments. And we feel that we can revisit many of our past moments at will. We all have a reservoir of many thousands of memories, so a key part of regression is identifying those that are relevant to the issue – that are part of the causal model that creates the problem reality tunnel. A common means of doing so is to use some form of metaphoric device – like the Flux Capacitor in Back to the Future, the Tardis in Doctor Who, or the Time Machine in H.G. Wells' classic – to guide the client and to keep communication of their experience clear.

The one I use most commonly is a time line. Imagine that where you are currently sitting is a point on a line that represents your entire life, with the past going off in one direction, and the future in another, and with you sitting on the point that is now. The time line can be in the client's imagination, or they can physically walk along a representation of the line on the floor.

A different metaphor would be to have the client imagine their past as a library, which, as they walk along the main corridor, has passages that open up for each year of their life, and a book on the shelves for every day of that year. Another possibility is a DVD library (especially for young people). The principle here is to just have a means by which clients can navigate the narrative of their life in a form that works for them, in such a way that you know where they are and they can follow your directions. You can also see how all three utilise a third person perspective, thus dissociating the client from the experience. The advantage of this is that they are less likely to abreact, and don't have to re-experience the past event – often a major reason for a client's reluctance to regress. In the event that the client does begin to associate into a negative emotion then encouraging them to return to their place above their time line usually makes them comfortable again. A second possibility is to set up a safety anchor (the principles of which are explained in Part 2.6) and fire it when they begin to demonstrate a strong feeling, and a third is to get them to open their eyes and calm them. In my experience, if you follow the principles of the intervention, and pace your client, this doesn't happen very often.

Time line reconsolidation

I've found that most people readily take to the time line idea, although sometimes it takes a bit of explanation. Let's imagine that Helen is sitting in front of me and, based on the information I gained in Part 2.3, I've decided this is the right intervention for her. I'd say something like this:

"I just want you to imagine your life as a line, with you sitting on 'now' and your past coming from one direction, and your future going off in another, almost like a road or railway line. Now, if your past line came from a direction, where would you point? And your future?"

There are no right or wrong ways to have a time line, they just have to be capable of being navigable. Sometimes clients will come out with something like "it's a ball of wool", or "a bowl of spaghetti", or sometimes have the memories all over the place. As with any problem posed by my clients, I leave it to them to solve it:

"So, if for now we wanted to make it possible for you to be able to go up and down your time line, and for us both to know where you are, what would you do to your time line to make that possible?"

I've had clients who peg it out on the ground, who unravel it and stick it or make it into a collage. The point is that they solve it using their model of the world; you avoid imposing your ideas wherever possible.

Having identified their time line the next thing is to dissociate them by having them move above it (although being beside it or below it works just as well). I usually do this without utilising a trance induction, and for the reason I mentioned in idea nine on page 123: in order to access a memory related to their problem it really helps if the memory loop related to the problem is firing. If I spend 10 minutes relaxing them, then the feelings firing in their brain at that moment are likely to be lovely fluffy ones. Remember priming? What is on your mind is brought to mind, so how likely is it that they will be able to access a negative memory when they feel relaxed and calm? I want to utilise the thoughts that I've been bringing to the surface by asking them about how they know they have a problem.

As I said with idea nine, all techniques work by utilising trance states, so in my opinion they carry the trance induction within them. Getting a client to follow the steps of any intervention described in this book creates the level of trance required to facilitate a change.

Step One: Getting away from the time line

Often, especially with people who are nervous of being 'hypnotised', or have a fear of failing (like at what I'm about to ask them to do), I distract them by saying:

"Before we start I'd just like to do an experiment, I'm not going to hypnotise you...."

This tends to reduce their anxiety, and not give them something to fail at. Then, at the conclusion of the following 'experiment' I simply continue with the sequence of this technique, so we never actually 'begin' something they could fail at.

"If you close your eyes and picture the time line you just described, and it had a colour, what colour would it be?"
Response.
"Excellent. Now, if you were to move yourself above the line, would it be easier for you to move the lines away from you, or for you to move yourself away from the line?"
Response.
"Good. Now, if you wanted to move along your time line, is it easier for you to move, or to stay still and move the line?"
Response.

I phrase it the way I have because I found that if I just said "Get above your timeline", people were able to say "I can't". By giving them what Milton Erickson called the 'illusion of choice', (in that whichever choice they make causes them to do what I want them to achieve - to dissociate) between moving above the line or moving the line, it causes them to have to see which one would work best - our minds tend to keep within the choices we're given (the *or* is a language pattern called *exclusive/inclusive or*) - and so sidesteps resistance, or it occurring to them that they can't do it. I found it reduced the "I can'ts" to almost zero. If you have a client who says "I can't", remember that this is their problem, not yours, so ask them a question to help them with their problem, such as, "If you could do something which would mean you *could* be away from the timeline, observing yourself on it, what would you do?"

Whichever one they choose (and they could be above it, below it or beside it) the principle remains the same, that they are dissociated from the experience they go back to in their memoragination. For the purposes of my description the following assumes that they are above the time line.

Choice made, I continue:

"So, just find a height above the time line that feels comfortable and safe for you, a height that, by going back to it at any time, will enable you to remain comfortable. Let me know when you're there."

This establishes this place as a safety point, so that if the client begins, at any time, to associate into a negative feeling you don't feel is helpful at that point, you can say:

"and how much higher would you need to get above your time line before you're back at that safe distance, able to view the event comfortably?..."

Response

Step Two: The key question

"Good. So, from your position above your time line, if your unconscious were to know the first event connected to your problem, which, by going back to it, would mean that you could let the problem go, completely and for good, would it be a time before you were five, between five and ten, or after ten?"

Before progressing to the response, let me deconstruct some of the key features of this question, because it's a precision instrument.

"… if your unconscious were to know the first event connected to your problem…": by asking the client's unconscious, rather than the client themselves, it often reduces the pressure some clients experience when asked to be responsible for an answer. *If* is a magic word. It invites the client (in this example) to create a counterfactual world where letting the problem go is possible. As they develop this world, they forget that it's one they made up, and actually accept the process as happening within their own belief system.

…*"which, by going back to it, would mean that you could let the problem go, completely and for good…"*: this is what I call a *TAOTM question* because it utilises cause and effect, similarity, or difference, to cause a client to do something **and** by doing it gain something else. This example uses cause and effect in the manner of the formula 'if X happens Y will follow", i.e., the act of going back to the memory will lead to the letting go of the problem. The presuppositions inherent in this structure are a common feature of many of the language patterns contained within the techniques I describe in this book. The power of presuppositions is that they're automatically accepted by the unconscious, often bypassing the conscious awareness of the client. Also notice the phrase 'completely and for good'; obviously the two terms can mean the same thing, but the ambiguity of 'for good' also suggests an ecology of change, so that going back to the memory will only lead to something positive.

…*"would it be a time before you were five, between five and ten, or after ten?"* There is nothing magical about this division of life; it just gives the client another illusion of choice. In my experience, most core events in our life occur below the age of 10-12, so this points them in the right direction, but gives them permission to choose a later time.

Some clients come with a belief in past lives, and their memories often live up to their beliefs, while some just seem to manifest them spontaneously despite their beliefs. As a therapist, my only interest is in the causal connection between the memory and the present issue, so this technique can just continue as if it were a memory from within this lifetime, nothing special or extra needs to be added just because it's a past life. A memory is a memory is a memory. What I think is important is that all memories should emerge cleanly from the client, not as a result of prompting or priming from the therapist. I know there are many therapists who believe in the reality of past life experiences and some who even insist on their clients experiencing one as a prerequisite for change. I disagree with the concept of the therapist deciding the nature of the client's reality in order for them to get better, and much prefer to work within their model of the world. If that includes past lives, great, if not, also great.

On most occasions the client will be able to give an affirmative answer after just a few seconds. This often surprises people, possibly because of the Freudian idea that such memories are 'buried deep'. But Barabasi's research on networks suggests otherwise: hubs are accessed regularly because of their relevance, so are usually brought to mind easily. On occasions where they aren't it might be because the memory loop containing the memory isn't sufficiently 'lit', in which case switching to the *Affect Bridge* variation described on page 169 might reap dividends. First, however, I would try one or more of the following devices to assist the client:

They say, "I don't know,"
I say, "I know you don't know yet, and what I'd like you to do is just to respond to my questions, just allow whatever comes to mind to be spoken."
"Are you indoors or outdoors?"
"Is it daytime or night time?"
"Are you on your own or with someone else?"

This is something I learnt from Gil. The provision of three choices often triggers aspects of the event that brings to mind the rest of the memory. It helps light more of the loop.
Or
"I know you don't know yet, and keep not knowing. Whatever you do, don't think of the event we're interested in. Keep your mind blank, keep it blank until the next memory comes to your mind, and tell me what it is when it comes."

If I say to you "don't think of a blue tree" what happens? That's right, you think of a blue tree. It's the same principle here; the mind has to process a negative, so in order to not think of the memory it has to bring it to mind.

On most occasions these two options will give you the desired result. If they don't, in the main, I'll adapt my approach by utilising the principle of the *Affect bridge* that I'm going to describe a little later.

So, let's assume one or other of these 'fixes' has enabled Helen to access a memory.

"OK I'm getting something."

"Excellent, so from above your timeline look down at what you're seeing; what's going on?"

Although it's useful to hear the content of the memory from the perspective of the client, I'd like to make clear that it's not essential. One of the things I like about dissociative regression is that it's an experience that can remain completely private to the client. As long as they follow the steps of the intervention it can work perfectly well without you knowing any detail of the client's memory. This can be a very attractive feature for clients who feel embarrassed and humiliated by their past. On the whole, however, I've found that most people are perfectly happy to tell you what they are experiencing, and that certainly helps your work.

"I'm in the living room at home and my Dad has got me to sing a song for some relatives who've come to visit. I'm eight years old and I got the words wrong and my Dad shouted at me and called me stupid."

What I'm listening for are clues as to how this event could relate to the problem the client has come to see me for. What is the TAOTM relationship between this event and their issue? While it's not as important for me to see the connection as it is for the client, being able to do so will help to guide my choice of questions. If the initial information doesn't make the connection clear then I'm likely to ask for more detail about what's going on. At the same time I'm also looking closely at the client to check on the level of comfort as they process the memory; some clients find it difficult to remain disassociated, so if I see any sign of negative emotion I would encourage them to get further away from their timeline until they can look on the event comfortably.

Step Three: Establishing a TAOTM connection

If I think the event is clear enough for a connection to be made by the client I'll proceed with the next question. Sometimes even if I don't think it's clear I might choose to proceed because clients will often see a connection even when I haven't.

"If there was a connection between this event and the problem you've had up until now, what would be the connection?"

The principle here is very important: what we're looking for the question to achieve is for the mind of the client to recognise a TAOTM connection between the event brought to mind and the presenting problem (i.e. how the event *caused* the problem, or is *similar* to situations now). This question places the client right in the heart of what I described as the 'calculation gap' in Part One, within the mechanism that identifies patterns between past and present – whether they exist or not. We have no way of knowing whether, before the question was asked, the link between event and issue had already been established by the mind, or if asking the question causes the brain to establish it. It doesn't matter – there is no 'truth' to find, so if the 'truth' the brain recognises is this connection, then changing the connection will change

There is no 'truth' to find

the brain's perception of the problem because it is totally dependent on the automatic output of TAOTM.

In the case of Helen, it's perfectly plausible that this memory in her living room could be the initial experience of embarrassment, significant enough for it to be marked out by the brain as a reference experience to be used to assess future situations. In other words, every time Helen walks into a present situation where her brain finds sufficient similarity between it and the living room memory, it sets off a thought chain that leads to the emotional response and behavioural actions that Helen calls her 'problem'. In Barabasi's terms, this memory is a hub.

Obviously, I'm hoping that Helen will see a connection between the embarrassment in the living room and her lack of confidence when it comes to speaking in front of people. Most clients will, but for some people such introspection is new to them and they may take longer to intuit the relationship. I really believe that such insights are much more powerful if they come from inside the client rather than if they're my insights accepted by them, (or 'outsights', as I like to call them). If they need more help to see, or become more certain of the connection, I will give them more information to sort for *similarity* by saying,

"If you were to go forward to the next event connected to this feeling how much further forward would you go?"

How much further forward they go isn't relevant, what they go to is. Again, I'll ask them what's going on, listening for similarities between this new event and the previous one. Then I'll ask a variation of the previous question, *"If there's a connection between this event and the previous one, what would the connection be?"*

This extra contextual information will usually enable the client to see a causal link between the events and their problem. I've never had to ask a client to link more than three memories before they get the relationship between these events and their issue. The reason I say this question is a key principle is because, in my opinion, the algorithms of the mind are the means by which the brain constructs belief. So, the presuppositions inherent in the question I asked, i.e. "If there was a connection between X and Y (similarity, cause or

> *Because the connection is presupposed by the language of the question, the mind accepts its existence*

155

difference) what would the connection be?", leads the mind to seek such a connection. And, because the connection is presupposed by the language of the question, the mind accepts its existence. So it doesn't actually matter whether this event *is* the first event connected to the problem, and of course there is no way of knowing that that is the case; all that matters is that the brain believes it to be. The brain works on plausibility, not truth.

The principle of the *key question* is that it presupposes the existence of a core memory and that by going back to it the problem can be resolved. The principle of the *connection question* is that it makes explicit the perceived relationship between the memory and the problem. In a way, by forcing the brain to perceive such a relationship it causes it to believe it - and 'what the Thinker thinks, the Prover proves' rides again.

Back to Helen and her response to the connection question...

"It's the fear of looking stupid in front of people. They don't know me; if I make a mistake they'll think I'm an idiot."

And there we have it: the core belief from which emerges what the client labels as a lack of confidence. In some quarters this is labelled a social phobia -a fear of other people's opinion - and it's probably one of the most endemic fears people suffer from.

In previous books I've labelled this phenomenon *premature evaluation*; the young mind makes a decision about its *self* based on its present level of experience. Unfortunately, this decision forms the basis for a belief which persists into adulthood, by which time it's taken as incontrovertible truth (i.e. an invariant belief sustained within a closed loop). Our job here is to intercept and reprogramme that belief by opening the loop to a richer perspective.

156

Step Four: Opening the closed loop to new learning

"As you look down at that event, if there was something the child that was you could learn, that by learning it would mean you could let go of that fear of looking stupid, what would you teach her?"

As always, the presuppositional nature of the question is key to the success of it, the way the TAOTM question sets up a cause-and-effect relationship between the learning being passed to the child and the letting go of the fear. Notice how much more powerful the above question is, in terms of the end effect of it, than simply saying, "as you look down at that event, if there was something the child that was you could learn… what would you teach her?" In the way that I've previously phrased the question, if the child is seen to have learnt what her adult self is teaching her, her brain is naturally led to infer that the fear of looking stupid must disappear.

Some clients will come out with a list of things for the child to learn, others might just say one or two things. The amount isn't important, but the client having the chance to express what he or she believes needs to be learnt in this situation, is. So I'll probably ask, "anything else?" until they've said everything they need to.

Sometimes clients will say, "I don't know", or, "Nothing, it was about the child being stupid/ugly/evil", etc. This is really just a sign that the client is stuck in their current perspective, and is usually the result of one of three nominal processing errors made by clients when they were children and experiencing an SEE:

1. This is my fault.
2. It cannot mean anything else.
3. This is about me as a person.

Therefore what you have to keep in your mind are the following TAOTM perceptual positions **(i.e. "What's that about?")**

1. How is this not about them?
2. What *are* the shades of grey?

3. How have they linked their identity to this event (the behaviour in it or the environment in which the event took place)?

Here are some sample questions that look to reframe one of the three errors (**"How can I use that?"**):
"How was this not about you as a person (self)?"

*"As you look down at the event, if you had been that other
person, would you have behaved in that way?"*

*"What was their intention" (the person central to the event –
parent/teacher etc.)?*

"What did they want you to learn by them doing what they did?"

When they've come up with something that fits any one of the three TAOTM positions, use the most appropriate version of one of the following:

*"So was it really about you, or about the limitations of the other
person?"*
> or

"What was it about them that made them behave that way?"

*"As you look down, if any other child had occupied the space you
did, would they have been treated the same way?"*

"So was it about you as a person?"

Often, as hard as someone can be on themselves (people can be their own best friends or their own worst enemies), they are usually more forgiving of others, so moving them to a perceptual position where they see the child through the eyes of another, or the child as being someone other than them, can work wonders – particularly if they're a parent:

*"If the child that is you in that event was your child, what would
you want them to learn?"*

*"If that child was yours would you love him/her, be proud of
him/her?"*

"What are the qualities that child has that makes you love/be proud of him/her?"

In Helen's case, she comes up with:

> *"I'd teach her that it doesn't matter what other people think. She should just have fun being her, and trust herself. She's as good as anyone else, and people like her. Making mistakes is natural."*

Some clients will come up with a long list of things to learn, others with just one. Both are fine, and it doesn't hurt to say the following; before moving on:

"So if the you at that age were to understand that...it was not about you...is there anything else left to learn before you let go of x?"

In most cases, avoid the urge to add to their list, and if you succumb, phrase it as a question like, "And would it help the child to learn X,Y or Z?"

Step Five: Passing new learning into the loop

> *"If your unconscious mind could use your imagination in the most powerful and positive way to pass that learning down to the child that was you, so that as you look at her, you know she knows it now, just notice how it does it, taking the time it needs to allow the child to fully absorb the learning, and when she has ..."*

There are many therapists who direct this part of the intervention by suggesting their own metaphor for learning transfer: they suggest passing the learning down in balloons or rolling them down in balls etc. Either of those could be perfectly good, but, as I keep saying, I think the best idea is the one the client comes up with and my phrasing of this suggestion allows the client's imagination to produce the most appropriate image for her. When saying this to your client, pace them and allow them enough time to do what you're asking them to accomplish. When you think they have had enough time, or you could ask them to nod their head when they have, you could move to the next step of the intervention, but just notice first how the structure of this suggestion where it says, "...so that as you look at her, you know she knows it now...", presupposes the image of the child changing in a way that means learning is taking place, which also, because of the previous question, means that the fear can (and actually must) disappear. It's a subtle request for the driver submodalities of the image to change.

Step Six: Moving before the Event

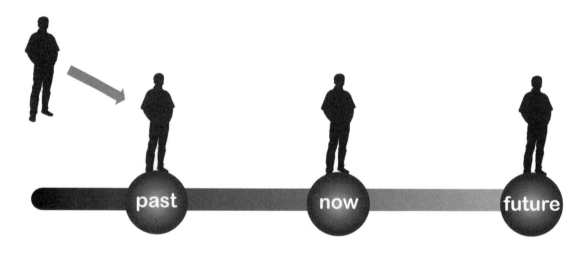

The next step is one which asks the client to reorientate themselves above their timeline and can sometimes cause difficulty for those less blessed visually: It's why I usually mime the progression of the exercise in front of them before I start so they can see what I'm asking them to do at this point; I've found it really helps this stage go smoothly.

"... just move along your time line to just before this event occurred so that it's down below and in front of you with you facing the direction of now, and let me know when you're there. Good. Now, as you look down at that event from before it happened, where's the emotion gone? Is it there or has it gone?"

This is a very powerful part of the intervention, and there are several explanations as to why it works. The simplest that I find plausible is this: the mind has been led to accept that this memory is the first event connected to the problem. By shifting the perceptual position of the observing client to *before* this event occurred means that the emotion or the belief present in the memory has not yet been experienced by the child, therefore it can't exist in the event as they look down into it from that position. The brain is put into a bind that causes the negative emotion or belief to disappear. At least that's how it works on a good day. There will be times when a client says, "It's still there," instead of, "It's gone!"

Panic not. There are a number of what I call my ' get out of jail free cards'. The first is the one I usually try first:

"if there was an event, even earlier than this, how much further back would you need to go to find it?"

Clearly this is presupposing that the core event is even earlier than this, and many clients will immediately say something like, "Three years". You simply say:

"Great. So, if you go back to that memory now and look down, what's going on?"

You then repeat all the steps they were taken through with the previous memory. In the happy event of this causing the emotion to disappear, when I bring the client back along the timeline I usually stop them at the first memory they chose and just make sure the emotion has disappeared from that event too; it tends to be a good convincer for them.

If they say that there isn't another memory then I'll try an inductive question, such as:

"If there was one thing left to learn, which by learning it would mean you could let go of the fear, what would it be?"

It's inductive because it's suggesting that one thing will lead to the solution of everything, and the structure of the suggestion is such that by getting the child to learn that one last thing the client is led to believe it will naturally lead to the fear disappearing.

A third option is to say:

"How much higher would you need to get above your timeline for you to be able to see the memory without the emotion or belief in it?"

They say, "A long way", and you say, "Excellent, so just go to that height now and notice the emotion gone. And with it gone, come back down to that point above your timeline."

If these three options don't work, then it might be time to switch to another technique. I explain how to do that in Part 2.8. For now we'll assume it has. With the emotion gone, there are just a few steps left to the completion of this intervention. There is an opportunity at this point for the client to associate into the memory to enjoy the positive difference the disappearance of the negative emotion has made.

Clearly this would not always be appropriate; the fear of driving might be removed by reframing the memory of an accident, but it's unlikely it will make the accident an enjoyable thing to be associated into. These kinds of examples will be obvious to you, but in any case I usually ask the client:

"Would it be a good or useful thing to go into yourself as a child now and experience the difference this has made?"

If they say yes, you can say something like:

"And just go into your body now and notice all the differences this has made ... in how you feel ... so much better ... and you can just imagine how this would change your experiences as a child ... all the ways this would help you grow into the person you want to be ... almost like a pebble in a pond... the ripples of this can flow all the way along your time line ... changing your understanding of those things that happened that used to be part of the problem you once had ... so that from today your unconscious mind can store this memory in this new way and use it in the best way possible to help you ... grow more XXX (in this case probably confident, but use words they gave you when you were eliciting their solution state) ... and when your unconscious mind has done that bring yourself back above your time line and let me know when you're there."

The moment when the event is experienced in a different way by the client is the moment of inception. A new idea about an old idea has been planted. The rest of the intervention is designed to turn that moment into the start of their solution state becoming true by utilising the Butterfly Effect to take them out of protection and into growth.

When they let you know they're back above the time line you move onto the next step:

Step Seven: Reconsolidating the entire memory loop

"And now just allow your unconscious mind to bring you back along your timeline only as quickly as it can access those memories that used to be connected to the problem you once had, and learn from them whatever is left to learn that means that by the time you're back above now your unconscious has everything it needs for you to be free ... to be able to continue to use it so that as the days go by you begin to notice more and more the way you're changing ... becoming all those things you most want to be. And you might be aware of some of those memories as you come back along your timeline, or you may not, it doesn't matter... just let me know if there's any memory we need to pay attention to, or let me know when you're back above now."

Some clients may get stuck on the way back above a particular memory, and if that happens I usually just assume it to be a sign there is something left to resolve in the memory. Asking the inductive question and passing the learning from it to the child usually resolves it and the client can resume their journey back to the present. Once there we conclude, as we do with every intervention we do, with a future pace, because I think it's vital to link the incepted idea to the solution state becoming true. In that way the new idea becomes the cause of the client's desired outcome (the effect). By working within TAOTM the change becomes more plausible to the brain. I talk more about this in Part 2.7.

Step Eight: Connecting the change to the solution state

"If you were to go out into the future to an event which, if it had happened in the past, would have been connected to the problem you once had, look down at that event and notice how much it's better."

Notice how there's a presupposition that the event will look better, which tends to stack the deck in your client's favour. When they look down and report that it does feel better you can then proceed with something like the following:

"And just notice all the things around you that are different now, people and how they respond to you...new choices and opportunities that appear...all the things that help you to be doing things so differently...and it might surprise you to see some of the new things you start to do as your confidence in yourself grows...and as you look down...whatever capabilities of yours that seem stronger...or maybe even new...that help this change to happen just mean that it's easier to see what it is this new you believes about themselves or the world that makes them the person they are...the person you want to be...so if I were to ask your unconscious mind to keep this you on your time line...almost like a beacon...something that your unconscious can use to guide you in the choices you make and the opportunities you notice....the actions you take and the resources you acquire that lead you...every day in large or small ways... to become more and more the person you want to be...so much more quickly than you might have imagined was possible once...so however your unconscious does this... now...you can come back towards now..."

It can also be good practice to associate them into their future self and anchor the feeling they have of being who they want to be. The future pace is a key part of your work. It replaces the old relationship between the core memory and present limiting behaviour with a new perspective of the change to the old memory being the cause of a new effect - the solution state perceived in this description of their future.

You can then bring them back to now, and as you do, use the information you've garnered from your solution state elicitation to prime them with your suggestions. A short example of that for Helen, based on her saying how her evidence would be feeling warm, cosy and safe around people, in control with her breathing low and slow, could be:

"...so that from today you may begin to notice how you're beginning to feel different around people...more in control...and in the beginning it might feel strange to realise how the company of people can make you feel warm...even cosy...with the right people...but sooner than you might imagine the feeling of safety just grows to the point where you notice what makes that true...and whether your breathing...slow and low...is the evidence...or something else entirely doesn't matter...you know it is..."etc

When you've finished that you can get them to open their eyes. I'll usually make that section about nine minutes long and record it so the client can listen to it every night for a period of time so that their unconscious becomes more and more primed to the radio station that equals their solution state. I limit it to under ten minutes because I find that if it's longer clients struggle to find the time to listen, or if they listen last thing at night, too tired. And while direct suggestion might require longer to install an instruction, ten minutes of Wordweaving™ every night is enough to adequately prime their imagination.

Beyond spending a few minutes giving the client the chance to relate anything about the experience that might serve to reinforce its impact, that concludes this intervention. Most people's response to it is, 'That was interesting'. Because people are working from a dissociative position they are less likely to run from your office screaming 'Eureka!' than if you're using an associative approach, but the results can be just as good over time. One of the things I like about regression generally is that the change is generative; each difference that occurs as a result of it tends to generate and amplify further change, so six months later the results can be significantly greater than they appear at first, whether or not they've initially run happily from your room. I think the Butterfly Effect is the reason why.

Within the overall process of individual therapy there might be a call to use regression on more than one occasion - often clients have more than one negative emotion or limiting belief contributing to their situation. It's possible to use time line several times in a single session, but I usually prefer to limit it to once to enable me to calibrate the difference it has made when I see the client for the next session. On most occasions change from this intervention, particularly if strengthened by the use of Wordweaving™, can be perceived within a short space of time.

One of the things that can cause resistance to the use of regression is the fear that, because a problem in the present-day appears to be so great, it must be based on something equally terrible in their past. Of course it's all a matter of perspective: what was terrible to you as a child is likely to be of little consequence to you if it were to happen to you now for the first time as an adult. If I steal a sweet from you when you're five it's likely to be the end of your world; steal a sweet from you now and you can just go and buy another sweet.

On most occasions the memories we go back to are our general challenges of childhood: the first day at school, sibling rivalries, fear of not being loved/liked/approved of etc. Of course there will be times when clients regress to genuine trauma, including sexual abuse. Disassociated approaches to regression can be tremendously helpful in reframing these events particularly when combined with some structure interventions, which I describe in Part 2.5.

Associative Approaches

I said earlier how I felt that more harm has been done by the inappropriate use of regression than by any other therapeutic intervention, and I think this is particularly true of its associative form. Much of this has been the result of a hangover from the days of Freud when the belief was that experiencing emotion fully would lead to its discharge, a process known as catharsis. In this model, the more the client cried, wailed and thrashed about, the more negative energy would be permanently released from the sufferer. A number of associative techniques have evolved from this principle, none of which I intend to cover in this book because Reconsolidation theory tells me that they're going to do harm, not good.

Energy cannot be destroyed it can only be transformed

However, that doesn't mean that associative techniques can't be effective, and of all the people I've studied who use associative regression within their therapy, by far the most effective has been Gil Boyne. He was fond of pointing out that "energy cannot be destroyed, it can only be transformed[86]." So the purpose of his regression is to take whatever emotions are represented by previous events and transform the meaning of the event, or the emotion contained within it, into something positive. Being a committed Christian, his approach tended to reflect that in the way he often moved people from an emotion like hate to love and forgiveness. Don't get me wrong, I'm all for love and forgiveness, but I'm happy for clients to choose whatever *they* need to transform their negative emotion from and to in order to let their problem go. Gil is the only hypnotherapist who trained with Fritz Perls, the founder of Gestalt therapy, and many people aren't aware of how much his innovations have influenced the practice of therapy throughout the world. What I want to achieve in this section is to highlight the key principles of his approach, particularly the similarities between them and the principles of Time Line Reconsolidation that I think cause both to work.

Identifying the emotion in the client

Clearly for us to work associatively, it is necessary for the client to access the feelings connected with their issue. This can be done in several ways: Gil's favoured way was to build it by direct suggestion as he counted from 1 to 10 after having induced a trance in the client. This is an example of Gil working with a lady called Bunny who had suffered from a psychosomatic frozen shoulder for many years:

The Boynian method for tapping into the key emotion

"You know there's a feeling that you have often... it's very familiar to you.. it's a feeling that has to do with feeling helpless about that pain that you had in your arm for such a long period of time. As I count from 1 up to 10 I want you to become aware of that feeling...1, 2, 3, it's a feeling there's something wrong with the arm 4, 5, 6, it's a feeling that's growing stronger now 7 like the floodgates on a dam opening up... flowing across you in a great wave... number 9... it's a frightening feeling because it makes you feel very helpless number 10..."

My method for tapping into the key emotion

I often identify the key feeling by focusing on the submodalities of the client's problem pattern in the following way. This can be done in or out of trance:

"As you think about your problem, if you could point in your body to where you get the feeling that lets you know you have it, where would you point?"

Client points towards her stomach (the kinaesthetic submodality of location).

"Great. On a scale of 0 to 10, how strong is that feeling?"

Client: *"About six."*

"Excellent. As you focus on that feeling if there was something you could do to it that would make it even stronger, what would you do?"

I'll be describing the use of submodalities in more detail in Part 2.5. Often clients will be able to increase the feeling with only that limited input from me. On other occasions I might need to guide a little more, as below:

Client: *"I'm not sure what you mean?"*

"Well for example, if the feeling in your stomach had a shape what shape would it be?"

Client: "A circle."

"Good, and if it had a colour, what would the colour be?"

Client: "Red."

"Now, if you could do something to that red circle that would make the feeling stronger, what would you do with it?"

Client: " Well, if I make the circle bigger it makes it stronger."

"Brilliant, so if you could make that feeling an 8 or 9 how much bigger would you need to make it?"

Client indicates most of their stomach.

"Great, so now it's an 8 or 9..."

As you'll see in the chapter on submodalities, there are many options you can choose, and they'll be unique to each client. The principle is to create an equivalence between the feeling and the submodalities that describe it. Once this has been achieved, a change in the submodalities will lead to a change in their experience of the feeling, and by making the change in the smds equal the feeling getting stronger, the easier accessing the relevant memory will become.

Both methods bring results. If clients are slow to access feelings then the smd approach gives them more time and a feeling of control over the process, but Gil's is probably quicker.

Subconscious spelling

Once the client has become connected to the emotion that is connected to the issue, we want to begin to identify the reality tunnel it's contained within. One of the methods that Gil invented is subconscious spelling. He said the following immediately after counting Bunny from 1 -10 as described on page 167.

" I'm going to count from three down to one and when I do I'm going to ask you a question. You won't have to think about the answer it will come from your subconscious mind. It will come up by spelling letter by letter."

Bunny spells F E A R.

"I'm going to tap your forehead and I want you to speak one or more sentences using the word fear."

Bunny responds with, "I fear the way things will turn out." If you think about it, this kind of phrase is identifying that Bunny has a fear of a negative consequence within her problem pattern. We know that this is the end result of a calculation the brain is making based on prior experience, so for Bunny to be aware of the age progression her brain is making, we know she's in the reality tunnel we're interested in.

Gil taps on the forehead as a pattern interrupt, to motivate a quick response. An important learning from Perls was encouraging people to 'get out of their own way', i.e. not to let their conscious thinking get in the way of an unconscious response.

The Affect Bridge

At this point Bunny could be regressed back to the event that created this fear of the future. If you haven't used subconscious spelling, or it hasn't revealed anything, then a further option is to use a version of the Affect Bridge I developed that fits within the timeline model:

Get the client above their timeline and ask them to go back to a time recently when they had their problem. Have them look down into the event and ask them,

"If you could point in your body to where the feeling is in the event, where would you point?"

Once they've identified the feeling you can get them to follow it back into the past, with them remaining above the time line, by saying,

"if you could follow that feeling back along the time line, all the way back, earlier and earlier, all the way back to the very first time you had that feeling, so you can look down at that event now ... are you below 5, between 5 and 10, or over 10?"

Clearly this is a mixture of both the associative and dissociative philosophy, in that the client accesses the emotion sufficiently to trigger the memory, but still remains dissociated in perspective (but after all, we don't live in an either/or universe). This can be useful because sometimes regressing somebody fully associated can be a bit like dropping them in front of an approaching train: you don't know something bad is there until they arrive. Here they get the benefits without the risk.

With whatever method you've chosen to get the client to access the feeling connected to their problem in order to regress them, when the moment comes to take them back there are two ways I recommend. You can either continue to use my semi-dissociative Affect Bridge:

With the client experiencing the emotion on a scale of somewhere between 7 and 10, and with their eyes closed, say to them,

"Just follow that feeling back, focusing on a feeling within your body as you get younger ... smaller ... just letting the feeling take you back into your past ... younger and younger ... focusing on the feeling until you arrive at the very first time you ever had this feeling ... and as you do tell me what is going on..."

Or use Gil's fully associated counting back method:

" I'm going to count from 10 down to 1 and as I do we're going to go back to an

earlier time that is to do with this very same feeling... 10, 9, 8, you're drifting back...7, 6, 5, you're growing younger now... 4, your arms and legs are shrinking, you're growing smaller now...3, 2, 1... where are you now are you indoors or outside? etc..."

One of the best techniques available when using associative regression is one Gil adapted from the work of Fritz Perls: the Gestalt chair. This is available whenever the memory involves the client and another person, and works best with someone the person knows well. Originally, Perls would have the client sit in front of an empty chair and talk to the chair as if the other person from the memory was present. Then they would get the client to sit in the empty chair and speak as the other person in response. Gill realised that this could all be achieved in the imagination:

"I'd like you to imagine yourself seated safely in front of X."

The success of the Gestalt Chair technique depends on several factors. The first is that it is only as good as the involvement of the client. They have to speak to the other person as if they're there, and when they are the other person they need to speak in the first person. Sometimes people can be a bit shy or feel awkward to begin with, so it's really important to encourage them and make sure they fully involve themselves in the exercise. I'll often encourage them to adopt the physiology of the other person: it really helps them 'get into character'.

The second point is remembering what the exercise is there to achieve. It is very easy for this exercise to just become a screaming match between the two parties, or for it just to meander pointlessly. Keeping two questions in your mind as you listen to the dialogue develop will really help you reach a resolution:

The first question is,

> *"What is it the client needs to say to X, that by saying it will mean they can let go of the problem?"*

The second question is,

> *"What is it the client needs to hear from X, that by hearing it will mean they can let go of the problem?"*

Notice that these are TAOTM questions. Keeping these two questions in mind will enable you to guide the client, in either position, towards closure. As I said before, this might be forgiveness or love, but it needs to be whatever would be what the client needs to feel for the issue to be resolved.

Let's return to Helen, and assume that, instead of having chosen Time Line Reconsolidation I instead used the Affect Bridge to take her back to the first event. Once there she tells me the following:

> *"I'm in the living room at home and my Dad has got me to sing a song for some relatives who've come to visit. I'm eight years old and I got the words wrong and my Dad shouted at me and called me stupid."*

> *"Be the child. Sit in a chair in front of your Dad, using your imagination to keep yourself safe. Consider the problem you've had up until now, and say to your Dad what you want to say to him."*

"It's all your fault! All these years I've been scared of making a mistake, of looking stupid. You made me feel so foolish in front of these people."

"Be your Dad. Sit as he would sit, and use whatever gestures he uses. Answer your daughter. Why did you make her feel stupid?"

"I didn't mean to make you feel that. It was my brother's family, and they've always made out that they're better than us. I just wanted them to see how talented you were."

"So were you shouting at your daughter because she was stupid?"

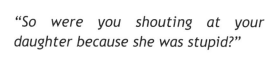

"Hell no. Helen's always been clever. I was just frustrated because I saw them smiling when she made the mistake. I suppose I was just embarrassed."

"So was this actually about you or about Helen?"

173

"It was about me. My brother was always the favourite, and I think it just brought back how stupid I felt around him."

"Be Helen again. You've heard what your Dad has said. Is there anything else you want to say that would mean you can let your fear go now?"

"I don't think so. Except I think I can see why you pushed so hard, and I felt what I did was never good enough. I wish you'd praised me more; I used to try so hard."

"Be your Dad again."

"I'm so sorry. I so wanted you to be better than me. I never felt good enough compared to my brother, and I wanted to push you to fulfil your wonderful potential."

"Helen, having heard your Dad say this, is there anything else he needs to say before you can move on?"

"No, I don't think so."

"Helen, is there anything you want to say to your Dad, that by saying it means you can let your old fear go?"

"I've always known you lacked belief in yourself. I just never realised that my doubts about myself were really yours about you. It wasn't your fault."

"Be your Dad. Do you love Helen?"

"Yes I do. I love you very much."

And repeat the question of Helen in relation to her Dad.

As with step six of time line reconsolidation, this point is the incepting moment when the closed loop has opened to a new idea. Because the client is associated, tears are highly likely at this point, which is great, because the resultant endorphin flow can increase their sense of well-being, which you can connect to being a consequence of having let go of her fear in the following way:

"And how nice to feel those feelings flowing through you...letting go of what's past...and enjoying the feelings that mean you can move forward...your unconscious taking the learnings from today to use in the most powerful way to help you begin to notice the changes..."

As with every other intervention, then do a future pace and incorporate your Wordweaving™ of the solution state.

Clearly, what I've presented here is a potted version of a Gestalt Chair session where everything goes swimmingly. Naturally there are times when it takes more negotiation before a resolution is reached and strong emotions are expressed, but it's a little like fishing: the resolution is on the end of the line, and your job is to gently coax and manoeuvre it into the net, and make the client think it was all their doing. As long as you keep the two core questions in your mind, you'll always know whether to give more line, or reel some in.

A common comment is, 'How can the client know what the motivations of the other person were? How can the client say what the other person would say?" I have two perspectives on it. The first is that mirror neurons mean that we've been running simulations of people close to us all our lives; in a sense we have a memeplex in our heads for mum, dad, brother, sister etc. Think of any subject - like an opinion on global warming - and give your views as one of your parents. You instinctively know what they'd say, don't you? My beloved grandfather has been dead for twenty-five years, and I still go to him in my head for advice. I'm pretty sure he didn't tell me one of my favourite phrases - "It's not supposed to be easy, just possible" - until after he was dead. If 80% of your reality is the product of your brain, then death is not the end of your connection to who you love. So my first answer is that we carry an imprint of these people with us; that is where these perspectives come from. My second answer is that it doesn't matter whether they

> *If 80% of your reality is the product of your brain, then death is not the end of your connection to who you love*

would have said those things, or if their motivations were what the client suggested them to be. So long as the client accepts them as valid, they're as true as they need to be.

In my opinion, one of the most important steps in any regression is to make transparent in the eyes of the client the connection between the event they regress to and the problem that brought them to therapy. With Time Line Reconsolidation it is achieved when you ask the question from above the first event "If there was a connection between this event and the problem you've had up until now, what would the connection be?" In TAOTM speak it's priming a cause and effect relationship between the two. Gil did something very similar, but from the other end of the connection.

He would often get clients to visit one or two more memories connected to the feeling, or perform a Gestalt Chair, and then bring the client back to now and say something like (in the case of Bunny):

" I want you to look back at the experience of the child and any related experiences she had as she grew. You know the terrible feelings the child had and some things that happened in her body like the pains in her arms and shoulders, and I want you to see how those feelings and those thoughts affected her as she grew, affected her experiences as a young woman, as a mature woman, has even been affecting you right up to this very time. And when you're ready to talk about it your arm will lift onto your lap."

When the client has described the consequences of the event in her later life, so that she can see fully how these events have led to her present problem, Gil moves to a resolution by getting the client to repeat a version of the Gestalt Prayer, usually beginning with a question that sets up a cause and effect relationship between the prayer and the problem:

The Gestalt Prayer

"You know there's a lot of energy tied up with this problem and you're carrying it. Would you like to put down that load?"

Assuming he gets a positive response - and why wouldn't he? He then proceeds with the prayer:

"I want you to repeat after me. And even though it is hard to say or you find it very difficult, it's a starting point:

"I now forgive everyone who has harmed me in any way. I bless them with my love. I wish for them all the good I wish for myself.

"I now forgive myself for every mistake I have ever made. I now know that each mistake was a stepping stone to greater understanding. I freely forgive as I would be forgiven. So be it.

"I now know that I don't have to live up to any childhood patterns or conditioning anymore. And that means...

"I am not put on this earth to live up to your expectations of me. And that means...

" And you don't have to live up to anything I have ever expected of you. And that means...

"I now understand that I am I and you are you. And that means...

"So from now on I'll do my thing. And that means...

"And I'll let you go right on doing your thing. And that means...

"If we can ever discover each other as two loving friends it will be wonderful and that means...

"But if that never happens, I can accept that too, because that's just the way it is. And that means..."

You may recognise the 'and that means' phrase as being a clever way of using equivalence to prime a positive consequence to what they've said. So, for example, in response to the phrase, *"So from now on I'll do my thing. And that means...",* Helen might say:

"I can start to do the things I want to do, just because I want to do them."

This can then be used within the suggestion/Wordweaving™ portion of the session to prime her Prover to bring things to her attention that show that this is now happening. An example might be:

> *"So it might not be until later that you look back and realise how you're beginning to do things differently...just because you want to...explore new opportunities and choices that seem to appear around you...so that as your confidence in these changes begins to grow...so does your confidence in you..become something you believe in more and more..."*

The Gestalt Prayer has within it some very clever perceptual changes and reframes that I find useful in helping a client to change. If its spiritual tone doesn't feel comfortable it's not at all difficult to use its principles without it, as I do.

In this chapter we have been dealing with the *reframing* of context within a memory, i.e., the meaning the event was given by the child at the time. Working associatively there are other things you can do to the memory to change the client's perception of it by working on the structure of it. I explore that in Part 2.5.

Conclusion

Whether you use a dissociative approach, or work directly through the feeling should always be decided based on the client, not on your own preference. Whichever one you use I think there are several key principles common to both of the methods I've described here which make them effective:

Principle 1:

> Make sure the client has the memory loop connected to the issue firing when you begin the process. If they're not in (or at least close to) their 'problem' reality tunnel, they're going to go along a different one, or nowhere at all.

Principle 2:

Ensure that the client sees and accepts the causal connection between the memories they're regressing to and the problems they're experiencing in the present. If they accept the cause and effect relationship between the event and their problem, then when the event's meaning changes, so must their belief about the need for their problem.

Principle 3:

Give an opportunity for their adult perspective to enrich the perception the child had that led to the problem. By adding new information to the closed loop it ceases to be locked into a 'groundhog day' feedback system where the rich get richer, and allows new interpretations to lead to new behaviours and choices.

Principle 4:

Create a new causal connection between the work done in the session and their progress towards their solution state.

The degree to which the client engages in all four of these principles determines the degree to which a therapeutic change will be achieved. Often it's the client not being fully connected to one or more of these steps that causes regression to fail in its intention.

The only reason to regress a client is to change their perception of the memory. Every time a client talks about something from their past there is an opportunity to change their perception of it. The techniques outlined in this chapter enable you to empower the client to see their past in a new light, and not just any light, one that frees them from the baggage they've been carrying. As Epictetus said aeons ago, "It's not what happens to us that matters, it's what we make of it."[87]

Structure interventions - What thoughts are made of

What's this about

Our thoughts are made of the same thing as our reality tunnel - submodalities. They can be thought of as the basic units of thought. Within our submodalities lie the code for our feelings about our thoughts, and hence the meaning we give them.

Just like a Word document on your computer, our thoughts can be re-written. By utilising smds in specific ways we can change the thoughts, memories and feelings that flow through our minds and reshape any part of our memoragination to replace limits with possibilities. This chapter shows you how.

In Cognitive Hypnotherapy, when we talk of *structure* we are mainly talking about how we experience the thoughts we have. In the beginning this is often strange for people because all of us know that we think, but most of us give little thought to how we think. When you think about something that happened to you, are you in the picture or are you seeing it through your own eyes? When a thought you have leads to a feeling, where in your body do you feel that feeling? Is it hot or cold, heavy or light, is it still or does it rotate? To a person new to this way of looking at thoughts these questions can seem strange, so you have to pace a client when you begin to ask them questions about this aspect of their experience. In NLP these distinctions are called submodalities, simply because our senses are often called modalities and the criteria that characterise them are hence called sub-modalities. Simple really.

Submodalities appear to be a method of describing the way in which our thoughts are given meaning, that's why they're important. They are the basic units of thought from which trance phenomena are created - and hence our reality tunnels. For example, you think about something coming up next week - a presentation, a job interview or a trip to your in-laws - *how* you think of it emotionally will be the result of the way the thought is represented in terms of its submodalities. So, if the thought of something that makes you nervous is in colour, then changing it to black and white might reduce the feeling; if the nervousness is in your throat, then moving it to your stomach might make it feel better; if part of the thought is a voice that says, "you're going to make a fool of yourself!", then changing the location of the voice, or its volume, or the voice itself, might make a difference. If this is new to you please trust me for now, and I'll give you the opportunity to prove it to yourself later.

Here again, we work to the uniqueness of the individual; each person will have submodalities within each thought that make the emotional difference. They are called 'drivers', and they vary from thought to thought and from person to person, although some drivers are pretty universal and form the basis of many NLP techniques like the Swish Pattern and the Fast Phobia Cure or Rewind.

Below is a list of the most common submodalities from the three senses that tend to have most effect:

A list of the most common driver submodalities.

Visual
Black & White or Colour - A quality that is a driver for many.

Near or Far - Where do they see the picture in their visual field if they were to point to it?

Bright or Dim - Usually the brighter the picture the stronger the emotion.

Location - Another visual field distinction; where do they point for the picture?

Size of Picture - Usually the bigger the picture, the stronger the emotion.

Associated or Dissociated - Are they in the picture, or looking through their own eyes in it?

Framed or Panoramic - Is the picture all around them, or on a screen?

Movie or Still - Are they looking at an event as if it's a video, or a still picture (or series of pictures)?

3D or Flat - Is the picture or movie in 3D, or is like looking at a photograph?

Audio

Direction - Does it come from your left, right, back, front etc?

Internal or External - Is the noise inside or outside your head?

Loud or Soft - If it's someone's voice, usually the louder it is the more dominant it is.

High or Low? (Pitch) Is it high like most women's voices, or low like most men's?

Cadence - What is the rhythm of what you're listening to?

Kinaesthetic

Location - Where in your body is the feeling?

Size - Is it big, small or somewhere inbetween?

Shape - If it had a shape, what shape would it be?

Intensity - On a scale of 0-10 how strong is the feeling?

Steady or Movement - Does the feeling remain in one place, or does it move?

Heat - Is it hot, cold, or somewhere inbetween?

Weight - Is it heavy, light, or somewhere inbetween?

The point of identifying these smd differences is that manipulating them can change the emotion that the thought is producing. Switching a thought from colour to black and white, and/or moving its location, and/or making the feeling smaller, and/or any combination of the smds listed above can produce an instant effect that can be quite magical for the client.

By getting them to 'play' with the qualities of the thought in this way they begin to get the idea that they can be in control of their thoughts and emotions. Once they get the hang of it, this sense of control it produces can be one of the major differences that moves them towards their solution state.

The theory is that every thought you have will comprise a combination of submodalities taken from one or more of these three senses, and that some of these submodalities will be key to the meaning you're giving to the thought you're having. What this means is that, by listening to your client and questioning them about the submodalities of their thoughts you can guide them in how to change the impact of their thinking by changing the structure of their thoughts. To give you some idea of how to do this, I'm going to go through five different submodality interventions and explain why, in my opinion, they have the effect they do. Hopefully by doing so you'll begin to see the principles which guide the way thoughts can be positively manipulated. In every case, the purpose of the intervention is to change the client's perception of the thought – changing it in the right way is as much an inception as reframing the meaning of something: it gives us the opportunity to make it the beginning of a change that leads to their outcome, and takes them from protection into growth.

1. Submodality Headache Cure

This is one of my favourite submodality exercises. Although I'm describing it in the context of relieving headaches, it can be used to remove pretty much any negative emotion or feeling. The principles are also incredibly useful for guiding clients who wish to use mind/body principles for healing purposes.

To begin, most clients will find it easier with their eyes closed because most people find it easier to visualise without external distraction, so I normally begin by asking them to close their eyes, but, as always, be aware that some people will find the complete opposite to be true. When their eyes are closed I then say:

"If your headache had a shape what shape would it be?"

As I've explained in previous chapters, the wording here is very specific. The use of the word *if* at the beginning of the sentence softens the question so you get many fewer people responding with something like, "What are you talking about, my headache doesn't have a shape?" than if you'd said, "What shape is your headache?"

What this question achieves is the linking of the headache with a shape, i.e. we are working within the realms of TAOTM by creating an equivalence: headache = shape.

"2 dimensional or 3d?"

The answer to this question isn't important, it just focuses the client more deeply on their visual representation of their headache.

"If it had a colour what colour would it be?"

Again, the colour itself isn't important, it's just a means by which we can alter the client's experience of their headache.

"If the background had a colour what colour would it be?"

By creating a contrast we can use colour as a means to reduce the headache, as you will see shortly.

"If you were to make the shape the same colour as the background would it need to get lighter or darker?"

You would think this would be a no-brainer, that if the headache was darker than the background, then it would obviously need to get lighter in order to become the same. And of course, in most cases that's exactly what happens. But occasionally, a client will somehow manage to do the opposite. This question allows for that and also, by the use of the magical word *if,* causes the client to try out this part of the exercise in their head in order for them to be able to answer the question. This makes it harder for them to say, "I don't know," or "I can't do that".

"Good, now make it smaller. Smaller and smaller...until it's as small as it can possibly be before it disappears. Tell me when you've done that."

Notice the consequence to further change that is being set up here; what's going to happen if the client is asked to make the shape smaller still?

"Good. Now make it smaller still...so you can look all over the background and try and find the shape and notice it's gone."

The previous step sets up a cause and effect relationship between making the shape smaller and it disappearing. Bearing in mind that the brain is already working with the complex equivalence linkage between the headache and the shape, so that by the shape disappearing, so must the headache.

"And now, if healing had a colour, imagine it flowing into the background....everywhere...bottom to top..side to side...until it flows over into everywhere it needs to flow for the headache to disappear...and just let it flow until it's done that and then open your eyes......"

Notice how imprecise this suggestion is in terms of where the healing needs to flow for the headache to disappear: using the word 'everywhere' means that the colour can go where the headache is or anywhere else it needs to for the headache to disappear. Also how the client is left to continue to do this until the healing has occurred or they grow old waiting for something else. They'll choose the healing.

If we put this in the context of Helen's situation, this technique could be used to take away any negative emotion she's experiencing about the problem during the session, which you would link to an anticipation of further improvement that takes her towards her solution state by the use of suggestion - such as *"and as you notice how that feeling has disappeared now we can both wonder how quickly your unconscious will learn how possible it is to control these feelings, so that soon it might be only after a situation which, in the past would have created that feeling, that you realise how free you've been of it..etc"* In Part 2.8 I also show you how it can overcome a sticking point in other techniques.

One of the things I love about this exercise is that it can also be taught to the client for them to use between sessions when, in my opinion, most therapy happens. So, equipped with this technique, Helen could find herself feeling nervous just before a meeting where she gets the feeling of a wide band around her chest constricting her breathing and make it disappear. It can be

Structure Intervention Principle 1:

Create an equivalence between an object and an aspect of the client's issue. When the link is established, what happens to the object happens to the issue.

tremendously empowering for people to realise they have control over their own feelings, so I'm a great fan of teaching clients the means by which they can create their own positive states without my help.

In terms of the underlying principle that causes this to work, in my opinion it is to do with its use of TAOTM. Essentially the technique guides the client to create an equivalence between the headache and a shape (headache = shape). By creating this linkage in the client's neurology, it follows that what happens to the shape happens to the headache. It's why it forms the basis of many guided imagery visualisations my clients develop when working on a healing issue (e.g. my wart/rheumatism/cancer = shape).

2. The Swish Pattern

This is a standard, if not classic, NLP technique that is taught on all Practitioner training courses. And rightly so. It's simple to learn, straightforward, and can bring great results. Most people use it to help stop habits like nail biting, but it can be used to move somebody's mind from any one state or outcome to another, or from one thought to another.

1. Get the client to create a picture in their head of the habit or behaviour they would like to change (present state). Make the picture as if they're looking through their own eyes (associated).

We could use the example of nail biting, where the client might imagine a picture where they see their fingers coming towards the mouth. It needs to be an image that represents to them the habit or behaviour they want to change.

In Helen's case, you could swish the picture she gets of her making a fool of herself - to a picture of her solution state.

2. Next, get them to create a picture of what they would like in its place (desired state) which, by having it, would mean they'd no longer be doing the habit or behaviour (present state). Have the client looking at themselves in the picture (dissociated). Also, ask them what they would do with the picture that would make it even more compelling: making it bigger, brighter, closer etc. It can help to separate the qualities of the present and desired states in this way. The more differences between the pictures, the more permanent the change is likely to be.

Again, notice how the instruction is structured to create a cause and effect relationship between the replacement image and the cessation of their problem (i.e. 'which, by having it...'). If the client finds after this exercise that this new image is present in their environment or behaviour it has to mean that they've let go of their problem.

Notice how with the desired state the picture needs to be dissociated, i.e. they see themselves in this new way.

I didn't actually think that this made much difference, but an experiment at Ohio State University changed my mind. The day before an election, researchers got subjects to imagine themselves going into the ballot cubicle and voting. Those who visualised themselves doing so from a dissociated perspective were 18% more likely to go and vote the next day than those whose image was from an associated perspective. The conclusion was that a dissociated position increases your motivation to pursue a goal.[88]

3. Have the client close their eyes (if they're not already) and bring back the picture of the present state.

4. Now insert in the lower left hand corner of that picture, a small picture of the desired state.

5. Have them confirm they have the big picture and little picture in their mind. Instruct them that when you make a swishing sound they are to make the small picture explode in size as fast as they can to cover the big picture, as that shrinks away into the distance. Speed is of the essence, they must do this in their heads as quickly as possible. Then get them to open their eyes and close them again.

Practice your swish noise before you try this, otherwise there is a risk of you drowning your client in spittle. Often you'll see the client physically react to your 'swish' noise by their head jerking, or eyelids fluttering.

You can probably spot the submodalities here that are being utilised: association /dissociation, and small/large image. The speed of the technique seems to 'force' the switch, so is a key element to it. I often find myself describing the effect of such smd exercises as 'jazzing' the thought so it loses its previous coherence, so when the thought is sent back to the cortex for reconsolidation it is sent with its new characteristics.

6. Repeat #5 a minimum of five times, i.e.:

"Big picture...little picture in the corner....SWISH! Good.

Open your eyes..close your eyes...big picture, little picture...SWISH!"

Within five repetitions people will usually report it being difficult to get the present state image up, or that it's less distinct, fuzzier etc. When they say something like this, swish another couple of times and then...

7. Calibrate by asking, "When you think of that old habit what comes to your mind now?" In most cases their mind will go straight to the desired state. If it doesn't, repeat #5 until the desired state is the only picture they get.

The principle that this technique utilises is that of universal drivers; that some smds tend to drive a change in the emotional construction of a thought, and most NLP techniques of this kind work by using drivers that work for most people (hence the term *universal*). If such a technique doesn't have the intended effect, it can be because the smds involved aren't drivers for that person (i.e., they are exceptions to the 'universal' generalisation). The principle still holds that there will be drivers present in the thought, so by identifying them you can modify this or another smd technique so that it utilises them.

> *Structure Intervention Principle 2:*
>
> Universal drivers are submodality qualities that drive the emotional meaning of a thought. For most people, changing them will change their experience of the thought.

I mentioned using Swish to replace Helen's negative consequence picture with her solution state. This can be a very helpful part of an overall strategy involving several different interventions, such as using timeline, giving her an anchor (Part 2.6) and swishing the picture, thus working in her memoragination at all three points, past, present and future. As with most clients, it's rare to use just one technique in isolation.

3. Spinning

This is one of the many techniques that sprang from the fertile mind of Richard Bandler, co-founder of NLP, and demonstrates perfectly why we should always seek simplicity. The principle here is to take a single driver and change its properties.

1. Begin by asking the client to identify or point to where they are getting the feeling they would like to change or get rid of. As always, the language is precise:

> "If you could point to where you get this feeling (like anxiety, fear, jealousy, sadness etc.) where would you point?"

Where they point is irrelevant, it just helps them to localise the feeling, focus on it and - most importantly - create a TAOTM link between what they feel where they're pointing, and their problem. So, as with the headache cure, if one thing changes, so must the thing it's connected to.

2. The universal driver used in this technique is the direction the feeling spins. As ever, the word 'If' at the beginning of the sentence can make all the difference. Saying, 'what direction is the feeling rotating?' is going to get you just a puzzled response with many people. The magic word 'If' will dramatically reduce this occurrence. Try both if you don't believe me.

> "If the feeling was spinning in a direction, in what direction would it be spinning?"

3. Whatever direction they choose say:

> "Excellent. Now notice the difference it makes when you slow it down. Does that make the feeling stronger or weaker?"

Note the presupposition in the sentence that assumes a difference will be noticeable, and I'm offering an illusion of choice by only offering two options.

4. If they say, "Weaker" :

> *"Good. Notice how much slower it needs to get before the feeling disappears. Let me know when it has."*

Usually the feeling ceasing to rotate will coincide with the cessation of the feeling. If the client reports that slowing it makes it stronger, then getting them to rotate it faster instead will reduce the feeling. Once the TAOTM connection has been established in the mind of the client between the rotation and the feeling, then you just have to explore how that relationship works with the client in order to change the intensity and nature of the feeling.

5. Assuming the more normal response of slowing the existing rotation = less, I then say:

> *"Great. So if you started spinning it the other way, how much better does that feel? And what would you call* that *feeling?"*

This step flips the TAOTM connection that 'the rotation is the cause of the feeling', into 'the opposite of the rotation must cause the opposite of the feeling'. On most occasions the client will report a positive emotion.

Other submodalities can also be incorporated into it if necessary. For example, you could say:

"As it's spinning, if it had a colour what colour would it be?"

 "And as it spins faster, does that make the colour lighter or darker?"

"And how fast could you make it spin before it changed to an even better colour? And what colour is that?"

As with many structure interventions, one of the great things is that the client can leave your therapy room with a tool that they can use for themselves. Once clients learn they can control their feelings, there's not much need for you; it's called empowerment. Why don't we teach this in schools?

With Helen, this would be a great tool for her to have available for use before meetings if she begins to get the feeling of panic.

4. Dropthrough

This is another intervention which focuses on reducing the strength of a feeling. Again, in my opinion, its effect is gained through its use of TAOTM connections between different thoughts. A theory of its operation goes something like this. We give our feelings names; things like anger, guilt, fear, boredom, power, confidence and content. Each feeling is unique to us, so while there will be a general agreement between two people that they are enjoying themselves, or scared, the details of those feelings - where they feel it and what the feeling actually feels like - will be unique to each person.

Part of the labelling of a feeling is through comparison to other feelings; we know happiness because we've felt its opposite, sadness. Some of these opposites are reasonably universal, but if you think of what your opposite of fear would be what would you say? Ask a few other people the same question and you're likely to get a range of answers.

Now imagine these opposites connected by other related feelings, like a ladder. The idea is that you connect the client to the problem feeling, and then have them 'dropthrough' to the feeling below it. They keep dropping through until they come to a positive. Here are the steps:

Elicit the emotion the client wishes to release, and get them to feel it in their body in the way I've described already ('if you could, where would you point for the feeling?'). In Helen's case it would probably be panic.

Then:

> "If you could drop through that emotion to the one beneath it what would you call that emotion?"

Client names it.

> " Fear."

This continues.

> "Good. If you were to drop through that emotion, what's underneath that?"

My advice is, don't let people settle at any level; as soon as they have named a feeling, repeat the question. You will often find that the deeper they drop the harder it becomes for them to find a name for the feeling and a greater use of hand movement attempting to describe the feeling often accompanies this. This is fine, the word is not important, knowing that it's not the previous feeling (i.e. the client is moving down the levels) is what matters. People vary in the number of levels they drop - for some it may only be three or four, my record has been thirty-two. I think the average would be about seven.

Something strange that often happens is that people don't always go straight from negative to positive; they reach a 'space' first. Brandon Bays[89], the developer of *The Journey* process, uses a version of this technique within her work, and calls this space 'the source'. That's a bit laden with spiritual overtones for me, something I don't want the client to have to accept for the technique to work, so I usually set up the exercise by describing the theory of emotions being connected, as I did earlier, and then say something like this before we start:

"As you drop through the negative emotions you may find that you come to a place. People use different names to describe it. Some call it the zone, or the place, or the source, the word doesn't actually matter, but it is somewhere that just feels good to be in. Dropping through that brings us to the positives."

There are some techniques that seem to work better if you explain the process and some that are better just to experience. I've found with Dropthrough that it works either way, but more people find this 'place' if you describe the technique first than if you don't. No surprise there, it could be attributed to simple priming - and it doesn't matter, if it brings the desired result.

Let's assume the client drops through to this space. Check that the space isn't just a negative space with no name by asking:

"And as you're in this (void/space/nothing) how does that feel?"

"It feels good...peaceful"

"And just take the time to notice all the good things about this place....all the things you can feel...all the things you can see....any sounds....all the things that make this such a nice place to relax...just drifting....floating ....being....at ease in this place....and you can imagine how useful it would be to have this place available to you whenever you wanted to...feel this way....whenever you want to (apply anchor now)...just take as long as you need to relax in this place for it to make the most powerful and positive difference to the way you used to be....and as you do.....if you were to drop through from this place, what's the emotion you come to next?"

(You'll see I've mentioned applying an anchor. I explain how to do that in Part 2.6.)

The client will name a positive emotion.

"Confident."

Stack this emotion as an anchor on top of the place where you anchored the feeling of the 'space' by repeating the application of the anchor as they focus on the feeling of confidence.

"Excellent. Now drop through that... what's that emotion?"

Stack that as an anchor too.

Only go to two positive emotions. The earth doesn't stop revolving if you go to three, it's just that this ladder actually seems to connect as a circle, and there is a chance that if you keep dropping through the positives you resurrect the negatives.

Verify that the emotions have disappeared:

"Open your eyes. Now where is the emotion you had before?"

In most cases clients won't be able to find it. If they can find any of it it will usually be less. If they can still feel any of the negative emotion say:

"Great. Now drop-through **that** emotion" -

and repeat the exercise.

Repeat it until the emotion has disappeared. Usually each time you repeat a cycle of Dropthrough on the same emotion, it is weaker, and the chain becomes shorter. I've never had to do more than three cycles for the feeling to disappear or become inconsequential.

Future pace:

"I want you to imagine a time in the future which if it had happened in the past, you would have felt inappropriate or unwarranted X (their presenting emotion), and notice if you can find that old emotion, or you may find that you can't.."

As with other smd techniques this is great for the client to use on themselves whenever they encounter a negative emotion. My experience has been that some clients can experience this technique once and never have their problem again, while others need to repeat it over a period of time to 'drain' the emotion out of the problem pattern.

Metaphors

If you try to strip metaphors out of your everyday language you very quickly find your sentences sounding bare, mere skeletons of what you're attempting to communicate. Three metaphors in one sentence, did you notice? Probably not, because they're such a natural part of the way we communicate, and I suggest that's true because they plug in (see I've done it again) to TAOTM. Metaphors work on the basis of a thing called isomorphism - something sharing the qualities of another thing - which I know by now you're going to recognise as meaning the same thing as an equivalence.

Metaphors aid our understanding because they help to connect the words you're hearing into the mental maps TAOTM has enabled you to create to navigate the world. Now I've pointed out how much of our speech is metaphoric it might begin to annoy you how much you see it - I'm sorry, I haven't suddenly started peppering (oops!) the book with them deliberately, they've been there all the way through.

There are many excellent books on the use of metaphor in therapy, some of which I've mentioned in the bibliography, and it's not my purpose to give you examples of metaphors to provide for your clients - in the main I believe the best ones are those they come up with themselves. Rather I wanted first to highlight that I consider metaphoric interventions fall within the category of structure because they are a means by which meaning is encoded within a thought, and secondly to introduce a class of structure interventions that don't depend on the direct manipulation of smds for their effect, ones that use the concept of *parts*.

Parts Work

In Part One I explored the nature of this feeling we have of having a self, a distinct aspect of personality that we feel is a constant part of our life, throughout our life. And I suggested that this was a trick, an illusion that helps our brain to plan more effectively. The fact that our self doesn't feel like an illusion is the core of the problems that stem from being human, because everything we do as an organism we attribute to the desire and direction of the self - so therefore everything we do is our fault. Without going over old ground too much, science has demonstrated that most of what we do has been determined by the unconscious - and by most I mean up to 90%.

We could neatly divide us into the conscious 'self' and the unconscious 'self' and envisage a tug of war in our heads where competing 'selfs' battle for who gets to work the remote that works your limbs - and some do. I'm not sure if that's right, and I prefer the model of a primary self (our 'I' or selfplex), a general unconscious intelligence that guides the workings of the body - including healing - and a number of 'selfs' or memeplexes (or Wolinsky's trance identities – see Part 1.2) that emerge as a response to a pattern match between a present situation and a stored set of information - an SEE and its memory loop. Returning to the example I used in Part One, John walking down the street is displaying his primary self if his attention is in the moment and focused on the external world. If he's daydreaming, his primary self is somewhere else while his general unconscious is steering him safely through the crowd, and when he spots Bruiser his 'scared of dogs' trance identity/self/memeplex emerges and takes over the controls.

All of us have multiple 'selfs', some of which aid us, and some of which hinder. In modern therapy Fritz Perls was the first to explore this experience we have of not being alone in our heads. He called these 'selfs' 'parts', and the Gestalt Chair technique was utilised, not just for the client to work through issues with significant people from their past, but also to get into discussion between conflicting parts. A client might say, "Part of me wants to go for the job, but part of me is holding back. I don't know why." If you think of your own experience, how often do you hear phrases like, "I wasn't myself", "Something came over me", "I'm in two minds", or "That wasn't like me"?

Perls might indicate a chair next to the client and say, "Sit in the chair and be the part that's holding back. Tell us what's on your mind." And from there a Gestalt dialogue would unfold between the client and the part. He even had 'parts parties' involving conversations and negotiations between several parts. Returning to the idea of isomorphic relationships, he would also listen to a client say, "I just get treated like a doormat!" and respond with, "Be the doormat, what do you feel like?" Interestingly, exploring the deeper structure of metaphors in this way has recently been taken in a fascinating direction by David Groves and his Clean Language mode[90]. But I digress - again I've given some book ideas in the bibliography.

The technique I'm about to describe evolved from Gestalt therapy, and is variously described as Parts Integration or Visual Squash. It is one of the most powerful interventions I've ever learnt, so don't be fooled by its simplicity. Here is my version:

5. Visual squash

It is common to hear people say things like, "a part of me wants to but..." and in these circumstances it's easy to move the conversation towards this intervention. It is also possible to gently lead them by saying, "it sounds like part of you wants X but part of you doesn't..." If they agree that that is a fair representation of their problem then the way is open. This is one of the techniques that I prefer not to explain. There is a magical moment in it that would lose its potency if you primed them beforehand.

1. Having framed the problem as a parts issue I ask the client if it's ok to take their hands. When you ask that people tend to offer them, and I gently turn their hands palm uppermost so they are in front of them and about 12 inches (30cm) apart. It works best if they are seated in an upright position with their elbows unsupported.

2. I identify the conflict and the parts involved. In Helen's case it might be phrased as the part that wants to be free to speak up, and the part that stops her.

"If the part that stops you speaking up were to come out on one of your hands, which one would it choose?

And the other part would come out on the other hand?"

I've never noticed any correlation between the parts and the choice of hands, but you can normally see which one they are going to choose for their 'problem hand' because it's the one they use to gesticulate with most when they're talking from their 'part'.

Something I avoid is referring to the problematic part as anything negative. The basis of this exercise working effectively is that all behaviour has a positive intention, including the behaviour generated by the problematic part, so to call one part good and the other bad tends to be counterproductive.

3. Ask each part to come out on one of the hands

"So if you could see this part on your hand, what would it look like?"

Some therapists prefer for the client to personify the part, by asking something like "does the part remind you of anyone", or "if the part was a person what do they look like?" I haven't found that doing so improves the success rate of the technique, so I leave it to the client's imagination. Mostly they come up with an image, examples of which have been a golden ball, a robin, a devil, a bowl of maggots and a lead weight. Notice how what this question achieves is to create an equivalence of the order 'the part = the bowl of maggots.

4. Separate intention from behaviour

I said earlier that the axiom that drives this technique is that all behaviour has a positive intention, so the next step is to discover the highest intention of each part.

I usually begin with the problematic part. I focus my intention on the hand, repeat the client's description of it by saying something like "So, this bowl of maggots...

"What is its intention?"

" Protection. "

"And what's the intention of Protection?"

"Safety. "

"And what's the intention of safety?"

You get the idea. There is no analysis to be done - this is a structure intervention, so I don't want any explanation or rationalisation from the client, or interpretation or going off-piste from me. The only variation I've found useful is sometimes to say, "And what will that bring you?" And I tend to do that once the client's words become positive, which they will. Sometimes the client will 'loop', having gone from one word to several more before saying that same word again. Treat it as a different word by saying, "And what's the intention of *that*?"

At some point in this questioning the words will become positive. Trust me here, because sometimes you might ask the question in excess of 20 times and hear nothing but negatives. I remember one client sticking to words like "hell, damnation, purgatory", for what seemed like forever, before getting to "redemption, forgiveness, and love". Sometimes you just have to strap yourself in and trust the process, they will get to somewhere positive, and in most cases I keep going until they say something like love, freedom, peace or contentment.

When I've got there, I'll repeat the process with the other hand. What you'll find will happen is that both hands will eventually arrive at the same place - love, freedom, peace, contentment etc. If they don't do it the first time though, there is nothing wrong with returning to the first hand and continuing from where you left off until they do come to a level of agreement. When they do, adopt your best quizzical tone and say,

"Love. Wasn't that the same thing the other part wanted?"

Often they will have become so absorbed (which I count as a trance state) that they don't realise this until you point it out.

5. Have each part tell you what is good about the other part.
Point at the first hand and ask:

"What does this part like or respect about the other part?"

Write down the qualities they say - you can use them later. Because clients tend to think of one part as 'bad' you might find them claiming that it has no redeeming qualities. When that happens I prompt them with questions like, "Is this part strong or weak?" "Is it determined to do what it does?" "Does it consistently do what it does?" This usually helps them to see that all things have qualities that can be useful in another context.

When you've achieved this step, have them acknowledge that their conflict is getting in the way of achieving their intention.

"Can each part recognise that they are making each other less effective at achieving their intention?"

When the client agrees that this is so we can move to the phase I described as magical.

6. Resolve the conflict by getting agreement that they will work together.

Look at the hands intently and say something like:

"So if these two parts could integrate....becoming parts of the whole....again...in whatever way they would begin to show you them doing this.....as you watch your hands.....whenever these parts begin to integrate....move together.....in their own time....slowly moving together....."

You can assist the integration by gently suggesting it by motioning with your finger, and watch for the first twitch in the hands. When you see it say:

"That's right, and as the hands continue to begin to move together...enabling these two parts to integrate you could just allow your eyes to close..."

With their eyes closed their hands will continue to move together. If you're adept at Wordweaving™, or otherwise spontaneously creating suggestions, this is an opportunity to make suggestions using the words the client gave as you were exploring the parts' intentions, or just remain connected to them by giving them occasional encouragement along the lines of "...that's right just allowing the hands to come together in their own time."

Sometimes the hands will stop - and often clients will report a feeling of resistance akin to trying to place the same poles of two magnets together. I take this to be a sign of a reluctance to integrate, or something left to learn before it is acceptable, so I say something like:

"And just allow your unconscious to continue to keep your hands stationary until it has learnt what it needs to learn to allow this integration to progress. And sometimes that learning will appear in your mind, and sometimes your hands will begin to move together again without your knowing what has been understood..and that's OK...just allow it to happen..."

Again watch for any movement, and encourage it when you see it.

As the hands are on the point of coming together you can suggest the following:

"And you might wonder just what you might feel when the hands touch...where you might feel it....what it might feel to you.......to have that integration.....as they come closer...and closer..."

Continue in that vein until they touch. You can then proceed with a future pace, as you would after any intervention.

You may find that clients have an emotional response when their hands touch, and many will report it a profound experience. So while it appears a simple, almost playful technique, I consider it to be one of our most potent tools.

6. Rewind

This is more commonly called the Fast Phobia Cure within NLP circles, but its use extends far beyond phobias - it's one of the principal tools in my kit when working with trauma. it is also called by some people the V-K double dissociation - one of its advantages is that it's heavily dissociative and it also avoids the need for the client to do any form of analysis or reframing.

1. Access the memory

The beginning can be similar to time line, in that you ask the client to access the first memory connected to their problem, so talking to them sufficiently to activate the memory loop of their problem (i.e., getting them to talk about what scares them) is a first step, and then asking the key question from time line is the next. Having them above their time line is a good idea because it means they'll be dissociated when they access it. You don't want your client to associate into their SEE and then have to get them out of it.

When they've accessed a memory and are looking down at it on their timeline we move into the technique itself:

2. Dissociate the client from the event:

"Can you imagine sitting in a cinema? And on the screen put this event, frozen, in black and white, on the screen."

3. Double-dissociate the client from the event:

"Now imagine leaving your body watching the screen, as you stand behind your body, maybe in the projection booth, so you're watching yourself watching the screen."

This is the V-K double-dissociation; both the visual and the kinaesthetic aspects of the memory are dissociated not just once, by looking at it on a screen (or from above a time line), but twice by having them look at themselves watching it.

4. Ask the client to run the film of the event forward in B & W to the end and freeze frame at the end.

"And now turn the movie into black and white and run the movie of the event from beginning to end, at normal speed. When you get to the end, freeze frame it and let me know you've done it."

5. Then, have the client associate into the memory and run it backwards in colour to the beginning as fast as possible.

"Now step into the film and rewind it, in colour, as fast as you possibly can. Let me know when you're back at the beginning."

People will vary in their ability to do this step at speed, so in the first few runs through I leave it to them to do it as quickly as they are able, and then, as they get warmed up to the task, encourage them to do it 'even faster'. When they let you know they've done it, proceed to the next step.

6.

"Now step back into the projection screen, get the event in black and white back on the screen and run it at normal speed, keeping it in black and white until you get to the end. Let me know when you're there."

7. Repeat steps 4 - 6 until the client can't get the feeling back, or until the memory is not accessible. On average about 5-7 times will seriously compromise the client's ability to feel the same level of emotion about the event, and if you ask them, "On a scale of 1-10 how strong is the feeling now as you look at the screen?" the response will usually range between 0 and 3. If it's higher (or anything less than 0) you can continue to repeat steps 4-6 until the emotion collapses. If there has been no change in the level of emotion from the beginning, try adding a soundtrack to it as they associate and rewind the memory. I usually say something like, "If you were to add a soundtrack as you rewind the memory, something silly, or funny, or ridiculous, like the Keystone Cops, or Benny Hill, what would you choose?" Just this simple addition can often be the difference that makes a difference.

8. Test by taking them out into the future and imagining a situation that once would have been an example of the problem. When they report that it feels better, use suggestions to prime them to anticipate those differences in the way they'll experience those kinds of situations from now on - in the vein of: (assume client has used the words 'in control' and 'relaxed' as part of their solution state evidence), *"so that as your unconscious sees the difference today can make to the way you begin to be in the future, you might be surprised just how quickly you begin to notice all the ways you're feeling different, so much more in control and relaxed in those situations that, sooner than you might once have thought, you realise that your confidence in those situations is so much better that you can really believe in what you've achieved here today."*

As you can probably see by now, Rewind is based on the manipulation of several smd qualities that tend to be 'universal': associated v dissociated, colour v black and white, forward v reverse, normal v fast. The fact that it manipulates so many pairs of qualities is probably a reason why it works so well with most people - the more pairs you manipulate the greater the proportion of people who will respond to one or other of them. If you focus on just one pair it can work brilliantly on those for whom it's a driver, but not for those for whom it isn't. So, if a technique doesn't gain the effect you expected, look at what smds it relies on, and see how you could adjust the exercise to use others.

With Helen you could choose to use rewind on her living room SEE instead of time line, or switch to it if using time line didn't cause the emotion to disappear. One is not better than the other. I usually base my choice on how possible it appears for the event to be given a meaning, and the client's ability to reframe. The nice thing about rewind is that it is mechanical: it doesn't ask anything more from the client than to follow the steps.

Conclusion

Structure exercises are extremely powerful and should not be thought of as just a backup for when context interventions are inappropriate or have proven ineffective; in many cases they are interchangeable. As always, your choice should be based on the information you've gained from the client, not because you happen to like the technique or feel comfortable doing it.

In this chapter I've shown you six interventions based on the use of smds:

Headache Cure

The principle of this is to create an equivalence between something (it could be an emotion, a headache, or a pain) and a shape. When that equivalence has been established in the imagination of the client, a series of steps guide them towards the shape disappearing. When an equivalence has been created, what happens to one thing happens to the other.

Swish Pattern

The principle here is to substitute one image for another by superimposing a desired outcome onto a present limitation, using speed and location as the key drivers. The speed and surprise of the swish sound (by varying the timing of when you say it) seems to cause the brain to skip from the old image straight to the new one.

Spinning

By taking one universal submodality and taking it from one polarity to another - large or small, near or far, clockwise or anti-clockwise, you can often take the feeling from it's original strength down to nothing, or even to the feelings positive opposite.

Dropthrough

This technique is predicated on the idea that the labels we give our emotions are based on the relationship they have with other emotions, including their polar opposites. By dropping through them, similar to the Swish Pattern, it tends to bump the brain from activating the original emotion in a situation to whatever opposite emotion is at the end of the chain.

Visual Squash

This involves the use of smds because an equivalence is created between an aspect of the self - the parts - and an image. As with the Headache Cure, what happens to the image happens to the part. The use of smds is more indirect than the previous examples because once the representation has been decided you don't directly manipulate the images - they provide a medium through which you investigate their intentions and then negotiate their integration.

Rewind

By manipulating multiple smd pairings the coding of the event is disrupted, so that when it is sent back to the brain for reconsolidation, the new coding of the event without the emotion present within it is what is stored. It means that it no longer acts as an SEE within the client's problem pattern. So, if we did this with John about his dog phobia, and the event you used the technique with was the core event, then it's likely that the next time he comes across Bruiser he won't have a negative response.

From now on, if you read any other techniques, NLP or otherwise, see if you can identify the principles which underlie them. If you strip everything off any technique what you'll be left with are its smds, because they're the code by which meaning is stored in the brain, and how the brain creates the meaning in the current reality tunnel. Being able to identify the principles means you have the means to create your own variations based on the needs of the client - or even discover a new one that nobody has ever thought of that you can name after yourself. That's what happened with Mrs Swish.

6

Process Interventions

What's this about?

All problems happen in time: they have a beginning, a middle and an ending although often it doesn't feel that way. In Cognitive Hypnotherapy we use a model that describes the process that begins with something being perceived in your environment, through to a behaviour that is programmed as a response to it. The importance of this is that each part of the process depends on the part before it for that response to take place. Change or disrupt any part of that chain, and the problem behaviour doesn't happen. (Here's how.)

The process quadrant of the client's problem pattern is the part that deals with how the client 'does' their problem, and the model we use to map the client's journey from stimulus to response, and a little bit beyond, is the Matrix Model.

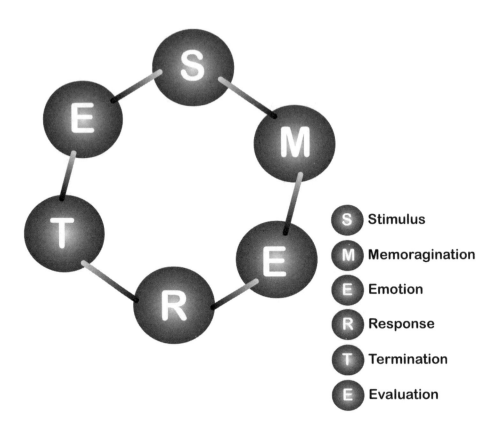

S Stimulus

M Memoragination

E Emotion

R Response

T Termination

E Evaluation

As you can see, it has six steps, beginning with **stimulus**. This is a piece of information that comes to the brain's awareness which leads to action being taken. In Helen's case it is anything that means she has to speak in public. It can be literally anything from our environment, or a thought you generate. As you know, every moment of our waking day the brain is comparing information from the environment with information from our memories in order to figure out what the best response to it would be. So, as the stimulus is perceived, it is filtered through our **memoragination** (all of our memory loops) for relevance. With Helen, it will be the living room memory loop.

If a match is determined between the stimulus and a negative memory an **emotion** is generated by dumping chemicals into our blood stream. For Helen it is panic. Emotions are our brains' way of getting us to do stuff, so the reception of an emotion will lead to a **response** – usually an action, which will continue until the need for it is judged to be over. Helen will feel the urge to get away. When speaking up is no longer part of her present or near future, it will **terminate**.

Following the termination of this thought-cycle, the model suggests that an **evaluation** process checks the outcome of the cycle against the thing it was originally developed to help with. The difficulty with this is that the evaluation seems to be done by the survival system locked within the closed loop of her problem pattern. So, if Helen suffers from the fear of presenting because of what happened when she was eight in her living room, which she believed earned her the displeasure of her father and made her look stupid, her unconscious evaluation of running out of the boardroom is likely to be that it was better than the alternative which was to stay and have her father withdraw his affection. The result of this evaluation is that this thought cycle is now reinforced to do the same thing again in any situation it deems similar, and because of the negative emotion present in the memory loop, the system is going to remain a closed one, so that the only information available to interpret future events that get connected to this loop through TAOTM will be what is contained within it. Her feeling can only feed on itself and become more of what it already is. The second level of the evaluation stage is that the selfplex - your idea of yourself - will also conduct a post-mortem on the behaviour cycle through its lens of 'how is this about me?' It too is caught within the closed loop without realising it, so any feelings of self-esteem that are connected to the event are also likely to become more of what they are - in this case Helen's feeling of being stupid can only use what it has within the closed loop to evaluate itself. It's a double whammy: the survival system reinforces the problematic behaviour, and the selfplex makes that behaviour mean something negative about its self. Both increase the negativity within the loop, each feeds off the contribution of the other, yet without either part knowing about the presence of the other. The bodge-brain in action.

Process interventions are those which cause a change to any part of the Matrix Model. Like a recipe, if you change any element of the model, you change what comes out of it. So anything that interrupts the thought-cycle or changes any component of it is thought of as a process intervention. For example, you could teach your client the Dropthrough technique so that whenever she feels the emotion that's part of the problem pattern she can do something about it. Now, wait a minute, I hear you say. Isn't Dropthrough a structure intervention? Well done, I'm glad you're paying attention. Yes it is - it works by changing the internal structure of the thoughts and feelings that drive the emotion. If a client experiences that emotion during a session, then I could use the Dropthrough as a structure intervention. However, this could also work consequently within her problem process, so by dropping through a feeling with me, she might find later that she can no longer do her problem: the structure intervention interrupted her process. I might also teach it, for her to use later if her process of doing her problem kicks in again. In this context its purpose is to directly interrupt the thought cycle **in the moment she's 'doing her problem'**, so I think of it as a process intervention. According to when and where they're used, some techniques can be described under both headings. Remember, this is only a model to guide your choices.

> *Any technique developed by anybody, anytime, anywhere works within one of the six points of this model*

Every technique mentioned in this book, or the others I've written (or, in my opinion, any technique developed by anybody, anytime, anywhere) works within one of the six points of this model. For example, a way of changing the client's perception of the **first step** that sets off the thought cycle - the **stimulus** - is to use hypnotic suggestion to prime their unconscious to perceive the stimulus in a way which would not produce a negative action. As another example, within a session, a Swish Pattern can also interrupt the process at its beginning.

The **second step** of the model is the search for similarity, difference and cause within the memoragination. This is best dealt with by the use of context interventions, or by using rewind.

The **third step** is **emotion**, and techniques such as Dropthrough and submodality change techniques will work at interrupting the problem pattern at this point.

The **fourth step** of the model is **response**, the action that is generated as the best choice of behaviour to deal with the situation the stimulus represents. In many styles of therapy, rehearsing different behaviour options is a key component of their work, and it can be very powerful. Our brain can be led by our physiology, just as our physiology can be led by our brain; so, in a situation where the brain expects one response but instead perceives you behaving in a different way, it can cause it to adjust the meaning it gives to the situation.

Termination is the point at which the brain no longer finds a match between the problem pattern and the present environment sufficient for it to demand a response, so the client ceases the behaviour that relates to their problem. This is the **fifth step**. This is another instance where hypnotic suggestion can use time distortion to prime the brain to create a perception of the environment that would encourage it to cease and desist from its current action.

Finally the **sixth step: evaluation**. Again, hypnotic suggestion can be great at helping the interpretation of what's just happened - as in, "...and it might only be afterwards, looking back, that you find yourself realising in just how many ways you were different this time...and whether those ways were big or small...what you expected or surprised you doesn't matter...it just means that things are changing for the better...more and more each time..." Changing the cycle within the Matrix Model provides an opportunity for the behaviour to be evaluated in a new way - i.e. it becomes a moment of inception.

I'm now going to give three examples of interventions that work within the Matrix Model that I haven't included anywhere else: Anchoring, the Circle of Excellence and Embodiment.

Anchoring

This is one of the most useful techniques from NLP. It utilises the capacity of every mammal to respond to a conditioned stimulus. Often people get a bit antsy when I compare them to Pavlov's dogs - you remember how he paired the stimulus of a ringing bell with the arrival of their dinner, so that after a few days just hearing the bell made them salivate? - but if you're driving along and you see a red light doesn't your foot go to the brake without thinking? And if you're the passenger and the driver doesn't seem to have noticed, isn't your first response to apply pressure to the non-existent brake in your footwell? That's a conditioned response, my friend. And in NLP it's an example of an anchor.

Neurons that fire together, wire together

We can become conditioned to respond to something automatically by repeated exposure - that's why advertisers group their adverts together in the hope that it will train your neurology to respond to their message. After 30 years ask British people what comes after, "Beanz meanz...." and they'll still chant "Heinz"; one of the most successful examples of conditioning the masses to create an equivalence between a product and a brand.

We can also get anchored when in a strong emotional state. You may have heard of the adage 'neurons that fire together wire together'. It suggests that if two things are present at the same time - intensely or repeatedly - they become linked within our neurology. It's the basis for many of our problems. I had a client who was assaulted as a child by a man who grabbed her by the shoulder from behind and dragged her into some bushes. The intense fear she experienced became linked to the grip on her shoulder, so that years later when she came to see me she still had a panic attack if someone touched her there from behind.

Within therapy, this idea of a conditioned response can be utilised deliberately to link a positive emotion with some form of a trigger. In NLP, the most common form of anchor is to apply pressure with a finger to a client's knuckle while they are in a strong emotional state, like relaxed, confident, powerful or calm. This kinaesthetic form of anchoring works well for many people, and didn't work at all on me. I made the mistake of thinking that, because it hadn't worked on me, anchors didn't work, and didn't use them on clients for about two years. What I've since realised is that the principle of anchoring applies to everybody, but you have to vary the trigger. Triggers are available in all modalities: a visual image can be used - how many people put lucky mascots on their desk before an exam? Auditory triggers, like key words or tunes, work brilliantly - am I the only one who runs faster if Eye of the Tiger comes on? (which can be a bit embarrassing in Tescos!) Many people turn to a favourite food for comfort, so gustatory clearly works, and smell anchors are particularly effective, e.g., peppermint.

Smell anchors are particularly effective

I came across the idea of using smell as an anchor in about 1997, when I was working at Hendon Police Training School. I was in charge of a unit helping students who were failing the intensive 18-week course. We had four weeks to improve their exam results or they faced dismissal, and our unit - called the Student Advice Centre - had SAC printed boldly on the door, so it wasn't the best of starts for them. The good news is that over three years we developed a model based on matching NLP representational systems to particular study methods and got to the point where we could guarantee between a 10% & 30% increase in exam results with only 2.5 hours of coaching. And the improvement was maintained after the coaching finished if they kept to the method. But that's a story for another book.

What I did come across during that time was a news story about how schools in Japan pump the smell of peppermint through their school air conditioning systems during exams because it increases short term recall. This got me thinking. I had read Ernest Rossi saying that memory is state dependent so I experimented with students studying in the evening in an atmosphere they found conducive, and had them periodically put a handkerchief impregnated with peppermint to their nose and breath deeply. My thinking was that this would anchor the smell of peppermint to a state they were in when they were studying. Then, during the exam they would produce the hankie and breathe in before answering a question, triggering the same state they were in when they were learning or revising what they were now being questioned about. In my opinion, it was one of the things that contributed to their sudden improvement. Years later, I heard that the British Olympians were carrying a smell on a wristband and breathing deeply whenever they had a positive training experience, like a personal best. Then, just before their event they would breath it again to take them back into their successful state. I've been using it now for years, not only with athletes, but with a range of other clients.

The great advantage of smell anchors is that smells go straight to the emotional system, not through the cortex, so they work on everybody with a sense of smell without any interference from our 'thinking' brain.

My point is that anchors work on everybody, but the same triggers don't work on everybody – except smell

My point is that anchors work on everybody, but the same triggers don't work on everybody - except smell.

For our purposes a definition of the principle of anchoring is that:

"Any time a person is in an intense, associated state, if a stimulus is provided to that person, the state and the stimulus become connected neurologically."

Creating an anchor

The best states to anchor are states that arise spontaneously in the client. Next best are vivid, highly-associated states from a client's past experience.

The following is a guide to deliberately create an anchor by getting a client to access a past experience. By following the steps you'll be able to see how to anchor a state that arises within a session.

For most clients it will be easier to do this if their eyes are closed. A trance induction isn't necessary because the exercise uses the trance phenomena of age regression, positive hallucination (in most cases) and sensory distortion. As I stated in idea nine on page 123, techniques contain their own inductions, so the trance arises spontaneously as the intervention unfolds.

I've written it from the perspective of doing a kinaesthetic anchor, but the principles remain the same if you choose another modality. With Helen, I would get her to choose a feeling she would like to have when about to speak up. It might be relaxation, or confidence, or personal power.

1. *"Can you remember a specific time when you felt really X? (happy, relaxed, calm, powerful etc)"*
2. *"As you go back to that time now ... go right back to that time, go inside your body and see what you saw, hear what you heard, and really feel the feelings of being really X'd."*
3. *"If you could point to the feeling in your body, where would you point?"*
4. *"As you feel that feeling, on a scale of 0-10, where 10 is the strongest it can be, how strong does it feel?"*
5. *If the feeling is an 8+ proceed to step 6, if the feeling is 7 or less say, "As you feel that feeling, if you could make it stronger, so it would be a..." (1 more than it currently is) what would you do to it?" Repeat until the feeling is an 8+.*

When it is, get them to nod, or tell you.

6. *"As you feel that feeling notice the pressure of my finger against your knuckle. And as you feel that pressure see the image of that specific time and notice the feeling in your body where you feel it." Apply pressure to the knuckle for 5 seconds."*

7. *"In a few moments you'll notice me repeat the pressure on your knuckle, and you could be curious when you feel that pressure about whether you get the image of that specific time before the feeling in your body...or whether you get the feeling before the image.." Apply the anchor on the knuckle. "What came first?"*

Their answer is irrelevant, asking the question just causes them to identify, and thus strengthen the trigger pathway.

8. Whichever they say, say, "Good, and if I do it again does it happen in the same order again?"

Again, the answer isn't important in itself, it's just training the pathway.

"So from today, every time you feel that pressure, and (depending on the order they get) feel the feeling and see the image, you can enjoy that feeling, knowing you have control, and wondering how much stronger the feeling gets every time you use this anchor.." etc.

As you can see, although it's a kinaesthetic anchor I've used other modalities to increase its effect. I would have used auditory instead of visual if I thought the client would respond to that better. If you're choosing to use a different modality as the trigger, smell, for example, I would simply waft the smell they have brought with them (so it's their choice of the equivalence between the smell and the state - you'll be amazed at what some clients choose) under their nose and ask them to take a deep breath instead of applying pressure.

Stacking anchors

An anchor can be a permanent resource. All that is required is that it is used regularly - it's definitely a case of 'use it or lose it'. A constant competition for neurons goes on in the brain, so if an anchor isn't used it will 'wear off' as the synaptic connections that comprise it are recruited for other purposes.

Potentially you can have as many anchors as there are emotions, but it would be difficult to remember where you put them all, and hard work to keep them refreshed. Instead I suggest you have two.

In simple terms, our states follow something analogous to a musical scale; some states take us up the scale, like excitement, power and strength. Others take us down the scale, such as calm, relaxation and peace. In most cases having one 'up' and one 'down' anchor keeps things simple. The principle of stacking is simply that every time you experience a useful state you 'trap it' using whatever firing stimulus you have employed - knuckle pressure, smell, etc.

This doesn't preclude having anchors set for particular situations. For example, focus might be a state that would be useful in both an 'up' or a 'down' context. One person might want to relax and focus on a task, while another would need to feel focused and excited. My wife and I have a relationship anchor. Whenever either one of us is appreciating a state that has emerged from being together - like watching a sunset on holiday - we hook our little fingers together. I also have one on the back of my right hand for enjoyable training experiences.

How would your life be if you could choose your emotional state in any situation?

One of the things I like most about anchoring is that it makes you realise you have choice. Clients are generally at the mercy of their emotions; if they have one they surrender to the actions it dictates, and it can be one of the most powerful life lessons any of us can learn: to realise that we can choose what emotions or states to have in any situation we are in. Just imagine that for a moment - how would your life be if you could choose your emotional state in any situation?

That is what the principle of anchoring can offer if you incorporate it into the way you live your life. I doubt that any of us will reach a point where we can do it perfectly in all situations, but we can do it most of the time.

One further utilisation of the principle of anchoring I want to include is something called the Circle of Excellence. It works by utilising a physical space as the trigger for a state, or a collection of states.

The Circle of Excellence

Help the client to identify a resourceful state they would like to experience more, or one that would be useful in a specific situation. In Helen's case, she might choose the state of confidence for occasions when she has to speak in public.

"Can you remember a specific time when you felt how you want to feel, even if it's in a completely different situation?"

"Yes, when I play netball I feel very confident, and I remember a match last season when I felt as good as I have ever done."

"Great. Imagine a circle on the ground in front of you. When you are ready, step into the circle and relive that experience. Step into yourself in the memory, become aware of everything that reminds you of just how confident you're feeling, and notice in your body where you're feeling it."

Give them time to fully experience the feeling, and use the submodalities of their experience to enhance it until the state is an 8+.

Test the circle by getting them to step out of it, change their state by distracting their attention in some way - I usually say something like, "Is that coffee I can smell...?", or make them laugh.

Then have them step back into the circle and notice how quickly and fully they access the state. You can repeat the exercise as many times as required until the state change is strong and instant, and you can add other situations where they felt the same way, or other situations where they felt an additional state that might be useful in that context. In other words you can stack the circle.

As with every technique, you then future pace the client, having them imagine a situation where this would be useful, and the difference they can see the circle making.

"So if you were to imagine the next meeting, placing the circle in front of you as you enter the room, and noticing the difference it makes as you step into it...all the differences in the way you feel and act that make things go the way you want them to....etc."

One of the things to pay attention to, and feed back to your client, is the change in physiology that occurs when they step into the circle. The Circle of Excellence will work best when the client adopts a physiology that mirrors the state, which leads us neatly on to the subject of embodiment.

Embodiment

Everyday examples of embodiment are not difficult to come by: when we feel physically tired we feel differently about ourselves from when we're rested - but that could be the tiredness affecting the brain, it's not direct evidence of the body causing it. How about this? People find it less easy to have a panic attack if they hold a pen between their teeth without letting their lips touch it. Try it and you'll find that this causes your mouth to curve into a smile, and the act of smiling makes it harder for the survival system to activate. It turns out that our brain uses physiological cues to influence our states.

Paul Ekman is one of the world leaders in the study of emotion and its bodily expression. His research involved many students being photographed adopting the facial expressions of the six or seven emotions that are hard-wired into the human brain.

Following her study of traditional cultures in the South Pacific the great anthropologist Margaret Meade concluded that facial expressions were transmitted culturally - i.e., we pick them up from those around us, and so anger in one culture might be physiologically expressed differently in another. This was the perceived wisdom for much of the last half of the twentieth century, but was comprehensively disproved by Ekman's research.[91]

If you met a tribesman in New Guinea, as an example of someone who has never seen someone from the West (assuming you are not one of my many readers in the jungles of Indonesia), they would be able to identify your anger, disgust, fear, happiness, sadness or surprise. Probably contempt also, but the jury is still out on that one.

While creating a facial action coding system Ekman found that as his students and volunteers expressed one or other of these 'primary' emotions for the camera, they reported beginning to feel the emotion that matched their expression. Adopting the physiology of a state tends to lead to the experience of the state. Welcome to the science behind 'fake it 'til you make it'.

Can I ask you to adopt the physiology of a depressed person for a moment? Feel how your state declines while you do so. Conversely, stand or sit like you're confident. Again, calibrate your feeling. We intuitively know what goes with what: the physiology has a correlate in the mind to a state or emotion. Our physiology dictates our state and our state dictates what's on our mind – it's hard to connect to memory loops in our memoragination that are different to the state we're in. It's another reason why 'what's on our mind is brought to mind'. Of course this flow of effect works both ways. Understanding this gives us the means to help a client control their being from every point within the mind-body connection. Using context and some structure interventions we can change the material of the mind (thoughts and memories) that lead the client to negative emotions and physiology. Using some other structure interventions (like spinning) we can teach the client to control their state, which will cascade its effect to their physiology and the more positive feelings will make available more positive thoughts. And using process interventions featuring embodiment, like the Circle of Excellence, the client can use their body to guide themselves into a more positive state which will, again, open up better possibilities for causal connections between the state and the client's memoragination.

> *Our physiology dictates our state and our state dictates what's on our mind*

For example, we can use embodiment in therapy by coaching the client to adopt a physiology that accompanies the state they want to have when in their problem context. I have watched the distinguished Ericksonian therapist Herbert Lustig work with a woman with anxiety disorder where in forty minutes he skilfully got her to recall a time when she felt comfortable and got her to practise being able to recall the feeling at will. In my opinion, central to his success was the subtle way he gave her feedback about the way her face looked as she accessed 'comfortable'. In effect, he turned a feeling her face had when sporting a particular expression into an anchor for *comfortable*: she learnt to recognise how her face felt when she was comfortable, so learning how to do that at will gave her control. She never had a panic attack again.[92]

In sport you often hear the expression 'putting on their game face'. I coach a boxer who is one of the nicest lads you'll ever meet, but as he walks to the ring his face undergoes a transformation and he suddenly looks a very dangerous young man. That's his game face, and with it comes a change in his overall physiology, and his attitude.

I'm sure you can see how this can be utilised to modify a client's response to a situation. Coach them into a physiology of excellence, focusing on a particular aspect, such as their face or their posture. If they maintain it during their problem process they'll find themselves unable to access the usual negative emotion that accompanies it. As their control improves, so will their anticipation of the next occurrence being even weaker - especially under the priming of your Wordweaving™.

Conclusion

The process quadrant of the problem pattern provides a means to track the client's journey from the initial prompt for their problem to begin, all the way through to their post-action evaluation. Every technique in this book acts within some part of the Matrix Model. In this chapter, I've highlighted those which demonstrate the principle of process techniques interrupting the client's running of their problem as it's happening, empowering people by their demonstrating to themselves that they have control of their emotional responses.

Moreover, these techniques can be tremendously useful in supporting the client's perception of their solution state emerging, and this drives home the message that most therapy happens in-between sessions. By giving them things they can do for themselves it helps to reinforce their internal locus of control and create a sense of personal empowerment.

In the main, these techniques tend to be supplementary to the main thrust of my treatment, in that I wouldn't depend on these interventions being the main difference that makes a difference. That won't always be the case. For some clients it will be their ability to control themselves in the moment that will be the strongest evidence that they're putting their problem behind them, while for others it is looking back at their past without an emotional response, or imagining their future without anxiety. People tend to have preferences for things, and this is just another of them, a preference for believing the evidence from the past part of their reality tunnel, or the present, or the future. While for most it is likely to be a mixture of all three, for some one will be stronger than the others. It's another thing to listen for within your client's description of their problem pattern and solution state.

The Future is What You Make It

What's this about?

Our brain is a survival calculator that seeks to create certainty in order to make us efficient in the use of our limited resources. Remember 'recharge or die'? We move towards what our brain's calculations tell us will reward us. And only that.

In Part One I suggested a theory of mind that proposes that our idea of the self - our selfplex - is another input of information that the brain has to consider, just like it does the information from the senses. This gives us a wonderful opportunity to invade our own memoragination and guide us towards the future we desire. By thinking the future how we desire it we prime ourselves to create the conditions to achieve it. We become our life's creators.

Martin Seligman was an eminent psychiatrist with a problem. He'd been elected to the post of President of the American Psychiatric Association (APA) and was searching for the inspirational idea that would guide his term in office, a direction that would move his profession forward. It came from an unexpected source:

"...I glimpsed what the backbone might be while weeding in my garden with my five year old daughter, Nikki. I have to confess that even though I have written a book and many articles about children, I'm not actually very good with them. I am goal-oriented and time-urgent and when I'm weeding in the garden, I'm weeding. Nikki, however, was throwing weeds into the air and dancing and singing. Since she was distracting me I yelled at her and she walked away. Within a few minutes she was back, saying, "Daddy, I want to talk to you."

If I can stop whining, you can stop being such a grouch

"Yes, Nikki?"

"Daddy, do you remember before my fifth birthday? From when I was three until I was five. I was a whiner. I whined every day. On my fifth birthday, I decided I wasn't going to whine anymore. That was the hardest thing I've ever done. And if I can stop whining, you can stop being such a grouch.[93]"

We tend to get the future we expect

From that moment, Positive Psychology was born. Seligman realised that, since its inception, psychology had been almost exclusively involved in the study of what is wrong with us. Seligman's moment of genius was to realise what an untapped resource were people living happy, fulfilled lives. Positive Psychology became the study of positive emotions, positive traits and strengths, and positive institutions. Its research has shown that happiness, positivity and optimism increase health, longevity and quality of life, and that people can take active steps to increase their default setting for optimism. A lot of it is managing the way you think of your future, because we tend to get the future we expect.

Optimism and pessimism are two poles of a continuum, and each one of us will tend to stick most often to a certain point on that line - it's what I meant by our default setting. Where we stand on this line is an indicator of the sum total of our beliefs about the way the world works: do things tend to work out, or do things tend to go wrong? Do you believe that the world is a positive place full of possibility, or a place where you need to guard yourself against the next twist of fickle fate? You can probably tell by the way I loaded that sentence that I'm an optimist, while my wife comes from a family of pessimists whose family motto is, 'don't get too excited because...', which sometimes creates an interesting difference in our marital reality tunnel. Over the course of all of our lives, our Prover becomes tuned to this class of information: does it bring you information that gives you cause to view the world positively or negatively? A balance between the two is ideal, because too far down the pessimism route and you can get stuck in protection.

While both optimism and pessimism have a part to play - being too optimistic can be as damaging as being a doomsayer - Positive Psychology has made a powerful case for suggesting that being up the optimistic end of the continuum is going to bring you the most success in terms of relationships, health and career. What I'm going to show you in this chapter can help to adjust the tuning of a client's Prover so it more readily brings to their attention the good things around them - especially the things that would be evidence for their solution state and keep them in a state of growth.

The first part of a client's future we need to think about is the consequence of their problem pattern; the brain's anticipation of the most likely outcome to a present situation that is linked to a negative memory loop. For many this will automatically change as a consequence of a successful intervention, such as Time Line Reconsolidation, Visual Squash or Dropthrough. When you do a future pace after the intervention in the manner described in this book, the nature of the presuppositions contained within it automatically produces a more positive outcome. However, for some clients it is the thoughts of the future that provoke their problem reaction in the first place, whether because they are so strongly pessimistic, or because they suffer from an anxiety condition (anxiety is always a fear connected to something that hasn't happened yet).

We tend to get the future we expect

So, where a client's evidence for their problem is focused strongly on the thoughts they have about their future, then these thoughts need to have the negative emotion taken from them; changing a future portion of their memoragination can be as powerful as changing a past portion.

Any structure intervention you can use on a memory from the past can be used on a memory of the future, because the brain is using the same processing areas to create them.

In Part 1.1, I described the evidence for the idea that the thoughts we have about our future are made up from what we've experienced in our past; it's difficult to imagine something we haven't come across before. So, if thoughts of our past and thoughts of our future are essentially the same thing, then techniques like Rewind, Dropthrough and Spinning, focused on the thought of the future, can work by taking the emotion from it. Once that has been achieved, the substitution of a future thought that is positive is more likely to prove sticky and not be overwhelmed by the habitually created old pattern. Bear in mind that I've mentioned this for clients who are predominantly future-oriented in terms of their evidence procedure (see Part 2.8). If clients are past or present oriented, then just the usual pattern of future pacing should suffice.

Future pacing

> *A core principle in Cognitive Hypnotherapy is that every intervention with a client is accompanied by a future pace*

This principle of future pacing is something that is given particular emphasis in Cognitive Hypnotherapy. I've suggested that problem patterns are the consequence of particular cause and effect, equivalence or difference relationships identified by the brain between present information and past experience. All the techniques described, in one way or another, redefine these algorithms so that the past experience no longer serves as a reference for the brain to guide our present actions negatively. A core principle in Cognitive Hypnotherapy is that every intervention with a client is accompanied by a future pace which establishes a positive outcome in the future as an effect of that intervention (i.e. it utilises TAOTM). Let me give an example to illustrate:

When doing time line you are asking the unconscious to connect the client to the cause of their issue (the effect). The reframing performed in a successful session of time line changes the causal event so that it no longer means what it once did. i.e., it is no longer the cause (the reference experience) of any effect in the present (their issue). What we can do now is create a new cause and effect relationship to guide the mind towards the solution state the client has identified as being the goal of therapy. In time line we do this by saying,

You can then continue, using the keywords you elicited from them during your

"Go out into the future to an event which, if it had happened in the past, would have been connected to the problem you once had. Look down and notice how much better it is."

Or

"Go out to the future to a point where the effect of today has had its full effect. Look down and notice how much better it is."

solution state information gathering. If you look back to Part 2.3 you'll see that Helen's evidence included the words *confident, in control*, and *relaxed*, so it might go something like this:

"As you look down notice what is different around you, the way people are toward you now, the changes in your environment...all the changes that show you're moving towards where you want to be...more confident...behaving in ways that support the you you're becoming...in control...all the things you're doing that make a difference to the results you're getting...and sometimes it might surprise you just how relaxed you feel because of how in control you are...in your future now...noticing the growing qualities that support your increasing confidence...resources and skills you've always had being given greater opportunity to grow...maybe new ones appearing now because they can...so that as your belief in your confidence continues to grow we might wonder how soon it will be before you realise it matches the belief of the you in your future that you're becoming...so much more quickly than you might have expected...so that soon you see yourself in the mirror already having everything you need to be the person you wanted to be...already...So that all I have to do is ask your unconscious mind...as you hold in your mind this future you...confident...relaxed...in control...to place her on your future timeline, almost like a beacon...guiding your unconscious mind in the choices and opportunities it begins to bring to your attention that move you towards being that person in the shortest, safest time...surprising yourself sometimes in the actions you begin to take...and as these happen more and more we might wonder when will be the first time you realise it means you've changed..fundamentally...a sense of inevitability beginning to be a part of your improvement...knowing you can be who you want to be...etc, etc."

Those of you who have read my two previous books will be aware of the language structures and suggestion loops that are part of Wordweaving™, and how I've incorporated Neuro Logical Levels into the future pace, flicking between the qualities of the future Helen and the present Helen with sufficient ambiguity for the two to meld together. Hopefully you can see that, if you are armed with solution state keywords for your client, you can substitute them for Helen's and the future pace will still read smoothly. (Read more about Wordweaving™ in Appendix One.)

The Change-Link Pattern

Another Wordweaving™ pattern that I utilise with my clients whenever they report back to me that they've improved is what I called the Change-Link pattern. It basically asks the unconscious to look back between now and the last session at all the things that have led to the improvements they've noticed, and use them to anticipate the next range of things that mean the improvement is continuing – i.e., linking the changes already noticed to the changes that might be anticipated. Once again I'm using TAOTM, where the changes noticed become the *cause* of the positive changes that will be noticed - the *effect*.

"And just imagine floating back along your past...all the way back to the last time I saw you....and it doesn't matter if you don't yet know....or if you never know...what it was exactly that made the difference...for your unconscious mind to assist you in the changes you've been noticing.....and it can be interesting that for you to have noticed the positive things which have been happening...something about you must have changed....the way you're thinking...feeling...and often these changes are happening so unconsciously that we're not even aware of them as they're happening...so if I were to ask your unconscious mind instead to take all the time in the world to come back towards now...noticing all the differences in you that have made this possible...the way you're behaving.............the differences in the way you're responding to people around you.............how they're responding to you positively.............those things about you that are growing stronger.....helping you in the most powerful and positive ways.....so whether there's something yet you can believe as a result of how you're noticing being different that could help this continue and develop and grow even stronger which means what it needs to mean for this change to be lasting....to be able to follow these improvements.......and changes in you all the way back to now....and just imagine how....if your unconscious were to use these changes as a platform for your future...how that future could begin to appear in front of you...just as you want it......with all the things that are important to you...present.....and just enjoy being aware of all of the things in this new future...all the things that can help you to move towards them....to continue to motivate you to move towards this new you....doing everything you need to do to bring this future towards you as quickly as it's possible....so just put that image of your new future wherever in your future seems right so your unconscious can help you move towards it in the way it supports you...assisting you in doing all the things that bring it closer....making you aware of everything that could keep you from it....so that the more you're noticing the positive impact of the way you're becoming on what it is you're doing we can both wonder how soon it will be before it almost feels inevitable that you're going to get where you want to be...just because you can...continue to do everything that keeps you moving forward...etc."

I've included this slightly adapted version from my book *The Question is the Answer* because the principle behind it is so important: every aspect of your work together is potentially available to influence your client's belief in their progress. And the most powerful way of doing this is to make it either the **cause** of some element of their solution state, or an **equivalence** of it. If your client's brain is primed to notice those things around them that equal evidence of growth, then it consolidates the incepted idea that your earlier work created.

Three Gifts

Positive Psychology has also provided us with a lot of research that can be used to prime your client's Prover toward a more optimistic choice of information from their environment. I think this is a very important thing to accomplish. If we can retune a client's mind to focus on the positives around them, then it will be harder to find matches between what is going on around them and something stored in negative memory loops. The more they live in a positive present, the more it means the unconscious is drawing on a positive past to give it meaning, and the easier it will be for it to create a positive future, resulting in a transformed reality tunnel.

The most powerful exercise the Positive Psychologists have developed, one that over a seven day period was more effective in raising the mood of people with depression than Prozac[94], is a very simple one.

Each evening, get your client to look back over their day and select three positive things that have happened and write them down. They are also asked to write down how they were responsible for those 'gifts' occurring. With clients who are very negative, or deep in depression, they might struggle sometimes to find even one good thing, but they are always there, so it's just about whether their Prover is tuned to notice them. It is often just a question of getting them to chunk down to notice smaller things, like seeing a butterfly, or a stranger smiling at them in the street.

As the days go by it will become easier to choose, and the choice will become larger. This is because the brain is being primed - what is on your mind is brought to mind - so if the unconscious begins to anticipate the task ahead each evening it begins to tune its awareness so that the client will have things to choose from. As the range of gifts gets larger, so does the their view of the world at large; it becomes more positive and full of opportunities for growth. During the day the client will begin to notice the things that will inform their choices as they appear, which helps them begin to appreciate what they have, and what is around them. I also believe that giving your clients a Wordweaving™ download to listen to each evening will accelerate that process. Here is an excerpt from one:

Allow your mind to drift back over the day....knowing that your mind notices far more than we're aware of.....until now...having the opportunity to reflect back over the day....and considering...that if your mind had noticed three things....three things that could be considered gifts to you....three moments that now...when you think of it...you realise brought you something....and everybody's different in what they notice...something somebody said...or did...something in nature that caught your attention... a moment of beauty....a learning...a smile....laughter...it really doesn't matter what the nature of the gift was...or whether it was big or small...just allow your mind to take the time to find these three things...as you wonder...what part you played in bringing them into your life...and at first it might not always seem obvious how you're connected to these gifts...to these coming to you...but it might begin to dawn on you how much more you are a part of their existence than you might once have thought...and you might even find that each time you do this your mind finds it easier and easier to find these gifts....and neither of us know yet when will be the first time you notice during the day something that you know will later be considered a gift....and how this begins to happen more often...and it's often the case that people are surprised where this begins to lead...to new directions....new opportunities...new feelings about themselves...all gifts that are connected....so that as your mind becomes more and more tuned to noticing all the good things around you it means that you're changing...growing... becoming more and more of who you want to be...doing more and more of what you want to do...and I'm not saying this will happen overnight...automatically....just that it could begin now...in the smallest of ways leaving you knowing that it's possible...that soon...looking back you realise you have noticed the different ways you're thinking...or feeling....and whether it's you or someone else who notices doesn't matter....it just means that your growing confidence becomes another gift....that leads to others...

230

Other exercises from Positive Psychology and elsewhere I've found useful include:

Gratitude: Find three opportunities in a day to thank somebody for something - beyond the run of everyday pleasantries. One of the biggest learnings I've gained in my life is how little it takes to make someone feel good, and how that feeling reflects back on you.

Savouring: We live at such a fast pace that we can go a surprisingly long time without appreciating the moment. Either set aside a period of minutes every day, or choose two or three things per day, and savour them. Take a sip of wine, or a bite of chocolate, and immerse yourself fully in the pleasure of it. Stop and watch the birds, or listen to them, or watch a sunset. Watch your children while they sleep, or your partner. Savour the things you know to be precious to you, bring them back into your appreciation, and try savouring things you didn't realise were. You'll be amazed at how much there is around you to savour. Make a Wordwweaving™ download for this too. I know I could do this for you, but if you give someone a fish...

Kindness: Do an act of random kindness everyday. Do it with no thought of personal gain, and do it at some cost or inconvenience to you if possible. Seligman and co discovered a remarkable thing; if you put people with depression into a situation where they served others, they recovered more quickly. Giving to others, of your time more than your money, is a potent way of feeling better about yourself.

Are you in growth or protection?: One final one from me, which I doubt that you'll be surprised by, is using growth and protection as a means of guiding your choices. When faced with a business decision or a life choice, Rebecca and I habitually ask ourselves questions like, "Which decision keeps us in growth?" or, "Are we in growth, or protection?" or "Where is that decision coming from?" We've found it works amazingly well to keep your life congruent.

Conclusion

I have described at length, throughout this book, why our future is so important to us; I think it's the end result of our brain's endeavour to become the most efficient survival calculator possible. We cannot avoid our brain's calculating the likely outcome of every situation that we experience. It will do so based on whatever match it makes between what it focuses on from our environment, and our past.

If we can tune our brains to find relevant the positive information present in our environment so that it seeks matches between that and our past, then it is much more likely that the anticipated future that emerges from this process will also be perceived as positive, leaving us motivated to move towards it and rewarding our bodies with the hormones that sustain our well-being. We can train our brains to pay attention to what we want it to; we can create our own reality tunnel.

Be Water My Friend

Once you understand the principles of this approach, and have achieved competence in the techniques described in the book (and any others you learn) you will never be stuck again, because 'resistance' in a client, or an inability to follow a step of a technique, is just feedback that can be used to move to another technique that continues you towards your therapeutic target. I'll give an example of what I mean:

Imagine I'm proceeding with a time line session with Helen regarding her issues of low self-confidence. She is above her time line and is asked the key question (see Part 2.4). She knows the feeling of no confidence but can't find the memory, despite my best questions. My options include:

- I could focus on the feeling of no confidence and switch to Dropthrough (structure intervention).
- I could focus on the feeling of not being able to get the memory and Dropthrough *that* and see where it takes me (remembering 'no failure only feedback' if it takes me nowhere useful).
- I could switch to consequence and take her to the end result of remaining the same. From this position often asking the question, "So if you could go to the first event connected to this ending how far back would you go?" will open up the memory; the change in perceptual perception often serves to bypass the block.
- I could change to a Parts Integration (structure) by saying "If a part of you wants to be rid of this feeling of no confidence, and a part of you wants to stay the same, which hand would the no confidence part come out on?"

Remind yourself of the other techniques in this book and see what alternative ideas for switching you can come up with.

If Helen accesses the memory but the emotion doesn't disappear from it when I move her before the event (and I've exhausted the other options given on page 161) I could:

- Perform Rewind on the memory.
- Dropthrough the emotion (with the option of returning to time line when the emotion has disappeared).
- Switch to Gestalt Chair - "If there was something you need to say to X for the emotion to disappear, what would it be?" and "If there was something you need to hear from X for the emotion to disappear, what would it be?"
- Use the Headache Cure to make the emotion disappear – or Spin it (with the option of returning to time line when the emotion has disappeared).

You have the option to continue with the technique you've switched to and follow it with a future pace, or switch back to time line reconsolidation once the purpose of the switch has been achieved. It just depends on your sense of what is left to accomplish to achieve inception from the point of choice that you've arrived at. As I hope you can see, the flexibility inherent in this approach make the possibilities almost endless.

The Two Simple Questions

You can step from any technique to another technique at any point, just by following the principles that underlie the two questions I hold in my head at all times during therapy, and which have guided us through this book. In response to whatever the client says, does or doesn't do, I ask, "What's that about?" When I am equipped with an answer I follow it with, "How can I use that?" I know it sounds a simplification, but these two questions allow me to flow from one client challenge to the next. From the two questions emerges a style that flows like water, sometimes moving through elements from three or four techniques until we reach the resolution of whatever outcome we're pursuing.

I've created a model to demonstrate the flow that utilises the questions. In honour of Bruce Lee's advice to 'be water', I've called it the Cascade Model.

Over the next few pages I will break this model down into its constituent parts:

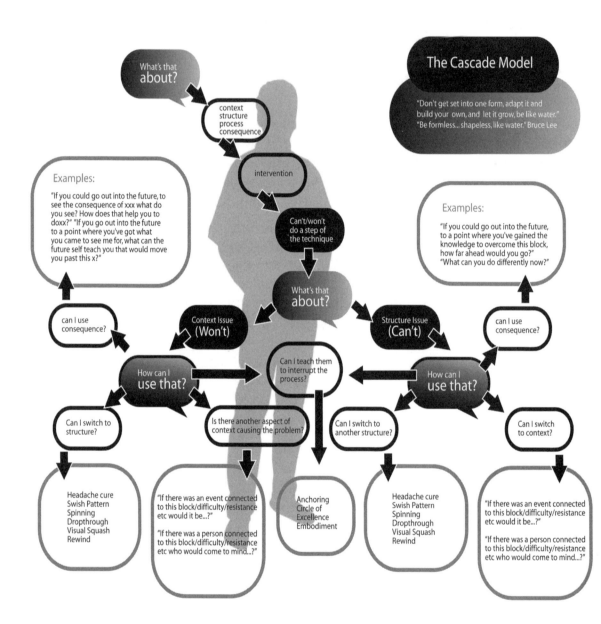

The Cascade Model

"Don't get set into one form, adapt it and build your own, and let it grow, be like water." "Be formless... shapeless, like water." Bruce Lee

What's that about?

context
structure
process
consequence

intervention

Can't/won't do a step of the technique

What's that about?

Examples:

"If you could go out into the future, to see the consequence of xxx what do you see? How does that help you to doxx?" "If you go out into the future to a point where you've got what you came to see me for, what can the future self teach you that would move you past this x?"

Examples:

"If you could go out into the future, to a point where you've gained the knowledge to overcome this block, how far ahead would you go?" "What can you do differently now?"

can I use consequence?

Context Issue (Won't)

Structure Issue (Can't)

can I use consequence?

How can I use that?

Can I teach them to interrupt the process?

How can I use that?

Can I switch to structure?

Is there another aspect of context causing the problem?

Can I switch to another structure?

Can I switch to context?

Headache cure
Swish Pattern
Spinning
Dropthrough
Visual Squash
Rewind

"If there was an event connected to this block/difficulty/resistance etc would it be...?"

"If there was a person connected to this block/difficulty/resistance etc who would come to mind...?"

Anchoring
Circle of
Excellence
Embodiment

Headache cure
Swish Pattern
Spinning
Dropthrough
Visual Squash
Rewind

"If there was an event connected to this block/difficulty/resistance etc would it be...?"

"If there was a person connected to this block/difficulty/resistance etc who would come to mind...?"

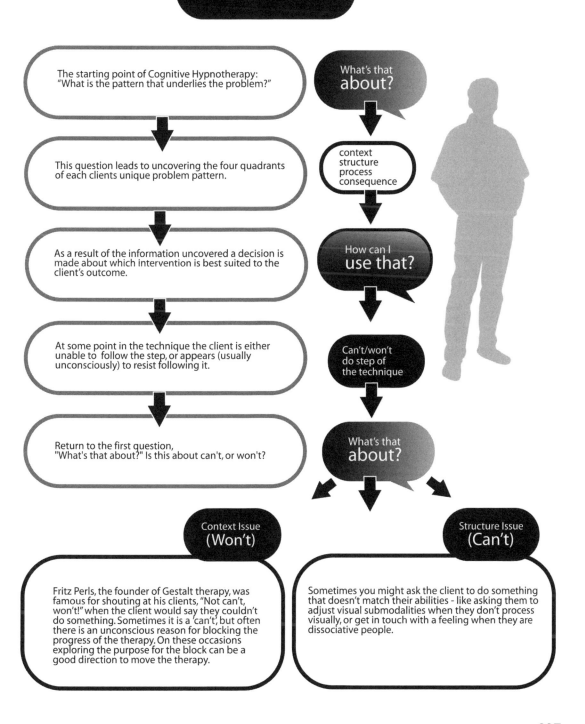

The Cascade Model

The starting point of Cognitive Hypnotherapy: "What is the pattern that underlies the problem?"

What's that about?

context
structure
process
consequence

This question leads to uncovering the four quadrants of each clients unique problem pattern.

How can I use that?

As a result of the information uncovered a decision is made about which intervention is best suited to the client's outcome.

Can't/won't do step of the technique

At some point in the technique the client is either unable to follow the step, or appears (usually unconsciously) to resist following it.

What's that about?

Return to the first question, "What's that about?" Is this about can't, or won't?

Context Issue (Won't)

Structure Issue (Can't)

Fritz Perls, the founder of Gestalt therapy, was famous for shouting at his clients, "Not can't, won't!" when the client would say they couldn't do something. Sometimes it is a 'can't', but often there is an unconscious reason for blocking the progress of the therapy. On these occasions exploring the purpose for the block can be a good direction to move the therapy.

Sometimes you might ask the client to do something that doesn't match their abilities - like asking them to adjust visual submodalities when they don't process visually, or get in touch with a feeling when they are dissociative people.

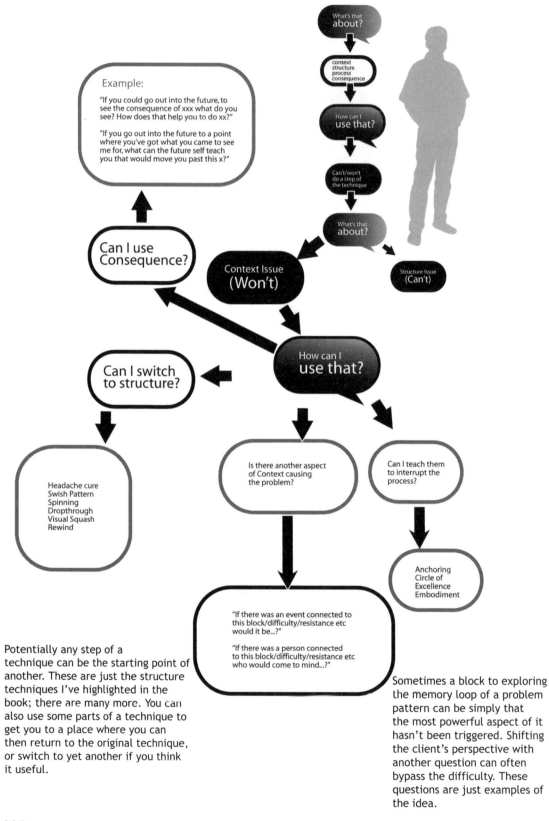

What's that **about?**

context
structure
process
consequence

How can I **use that?**

Can't/won't do a step of the technique

What's that **about?**

Structure Issue
(Can't)

Context Issue
(Won't)

Can I use
Consequence?

Example:

"If you could go out into the future, to see the consequence of xxx what do you see? How does that help you to do xx?"

"If you go out into the future to a point where you've got what you came to see me for, what can the future self teach you that would move you past this x?"

How can I
use that?

Can I switch
to structure?

Headache cure
Swish Pattern
Spinning
Dropthrough
Visual Squash
Rewind

Is there another aspect
of Context causing
the problem?

Can I teach them
to interrupt the
process?

Anchoring
Circle of
Excellence
Embodiment

"If there was an event connected to this block/difficulty/resistance etc would it be...?"

"If there was a person connected to this block/difficulty/resistance etc who would come to mind...?"

Potentially any step of a technique can be the starting point of another. These are just the structure techniques I've highlighted in the book; there are many more. You can also use some parts of a technique to get you to a place where you can then return to the original technique, or switch to yet another if you think it useful.

Sometimes a block to exploring the memory loop of a problem pattern can be simply that the most powerful aspect of it hasn't been triggered. Shifting the client's perspective with another question can often bypass the difficulty. These questions are just examples of the idea.

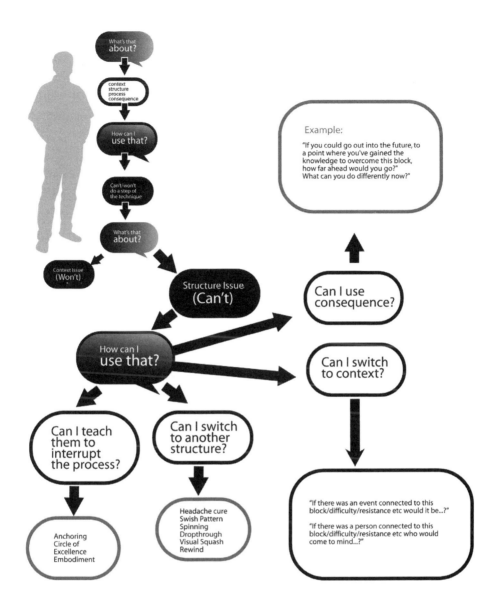

As with the previous page, any block to progress is a diversion sign, not a stop sign. One structure technique can take over from another, just by identifying the submodalities involved and utilising the one(s) which best fits the situation.

Similarly with context: If a structure intervention stalls, there may be an underlying secondary gain issue that would be revealed by switching to context, and a consequence is always available to gain a different perspective. The Cascade Model can quickly become second nature in your practice as a therapist, counsellor or coach. At its heart is TAOTM: the assumption that our brains are working on a causal understanding of the world, so the meaning of everything is dependent on the meaning of everything else. Change one aspect of the problem pattern, and potentially many more parts will have to change too, it's just a question of using the right technique to change the right thing. As your experience of using this model grows, so will your intuitive choice.

Our focus is on the stream of information that flows within the memoragination, which we can partition into three elements, the past, present and future. If you examine other therapeutic approaches you'll find that often their focus is mostly in just one or two of these areas. For example, Behaviourism, and to a large degree Cognitive Behavioural Therapy and Brief Strategic Therapy, focus on the present. Positive Psychology focuses on being mindful in the present and imagining a positive outcome. Gestalt Therapy is predominantly present focused, Freudian approaches tends to be more about the client's past, and traditional hypnotherapy on making suggestions about their future. In Cognitive Hypnotherapy we utilise all three, in differing proportions, according to the client.

On many occasions, a treatment plan of ours will include some regression, either to open a closed loop by reframing the negative emotion out of it, or using smds to do the same thing, or to utilise past positives as new hubs for the brain to begin to use to anticipate the future. A resource for the client to use in the present, such as an anchor will probably be included too, and in all cases, Wordweaving™ will be used to prime the unconscious to bring to the client's attention evidence for their solution state, and to make the work done in each session be the cause of their movement towards their outcome.

While in general all three parts of the memoragination will be explored at some point, with some clients this will not be true, because some techniques simply won't suit them or have the desired affect. It's a continuing fascination how some techniques, no matter how well delivered, work wonderfully for one client, but simply bounce off the walls of the reality tunnel of another.

One of the reasons for this is, I think, to do with some having a strong preference for where they look within their memoragination for evidence of their improvement. After a session is over, the client returns to the world and gets on with their day. How will they know that they are better? For some it will be because they begin to notice things during their day that feel better. For others it might be when they muse about old events that used to bug them and realise that they no longer do. And for others it might be when they imagine an upcoming event and feel comfortable about it, where in the past it would have made them anxious. For most of us it's likely that we're a balanced mix of each, which is why I said earlier that most treatment plans will cover all three bases, but some will be strongly biased towards one.

Where that's the case, the best time line in the world is likely to leave a present or future oriented client unchanged, just as a present focused intervention like Dropthrough won't make a huge difference to the belief of a past focused person. The secret, as is so often the case, is to listen to where the client puts most attention when telling you about their history. Most will tell you most about where they tend to focus - past people about their childhoods, present people about their week, and future people about how they can't see themselves ever getting better.

Inception can be achieved from any part of the memoragination, so use that information to influence your choice of technique and you're likely to have fewer occasions when your interventions fail to work.

Overall, using the Cascade Model within a client's memoragination, and basing your choices on what you train yourself to hear within the client's unique way of representing their world to themselves will bring you to the place that Bruce Lee described as 'the stage of artlessness'. Your understanding of the underlying principles becomes so intuitive that your understanding of why you make the choices you do will begin to blur, and, at some point, what I hope you will feel in your therapy is...you leaving. What I mean by that is, ultimately, to paraphrase Clarke Maxwell, what is done by you feels done by something greater than you in yourself. This is the emergence of your genius.

Finding something greater than you in yourself

A number of recent books have examined what makes a genius, and in general they treat genius as something that a person is - as in "Hawking is a genius". This is different from the use of the word in ancient times, which I much prefer. To the Greeks and Romans genius was a spirit or energy that resided in all things, and from which objects, creatures and people derived their special qualities - for example Julius Caesar's gift for oratory was attributed to his family 'genius'. This is more what I mean by my use of the word. I believe that everybody has a genius - an unconscious potential or gift, if you like. I think many people spend their lives with the feeling that there is something greater within them than their life is expressing, and to me that is their awareness of the restlessness of this untapped resource.

My particular genius has found its best expression in therapy and teaching – far from where I consciously directed my first career. Looking back now it first made an appearance when I was twenty-five years old. I gave my first presentation to a group when I was on a course for newly promoted Sergeants and we had to give a talk on a religion of our choice. I chose Taoism. I became aware during the talk of the feeling of losing myself in the act of communicating with the audience - I now recognise it as a trance - and when I emerged I became aware of a similar state in many in the group, a kind of communal connection. I had this feeling of something deeply significant having happened but, being the person I was back then, I waited for someone else to recognise it and do something with it. I now recognise it as an early flexing of my genius, and my limitations at that time led me to entice it back into slumber for another seven years.

But when I look back I realise that it was always there. I always had a fascination for why people did what they did, and a knack for knowing peoples' weaknesses – my first bit of therapy was when I was seven. I told my Nan that the reason she did the kind acts she told everyone about was for selfish reasons – they made her feel good about herself. I seem to remember a clip round the ear was my first payment. In my early years I used my talent more to hurt people and gain power over them than to help them. It's why becoming a therapist has helped me become a better person – when you are given the privilege of being allowed into someone's mind there is always something to love there, which makes it hard not to believe in the potential of everyone you meet - and in your own. It's why I think there is no better purpose in life than to find the place where your genius can come out to play – and if you can make a living with it so much the better – you'll never feel like you're working again. I think the luckiest people in the world are those who find the place where their genius can be released. The great minds are good examples, as are (in my opinion) people like Lennon and McCartney, Michaelangelo, George Best and Eddie Izzard.

To see genius as a thing you have, rather than a thing you are, means that we can see 'geniuses' make human errors without it diminishing our view of their talent. As I write this, Tiger Woods is being publicly eviscerated for his infidelity. The standards set by a genius in its groove are not the standards we should measure the owner of it outside of that groove – it's why we so often end up disillusioned by our heroes.

It can feel very un-British to talk of ourselves as having a genius, but once you understand the root of how I'm using it you'll realise it has nothing to do with ego in any way. I have a genius, but in some situations I'm a complete numpty. Who tries to open a champagne bottle with a knife?

While stumbling across therapy and teaching instantly felt as if I'd made it home after a long journey, it took years before I fully had the sense of my talent not being about my 'I'. When the penny dropped I allowed my 'me' to take over my therapy and my training, and it transformed both. In most respects this book is a conscious observation of the patterns my unconscious has evolved to use. In *Outliers* Malcolm Gladwell suggests that it takes 10,000 hours of practice to become a genius.[95] I think that 10,000 hours is the time it takes for your genius to feed, and learn, and mature. Not for you to *be* one, but for you to *have* one.

Developing the full potential of your genius will bring you to the stage of artlessness that Bruce Lee spoke of, and it's not easy. It requires the commitment to feed your genius at every opportunity. It will not come quickly, and you must be prepared to fail in order to learn to succeed. It requires recognition that what we tend to call our 'ego' - and which in this book I've called our selfplex - has no place in therapy, because 'it' isn't the part of you that's getting the results, so you have to be prepared to step away and let your genius take over. Developing your genius goes completely against the current zeitgeist that says you can be a 'Master' of something in a weekend, or be a world class singer just by standing in front of Simon Cowell.

The idea of being 'self-less' with a client can be a difficult thing to do because we can be so wedded to wanting to feel good through our 'making people better' (notice the TAOTM attribution). So many therapists are unsuccessful because they are doing therapy as therapy for themselves, needing the admiration or gratitude of their clients in order to feel better or more worthwhile. Notice that this is just another manifestation of Gil's 'universal neurosis', that we're not loved. It comes from being in protection, not growth. Using therapy as a means to fill that hole is doomed to failure. Seeking anything from the outside that will do that always is. For those who dare to take the step of treating each session as a mystery that will be revealed by your interaction, like the meeting of two travellers who share what they have to help one of them on the next stage of their journey, such a withdrawal of responsibility can be a wonderful freedom because if it isn't your selfplex doing the therapy, then its outcome has no impact on your selfplex-esteem. Who you are and what you do are not tied together in a way that leaves you vulnerable to the opinion of others. And you will find that by abandoning therapy as a means of gaining anything from it for your 'self', you inevitably will: you'll find growth.

This is the alchemy of therapy, whereby the bringing together of two forces leaves both transformed. And it is within the journey to find what lies beneath the techniques you employ that you will find the full expression of your genius, and the true brilliance of simplicity. This model, and I suppose the book as a whole, is intended as a guidebook for that journey, knowing that the destination is beyond anything that can be described in words.

Inconclusion

Ernest Dowd, in the USA, and I independently began using the term *Cognitive Hypnotherapy* around the same time, he with the release of his book, and me with the launch of the first Diploma Course in the subject. From the beginning we have meant different things by the term. His was predominantly the addition of traditional hypnosis to CBT approaches, and that has tended to be the case with Cognitive Hypnotherapy in North America ever since. In the UK and Europe, what you have read here has been the dominant development. If I had my time again I may have chosen a different label for what I've described here, but I've just googled the term and came up with 94,000 hits, with the approach described in this book dominating the results, so the genie is out of the bottle and it will be left to market forces to determine which meme comes to represent the term in the minds of the public and the therapy profession.

What I hope for this meme is coherence and cohesion. If people begin to develop variations of the version described in this book, such as Transpersonal Cognitive Hypnotherapy, Humanistic Cognitive Hypnotherapy or - shoot me now - 'somebody's name' Cognitive Hypnotherapy, or to describe themselves as using Cognitive Hypnotherapy *and* Counselling/NLP/Jungian Analysis etc., then I will have failed in making my central point, which is that this isn't a new therapy, it's a way of using *all* therapy. In the spirit of Bruce Lee, the framework of the problem pattern and solution state provides a means to describe everything that works from every other branch of psychotherapy, and a rationale of what to use from which approach at what point of treatment, with which client. Any variation to the model should happen within the model, so that it grows organically, not be the parent of hybrids.

I'm passionate about this point because the history of psychotherapy and counselling has been one of continual fracturing. It sometimes feels there was barely a disciple of Freud who didn't abandon or adapt his ideas to name an approach after themselves, Jungian and Adlerian approaches being just two. Such were the schisms that the Neo-Freudians probably outnumbered the Freudians within a generation. Sadly psychotherapy, hypnotherapy and counselling have continued in the same vein. Every new idea or technique has quickly had a fence erected around it, and only the acolytes of that particular temple are allowed access to its secrets. Even NLP, an approach that focuses on the subjective nature of our experience and uses models that it stresses are not true, just useful, has splintered into different factions, most claiming the superiority of their model. For me, this has left the field in a state of protection masquerading as growth, and that's a tragedy.

Claiming that a single approach is better than another flies in the face of the simple truth that no one approach works on everybody. What is true is that every therapy works on somebody, so what I'm striving for is a model which makes available everything to everybody: the *techniques* of Gestalt, CBT, Psychosynthesis, Transactional Analysis, EMDR, NLP, EFT and every other approach you can think of, can all be described as either context, structure, process or consequence interventions. In other words, you can fit each of these therapies into Cognitive Hypnotherapy, but you can't fit Cognitive Hypnotherapy into any one of them. I dislike the word because of its overuse in the NLP world, but it is a *meta-model*, which means a model that describes other models and creates or describes relationships between them. To think of it as being superior to any other form is to misunderstand its nature: as I just said, it isn't a therapy in itself, it's a way of organising your thoughts about all therapy.

It may turn out that, in time, we will discover a single, unifying truth that cures all ills, or the truth may be that we will always need an approach tuned to the uniqueness of the individual. In either case, it seems to me that the best way of finding it is by uniting in the quest, not by fighting to own the sole rights to treat particular conditions. Therapy is a mission, not a competition.

My abiding hope in developing Cognitive Hypnotherapy is to change the landscape of our profession: to replace fences with open space, to nurture the garden instead of fighting over the turf; to begin a reunification that returns the purpose of changework – personal empowerment – to the people as a central part of their education and their life. I told you I was an optimist.

To stay in growth this model must remain fluid. If something useful comes along that can't be described in terms of the model, then the model must be changed, and that change must be based on evidence of its efficacy. In 100 years time, Cognitive Hypnotherapy may be almost unrecognisable from what is contained in this book, but this philosophy should still be at its heart, with, "It works" as the sole reason for the inclusion of any part of it. And the knowledge that in a hundred years what we consider cutting edge will, in all likelihood, be thought of as we do blood-letting with leeches, should keep us humble.

A book begins with an empty page, and it begins to finish with one too. I spent quite some time staring at this particular empty page, wondering what to write here. When a book has taken up so much time and space in your head, knowing how to bring it to a conclusion should not only be a relief but obvious. It wasn't. But what I realised after staring into space is that, for a book whose central premise is the need for constant uncertainty, no conclusion should be drawn because Cognitive Hypnotherapy, to be true to itself, needs to be a constant work in progress. The end of this book is only a beginning, so perhaps it's appropriate for this particular book to end as I began it, with one small addition:

"Therapy should be a unified field bound by a communal curiosity about what can make us more skilled at being human. That's what I want Cognitive Hypnotherapy to be about; permanent revolution driven by curiosity, united by uncertainty, guided by evidence, and always in a state of growth."

This book has been a journey that, by writing it, has changed me, and I hope has inspired you to join us in our quest.

Appendix One

What is Wordweaving™?

NEURO-LOGICAL LEVELS

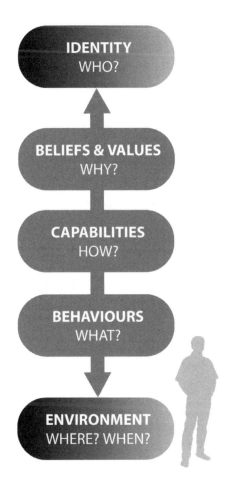

IDENTITY
WHO?

BELIEFS & VALUES
WHY?

CAPABILITIES
HOW?

BEHAVIOURS
WHAT?

ENVIRONMENT
WHERE? WHEN?

Wordweaving™ began with a simple question: What makes a hypnotic suggestion work? It turned out to be the kind of *Alice in Wonderland* question that sucks you down the rabbit hole. My initial training in hypnotherapy hadn't strayed far from the traditional model that trance renders people open to suggestion, the deeper the better, and then you deliver suggestions calculated to relieve the person's problem. I quickly found that reading the same script to different people had varying effects, and that trance depth – as far as I could observe it – had little to do with whether it worked or not. I got to the point where I thought that suggestions only worked on the suggestible, so actually felt I was cheating if 'all' I did with a client was read them a script.

Stumbling across NLP increased my discontent. It opened my eyes to the differences in the way people think and the way we each create our own 'model of the world'. With so many levels of difference between one person and another, how can one script possibly work on everyone whose only connection might be the problem they share?

Milton Erickson made an early impression. The idea of the client having all the resources they need to solve their own problems really appealed, as did his indirect way of making suggestions. The Milton Model was a starting point, but it was only a beginning, because I noticed that many therapists using it were certainly vague, but hardly artful. Surely suggestions had to have some point?

Years of clients helped me with this. I evolved a model that worked well at mapping the process of a client's problem (the Matrix Model). This enabled me as a therapist to accurately map a client's problem as it happened from beginning to end and guide what techniques and suggestions to use.

A slight variation of Robert Dilt's Neuro-logical levels provided me with a second way of thinking about where I wanted to aim a suggestion – i.e., where the unconscious could be guided to seek an effect of what you were saying. So, the first part of Wordweaving™ emerged, with a 'rule' to guide it, "Every suggestion pattern must be aimed at a point in the Matrix model or a Neuro-logical level."

The next step of my journey involved a book called *Trances People Live*, by psychotherapist Steven Wolinsky. Reading it turned my practice upside down. In a nutshell, Wolinsky suggested that trance states are part of everyday life – nothing new to me so far – but then made the point that problems are part of everyday life too, so trance phenomena form part of the way a client creates and perceives their issue. I quickly found that clients described their problems in ways that could be described by the standard trance phenomena – things like sensory distortion, age progression and positive hallucination. It came to me that there was a link between these phenomena and what Bandler and Grinder had described as 'universal modelling processes' – deletion, distortion and generalisation; what the mind does with information it receives through the senses in order to create the model of the world each person lives in. This to me was tremendously exciting. Trance phenomena became the means by which the client's mind created the perception of their problem, so a core element of any suggestion pattern had to be one or more trance phenomena – without them you were painting without any paint. Thus the next 'rule' of Wordweaving™, every suggestion pattern must contain a trance phenomenon. And, if you can, use the ones the client uses to create their issue – because you know they're ones they're good at. All you have to do is learn to listen for them.

The third aspect to Wordweaving™ is simply how you couch the suggestion. My preference is to use indirect language – particularly presuppositions – because they guide the client to find their own solutions. Direct suggestions tend to involve the therapist's model of the world in the solution the suggestion is aimed at, which I don't think is as good as using the client's. Also, by the use of the form, "you will…" the situation may be created where, if the instruction isn't fulfilled, everything else that the therapeutic relationship has created could be negated i.e., 'if that suggestion hasn't worked, what else hasn't?'

Consequently, a lot of the focus of Wordweaving™ training is improving the ability to utilise indirect language patterns – but for a purpose: to deliver appropriate trance phenomena to a particular part of their problem pattern in order to change the client's perception of that problem. With practice it is perfectly possible to be able to create such patterns spontaneously, based on the information you have gained from the client. Essentially, that is what *Volume I: The Science of Suggestion* is about – the model of Wordweaving™ and how to build suggestions in this way.

Trackdown

What was your favourite story, film, or game when you were growing up ?

Describe your understanding of the story or theme.

What is your favourite book or film now?

What are the similarities in the two stories ?

What are the similarities between those things the two have in common and your own life so far ?

What do you think your mother didn't like about you when you were growing up ?

What do you think your father didn't like about you when you were growing up ?

What didn't you like about them?

Look at yourself as others see you. How would they say you are like your mother and father?

How would you finish these three sentences......

I am OK if.......

I am OK when.....

I am not OK when.....

How are the things that you have written above linked to the themes in your favourite story and film ?

How could you use them as a basis for change?

Appendix Three

The Psychobiology of Belief

Originally this was a chapter, but I couldn't fit it into the narrative of the theory in a way that didn't make it dominate, and in doing so run the risk of driving away some of the people who might benefit from the rest of the book. It provides a model of mind-to-body communication that for me is compelling, but obviously unproven. I decided to include it for those who would appreciate it, but in a place where it could be ignored by those who are more comfortable doing so. It remains just another meme that will survive the competition, or not. Enjoy!

'Mr Wright' was going to die. He was suffering from an advanced cancer of the lymph nodes and had reached the stage where he had become resistant to all known palliative treatment. It was the mid 1950s and everything that could be done, had been. He had huge tumours the size of oranges in his neck, groin and stomach and his spleen and liver were huge.

Despite this Mr Wright hadn't given up hope. He had read in a newspaper about 'Krebiozen', a new wonder drug that he believed was going to be like the seventh cavalry, riding over the hill to save the day. And, sure enough, the clinic he was in was chosen by the Medical Association as one of the hundred places where the drug was to be evaluated.

However, the fly in the ointment was that Mr Wright's condition was considered too advanced for him to be eligible for the trial as he had a prognosis of no more than two weeks. That should have been that, but his enthusiasm was such that he persuaded his doctor, against his better judgement and the rules of the trial, to include him.

Injections were given three times weekly and began on a Friday. The doctor didn't see him again until the Monday and was astonished at what he found. When last seen Mr Wright had been gasping for breath and completely bedridden, but now he was wandering around the ward chatting to people. Yet only he had improved, others on the trial were either unchanged or had changed for the worse. When examined, in the words of his doctor, his tumours had "melted like snowballs on a hot stove, and in only these few days, were half their original size". Within ten days Mr Wright was able to be discharged from his 'death-bed' with practically all of his symptoms gone.

Sadly, within two months of the trial beginning, all the clinics were reporting that Krebiozen was having no effect (it has since been shown to be an inert and useless treatment, although some alternative clinics still offer it), and this was reported in the press. As the evidence grew, Mr Wright grew increasingly despondent and, after two months of health he relapsed to his original state. At this point the doctor did an amazing thing. Utilising his patient's innate optimism, he lied to him. He told Mr Wright that the papers were wrong, the drug was showing signs of being very promising. The reason for his relapse was that the drug deteriorated if left standing. A new 'super-refined double-strength' product had been produced that could reproduce the original effect.

The next day, and with much fanfare, the injection of the new drug was administered. It was actually water, and yet his recovery was even more remarkable than the first occasion. The tumours disappeared, his breathing normalised, he could walk again, and even returned to flying. He remained symptom-free for a further two months. At this point the AMA announced to the press "Nationwide tests show Krebiozen to be a worthless drug in the treatment of cancer." Mr Wright died within seven days of it appearing in the press (1957 report by psychologist Bruno Klopfer of the University of California, Los Angeles, entitled "Psychological Variables in Human Cancer").

Placebo: That Voodoo You Do

The placebo effect is the term given to the phenomenon whereby people respond to a substance pretending to be a drug as if it is the drug itself. In other words, if we believe we're being given a drug we'll respond as if we have. In fact, some people have got better from surgery when all the surgeon did was open them and then stitch them back up. The statistics to support this ability are really quite remarkable. In nine double-blind studies comparing placebos to aspirin, placebos proved to be as effective 54% of the time. You might expect it to fare less well against something stronger, like morphine, but it's not the case. In six double-blind studies the placebo was 56% as effective as morphine. Ernest Rossi has highlighted this percentage: (http://www.wrf.org/alternative-therapies/power-of-mind-placebo.php)

"In other words, the effectiveness of placebo compared to standard doses of different analgesic drugs under double-blind circumstances seems to be relatively constant...it is worth noting that this 56% effectiveness ration is not limited to placebo versus analgesic drugs. It is also found in double-blind studies of non-pharmacolgical insomnia treatment techniques (58% from 14 studies) and psychotropic drugs for the treatment of depression such as tricyclics (59% from 93 studies reviewed by Morris & Beck, 1974) and lithium (62% from 13 studies reviewed in Marini, Sheard, Bridges and Wagner, 1976). Thus, it appears that placebo is about 55-60% as effective as active medications irrespective of the potency of these active medications." (The Psychobiology of Mind-Body Healing)

There is an interesting psychology behind factors which influence the degree of effect. For example, blue sugar pills are less effective than red ones, and the smaller the pill the more effective it is deemed to be. Inter-personal factors include the relationship between doctor and patient, the level of confidence the patient has in the doctor, and the confidence felt by the doctor administering the placebo (presumably in the placebo effect). So the mind appears to be a potent factor in the healing process; evidence that mind can effect matter. And not always for the better.

In the 1970s 'Sam Shoeman' was diagnosed with end-stage liver cancer and given just months to live. As many do, he stuck obligingly to the timetable of his prognosis and died. And yet when the autopsy was performed it showed that the doctors were wrong; the tumour was tiny and hadn't spread. "He hadn't died from cancer, but from believing he was dying from cancer", says Dr Clifton Meador, who studies examples of what are called 'nocebos', the ability of the mind to produce a negative effect. "If everyone treats you as if you are dying, you buy into it. Everything in your whole being becomes about dying."[96]

If everyone treats you as if you are dying, you buy into it. Everything in your whole being becomes about dying

There are many studies that support this. One found that women who believed they are particularly prone to heart attack are nearly four times as likely to die from coronary conditions than other women with the same risk factors. And beliefs can be caught from other people. In 1998, in a Tennessee high school a teacher noticed a 'gasoline-type' smell and began complaining of nausea, headaches, dizziness and shortness of breath. The school was evacuated and over the next week more than 100 staff and students were admitted to hospital complaining of similar symptoms. However, after extensive tests no medical explanation was found, and no toxin found in the school. The factors that linked the people together was that they were more likely to be female, and knew, or had seen, a classmate who was ill. Nocebo can be passed to others as a meme!

I believe that this is all hugely important. Professor Robert Cialdini is probably the world's leading investigator into what factors influence our decision making, and he found that two of the most powerful are what he calls *social proof* - we are strongly persuaded by the actions of others (and the more the better), and *consistency* - we seek to retain a coherent sense of ourselves, so once we adopt a point of view, we act to remain consistent with it. Our personal environment - the people we mix with - will be a powerful influence on our behaviour and sense of self, and once we react to something, we'll largely act in a way that remains consistent with it.

A well-known example is where a group of students were gathered and told that they'd been selected because they were the most talented group of students in their state and were to be taught by the most able teachers. The teachers were told they had been selected because of their abilities, and were to teach the most gifted of students. As you might expect, this bunch of eggheads outperformed everybody else in their SATS. It was only after the results were released that it was revealed that both teachers and students had been selected at random from an average group. It was their collective belief in what they had been told about themselves and those with them that caused the surge in their performance.

The beliefs we hold can increase our intelligence and have a physical effect on our bodies. But where exactly does mind meet matter? Where does thought actually manage to create a physical response? Bruce Lipton might have provided a model that answers that.

The Biology of Belief

I mentioned Bruce Lipton earlier in the book in relation to growth and protection. He is an American geneticist who worked for a time as a researcher and teacher at Stamford University. As such he was steeped in the received wisdom of mainstream biology. In fact, as a teacher, he was a purveyor of it, until he had an epiphany.

There exists in cellular biology something called *the Central Dogma*. Now dogma is a strange word to use in science because its definition goes something like, 'a specific tenet or doctrine authoritatively laid down, as by a church.' It suggests something not open to question, a received truth, and Lipton makes much of this title, claiming it made him realise, as a lecturer in cellular biology, that he was teaching religion, not science. The term was actually coined by Francis Crick, the co-discoverer of DNA, who later had this to say about his choice:

"As it turned out, the use of the word dogma caused almost more trouble than it was worth.... Many years later Jacques Monod pointed out to me that I did not appear to understand the correct use of the word dogma, which is a belief that cannot be doubted. I did apprehend this in a vague sort of way but since I thought that all religious beliefs were without foundation, I used the word the way I myself thought about it, not as most of the world does, and simply applied it to a grand hypothesis that, however plausible, had little direct experimental support."[97]

So the label was a mistake, but, as is so often the case, it has tended to be viewed as a truth by many in the field. But not by all, and Lipton isn't alone in his resistance to it being thought of as a settled truth. So what is the central dogma? That DNA controls its own replication and acts as the blueprint for the body's proteins.

According to the dogma, the flow of information is from the DNA, to the RNA, to the protein, it can't flow the other way. Nucleic Acid (DNA and RNA) instructs proteins, proteins can't instruct nucleic acid. The premise is that, because the nature of its proteins defines the character of a living organism, and the proteins are encoded by the DNA, then logically DNA is the primary determinant of an organisms traits - physically and mentally.

This is the wellspring from which flows the idea of genetic determinism that dominates so much of popular opinion. Barely a week goes by without the press reporting the discovery of a gene that *causes* cancer, or homosexuality, or even a belief in God. Psychologically I can quite see that acceptance of the concept leads to a helpless position where what happens to you is outside of your control – 'It's not my fault I'm fat, thin, lazy or violent, it's in my genes'.

Lipton contends that this isn't just the popularly held view of the way things are, it's also the prevailing view within biology. As an outsider, and a non-scientist, looking in, I haven't found the evidence to support this. Certainly the idea of genetic determinism is present – because it does exist. Certain genes do predict the existence of certain conditions, such as Cystic Fibrosis and some cancers. But there seems to be a strong presence of scientists within the field who acknowledge other factors beyond the central dogma that exist and influence the growth and behaviour of an organism. It might be that Lipton is guilty of disambiguation – otherwise known as the straw man argument - where you propose a point of view your opponent doesn't actually hold, and by destroying that point of view enhance your own. If so, I think it's more in order to be heard to an audience whose attention he's trying to gain, than to hide any weakness in his own argument, but I'll let you be the judge of that.

To understand his hypothesis I had to begin with the basics; what's the difference between DNA, genes and chromosomes? You can see how much of a scientist I'm not, can't you?

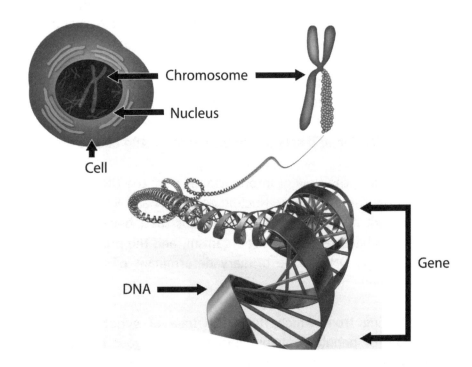

In a nutshell, the answer is that DNA is the smallest element of the three. It contains four molecules called 'bases' that combine in different ways to encode the information the DNA carries.

Genes are sequences of DNA that interact with each other to influence physical development and behaviour.

Finally, chromosomes are very long, continuous pieces of DNA (a single DNA molecule), which contain many genes, enveloped in a package of proteins. Every human cell contains 46 chromosomes (23 pairs).

Also contained within the cell are thousands of different proteins. In many ways they can be thought of as engine parts, each with a different job to do to make the engine work, and also combining in different ways to change the function of the cell. Genes are a protein library – a blueprint for making proteins.

Because the nucleus of a cell contains its DNA, and the DNA is responsible for the creation of proteins, it seems to be the general consensus within biology that the nucleus acts as the brain of the cell. This is the place where Lipton begins to swim away from the mainstream.

He cites experiments he performed that demonstrated that cells continue to function normally after the removal of the nucleus, only eventually wearing out from the inability to manufacture new proteins. He considers the membrane of the cell to be the brain, and has a detailed model for how it interacts with environmental signals to cause the genes to be expressed. And this is the crux of his argument that concerns us as therapists, namely that genes aren't self-emergent - they don't do things of their own volition, a signal from the environment has to turn them on.

Epigenetics is the study of molecular mechanisms by which the environment controls gene activity, and it has established that DNA blueprints passed down from our parents at birth are not set in concrete. Other influences from the environment, including nutrition, stress and emotions can modify these genes, without changing the basic blueprint. These modifications can themselves be passed on to future generations. Research (see wiki epigenetics) has shown that paternal grandsons of Swedish boys who were exposed during preadolescence to famine in the 19th century were less likely to die of cardiovascular disease, yet if food was plentiful then diabetes mortality in the grandchildren increased. Not only does this seem to contradict the Central Dogma, but also traditional Darwinism, which suggests that evolution takes many generations to have an effect. It appears that evolution can happen from one generation to the next, and that it is in response to environmental factors.

The primacy of the environment

Lipton reverses the Central Dogma by suggesting that it is the environment that causes genes to act. Essentially, environmental signals pass their message through the cell membrane via receptor and effector proteins which cause a gene to be read – the gene is covered by what is called a regulatory protein until the environmental signal tells it to expose the gene, allowing it to be copied. This model he calls the

Primacy of the Environment. Gene activity does not happen unless something in the environment requires it to. At a micro level the signals we're talking about are things like neurotransmitters and peptides, but at a macro level we're talking about everything that comes through our senses, and from our minds.

If you think back to Part 1.3 when I described algorithms as the mechanism of evolution I said:

"Complex biological systems possess many layers of physical structures, from DNA-to genes-to proteins-to organs/bones/hair, so, in Montague's words, "it's information processing all the way down" and, because Turing's model suggests that the mind emerges from the biological structure of the brain, it's information processing all the way up from cell to thought."

Our thoughts are information that is transmitted to our cells, and our thoughts are information transmitted from our cells

The neurotransmitters that cause a gene to be read are information carriers, the end of a journey for that information that began when it met our senses, was filtered through them, and then our belief systems, until the meaning it was given caused its onward flow into the body as a call to action, all the way down to the level of the cells. The combined cellular response is...us, living, breathing and acting on the world. Our thoughts are information that is transmitted *to* our cells, and our thoughts are information transmitted *from* our cells. We are part of a ceaseless cycle of information flow where talk of a mind/body connection becomes meaningless; each is a seamless part of the other.

If our thoughts are part of the information stream that causes our genes to be switched on, then Deepak Chopra was right when he said, "every cell is eavesdropping on your conversations." Here could be the source of the placebo and nocebo effect. Here could be the beginning of a clearer way of realising the power of human potential. Your thoughts can create you.

Lipton's model suggests that our cells respond to messages from our environment that causes the DNA within them to be expressed in order for the response to be possible. At the level of the cell the form of this message is in the shape of neurotransmitters, peptides and hormones. At the level of the organism the message is anything that causes our senses to pass the message on to the processing areas of the brain. Now, if our brain creates 80% of our awareness of the environment that our cells respond to, doesn't that sound like a mind/body connection? It's a big point, so let me reiterate it.

Every response to the world is ultimately occurring at the cellular level. The world we respond to is largely a projection created by the computations of our brain. Therefore, our thoughts are the major events that our cells respond to.

According to Lipton only 5% of cancers are genetically determined, which means that, potentially at least, 95% of cancers are caused by a reaction to our environment – or to ourselves. His work points tantalisingly toward a situation where your beliefs create the state of your body - for better or worse, as much as the state of your world, for better or worse.

If we can change our beliefs we control our destiny.

So can we? If our beliefs are simply the emergent consensus of a series of our experiences which are stored as memory loops, you bet we can.

The story so far

The thoughts you have can change your biology. Your thoughts can create both wellness and illness – can keep you in growth or protection. And you can choose your thoughts...

Learning resources

Cognitive Hypnotherapy is a growing school of thought, and we're committed to bringing the best information and training in it that we possibly can.

At the time of publication there is already an online certification course in Wordweaving™ available on our website www.questinstitute.co.uk, and more trainings, downloads, and resources are in development, so please take a regular look.

You can also subscribe to Trevor's blog there, which he uses as a major way of letting people know about the latest developments in the field.

Details of the Quest Institute Diploma in Cognitive Hypnotherapy, which includes NLP Practitioner certification, are also to be found there.

Glossary

A

Active Agent
In the context of this book, the feeling we can have as humans of being the cause of the things that happen to us. The belief that we have free will is an example of this.

Age regression
Trance phenomena during which attention is focussed on a past experience

Age Progression
Trance phenomena during which attention is focussed on a possible future experience

Algorithm
A set of rules or instructions for solving a problem in a finite number of steps

Algorithms of the mind (TAOTM)
The three ways the mind assesses information flowing through the senses by matching it against information stored in the memory; cause and effect (this is because of that), complex equivalence (this is the same as that), and this is different to that.

Amnesia
Trance phenomena which causes a block to recall of a particular piece of information

Amygdala
A part of the limbic system thought to be responsible for fear and anger responses. LeDoux believes memories connected to these emotions may be stored in this location.

Anchor
Linking a stimulus to an emotional response. Anchors can be physical - applying pressure to a knuckle, but work in any modality. Linking a smell to a positive state, for example.

Aspergers Syndrome
A milder form of autism characterised by social isolation and eccentric behaviour

Association
Where a person experiences a thought as if through their own eyes, often with the full emotional connections associated with the thought.

B

Barabasi's Law
A theory developed by Laszlo Barabasi that describes the two key factors in making a network scale-free. In Cognitive Hypnotherapy it is suggested that memory loops are organised as such a network and so conform to his law.

Behaviour
Neuro logical level that describes the actions we take, corresponds to the Response stage of the Matrix model

Beliefs
Neuro logical level. Things we take to be true that order our model of the world

Biological imperative
What is taken to be the core drive of every organism on the planet - the urge to survive.

Butterfly effect
The popular name given to the phenomenon first noticed by Edward Lorenz that, in a complex system, small changes can later have a large effect. So called because of the analogy that if a butterfly flaps its wings in the Amazon it could cause a storm three weeks later in Australia.

C

Calculation Gap
Term used by the author to describe the processing space between information arriving in the brain from our senses and our becoming consciously aware of it. It is within this unconscious space that the conditions for personal change exist.

Calculations
Term used in Cognitive Hypnotherapy to describe the action of the brain when contemplating possibilities based on previously stored meanings.

Capabilities
Neuro logical level that describes a person's strengths, resources, abilities

Cascade model
Developed by the author to guide therapy through the use of the two simple questions of the title ("what's that about?" and "how do I use it?").

Catharsis
A Freudian term usually taken to mean the purging or relieving of emotions - usually by their strong expression. Reconsolidation theory suggests this would actually have the effect of making them stronger.

Causality
The relationship of cause and effect. The principle that nothing can happen without being caused.

Cause and Effect
The concept that an action or event will produce a certain response to the action in the form of another event. Present in Cognitive Hypnotherapy as one of the algorithms of the mind, and in NLP as part of the meta and Milton models

Change-Link Pattern
A Wordweaving™ pattern that links the client's evidence of improvement in their experience to its continuation

Chaos theory
The study of unpredictable and complex dynamic systems - like the weather - that are highly sensitive to small changes in conditions. In this book it is suggested that the brain - as a complex system - is subject to chaos theory. See Butterfly effect.

Closed loop learning (or 'closed loops')
See single loop learning

Cognitive Hypnotherapy
A therapeutic approach that combines ideas drawn from Cognitive Theory, Evolutionary Psychology, NLP and uses a theory of trance states proposed by Steven Wolinsky within the approach to suggestion developed by the author (Wordweaving™) to create a brief therapy model

Cognitive Theory
Concerns itself with how we form our perceptions – how we come to know. Has at its heart the idea that we are all scientists devising and testing theories about how the world works.

Complex Equivalence
Used in Cognitive Hypnotherapy to describe one of the three algorithms of the mind (A=B). Where one thing is taken to be the same as, or have the same qualities as, another. In NLP one of the Milton and meta model patterns.

Computational Theory of Mind (CTOM)
The view that the human mind should be conceived as an information processing system and that thought is a form of computation.

Consequence
One of the four categories that form a client's problem pattern; The hallucination of the future imagined as a result of a present situation, itself based on past experiences that are deemed similar.

Consolidation
The process by which incidents are committed to long-term memory.

Context
One of the four categories that form a problem pattern; the circumstances within which a problem occurs (or doesn't) and the history behind its formation.

Cortex (cerebral)
The furrowed outer layer of grey matter in the cerebrum of the brain associated with higher brain functions.

Counterfactuals
In the context of this book the idea of the brain running 'as if' scenarios, exploring what could, would, or might (or their opposites) as a consequence of matches made between information present in a current situation, and information stored in our past.

D

Deletions
One of Bandler and Grinder's universal modelling processes – how the mind filters

information flowing through the senses and refines it from 2 million bits of information down to 7±2. Deletion refers to the removal by the unconscious of information from conscious awareness.

Difference threshold
A term used in psychology to describe the level of change in perceived information required for an observer to become aware of that change.

Dissociation
A trance phenomenon where our subjective experience is that of observing, either something we're doing, something we're thinking, or some future action we're taking. A detached, unemotional state. Also a term used to describe the observation of any part of our body or behaviour as independent of our self.

Distortions
One of Bandler and Grinder's universal modelling processes - how the mind interprets information flowing through the senses to make it what it expects to be. Why we mistake strangers walking down the street for friends.

Dogmation
A word invented by the author to describe the situation where the clinging to of a particular orthodoxy has led to a state of protection - i.e. nil real growth. A combination of dogma and stagnation. Who knows, it may catch on.

Dopamine
A neurotransmitter which helps regulate emotion and movement, and appears to be the chemical that 'rewards' us for taking approved actions.

Drivers
Those submodalities which are the key to the meaning given to an internal representation. The difference that makes a difference.

E

ELOC (External Locus Of Control)
Where a person looks to the outside world for their solutions and holds others responsible for their wellbeing - or lack of it. They are at 'Effect' in their world - things are always happening **to** them. The opposite of ILOC, where the person in that position is happening **to** the things. ELOC is the position most clients occupy in

the beginning of treatment. ILOC is a key thing to develop in them for change to be self-sustaining.

Emergent property
Something that is a quality of a system, without it being the purpose of it, and which requires all parts of the system for it to be present. The intelligence of a bee hive is an emergent quality of that system; no single bee possesses it, and it is a means by which an effect is arrived at (honey, and the growth of the hive) – not an effect in itself. Our sense of self could be an emergent property.

Emotion
A mental state that arises spontaneously rather than through conscious effort and is often accompanied by physiological changes. The third stage of the Matrix model, it being emotion which drives us to act.

Environment
Our surroundings. Within Cognitive Hypnotherapy's interpretation of Neuro logical levels, everything that is not mental (i.e. includes the body).

Evaluation
Last step of the Matrix model process. The mind compares the result of the process it's just run against the purpose it was originally designed for.

Evolutionary Psychology
The study of the psychological adaptations of humans to the changing physical and social environment, especially of changes in brain structure, cognitive mechanisms, and behavioural differences among individuals.

G

Generalisation
One of Bandler and Grinder's universal modelling processes – where we take an experience and use it to represent the entire category of which the experience is an example. Closely involved in belief creation and predicting consequence.

Global brain theory
In this book refers to Edelman's model of brain function he calls TNGS (Theory of Neuronal Group Selection) which suggests that the brain uses different patterns of neurons to create the same effect/thought (I have greatly over-simplified here).

Google-juice
A term coined to describe how, on the internet, if my website is connected to a high-ranking site, it causes some of that site's popularity (juice) to be passed to mine. In Cognitive Hypnotherapy it is suggested that TAOTM is the google of the memoragination, and emotion is the google-juice. The more emotion is present in a memory the more likely it is to become a hub, and the more likely that later events become associated with it.

Growth
In the context of this book, one of the two basic responses cells have to stimuli - to either grow towards it, or to move away to protect themselves. Bruce Lipton suggests that organisms as a whole are either in a state of growth or protection. In the latter state natural processes are shut down which can lead to a plethora of mental and physical problems.

Growthplex
A term coined by the author to make the point that over time our beliefs tend to organise themselves into a system that either leaves us living a life in growth, or in protection. If our sense of self is as a 'growthplex' we are likely to live a life of positivity, and optimism, and health.

H

Hippocampus
A region of the brain considered to be an important part of forming and retaining long-term memories.

Hubs
A term used by Barabasi to describe points in a scale-free network that are more highly connected than others. In terms of the internet, Amazon and Google would be considered hubs. In Cognitive Hypnotherapy, any memory which is deemed highly relevant to growth or protection becomes a hub within the memoragination which present situations are compared to more than other memories.

I

Id
A Freudian idea that divides the psyche into three parts: the superego - plays the critical and moralising role (The Parent in Transactional Analysis), the ego - the

organised, realistic part (The Adult in TA), and the id – the uncoordinated instinctual drives (The Child in TA).

Identity
One of the Neuro-logical levels. Identity comprises those factors from which the sense of self emerge. Includes representational system preferences, metaprograms. Identity is that person you know isn't someone else.

ILOC (Internal Locus Of Control)
Where a person maintains themselves in a state of agency – where they look to themselves for solutions and hold themselves responsible for their results – they are at 'Cause'in their world. The opposite of ELOC. ELOC is the position most clients occupy in the beginning of treatment. ILOC is a key thing to develop in them for change to be self-sustaining.

Inductive questions
Where it is suggested that one thing will lead to a change in a greater range of things i.e "if there was one thing you could learn that would mean you could understand everything, what would it be?"

Internal Representation
Full term would probably be ...of our external sensing. The version of reality we are aware of in our thoughts, either a memory, or the filtered information from our senses of the world outside.

Interval processing
From the work of Piaget, the level of thinking above nominal and ordinal, where finer levels of measurement in the relationship between things can be made – "I like curry more than pasta, but only just".

Invariance/invariant
The quality of remaining unchanged

K

Kinaesthetic
In the context of this book used to describe the physical and emotional experiences we have, as opposed to the visual, auditory, olfactory (smell) or gustatory (taste) ones. Usually explored through their submodalities. In NLP also used as a term to describe someone who related to the world strongly through this system.

L

Limbic system
From the triune brain model developed by McLean, the limbic system is those parts of the brain involved in emotional processing. Often referred to as the mammalian brain.

M

Matrix Model
A model used in Cognitive Hypnotherapy to describe the steps the mind and body make from the awareness of a stimulus to the conclusion of its response to it. The sequence it describes is Stimulus-Memory Matrix-Emotion-Response-Termination-Evaluation.

Meme
A cultural item - i.e. an idea - transmitted in a manner analogous to the transmission of genes (i.e selection and mutation - ideas that are fittest survive, and can change as they are passed from one person to another). In Dawkins view an idea is another form of replicator (the gene being the other).

Memeplex
A term coined by Blackmore to describe a collection of beliefs arranged and organised around a central idea.

Memetics
The study of memes as a form of replicator and its ramifications.

Memoragination
A model proposed by the author. It suggests that the memory and personal imagination are part of one mind-system that links our past, present and future using TAOTM in order to make sense of our present, and guide our next actions through the creation of a reality tunnel.

Memory loops
A chain of memories connected by a particular context - from the first reference experience, usually a significant emotional event, to the present day. The second step of the Matrix model.

Meta-model

In the context of this book, a term used to describe a model that organises other models (or groups of models) Meta means 'above', not in terms of superiority, only in terms of logical levels of organisation. In NLP used to describe a question model that recovers information from a client's deep structure.

Milton model

An NLP model of hypnotic language developed from the observation of Milton Erickson by Bandler and Grinder.

Mirror neurons

A neuron that fires both when an animal acts and when the animal observes the same action performed by another. Thus, the neuron "mirrors" the behaviour of the other, as though the observer were itself acting. Possibly a major source of our ability to learn, and this book suggests they could also be an important component of our sense of self.

Model of the World (MOTW)

A term used in NLP to describe the sum of the ways an individual subjectively experiences the world they live in.

Multiple Personality Disorder

A contentious psychiatric diagnosis that describes a condition in which a person displays multiple distinct identities or personalities, which often act independently of each other.

N

Negative Hallucination

Trance phenomenon whereby the person doesn't notice something that is in view.

Neuro Linguistic Programming

Defined as 'the study of subjective experience' and originally developed by Bandler and Grinder, it has grown to include a number of models that are useful in developing excellence in a wide range of human activities.

Neuro logical Levels

Developed by Robert Dilts who was inspired by Gregory Bateson's work on classifying natural hierarchies. Dilts applied these ideas to the nervous system and proposed that different logical levels are an expression of different types of neuro-logical organisation that operate at different levels.

Neurology
Either,
the study of the anatomy, physiology, and diseases of the nervous system, or a term
used to describe the nervous system itself i.e. 'our neurology'.

Neuron
A brain cell.

Neuroscience
The study of the brain and mind

Neurosis
A Freudian term used to describe the kinds of issues that clients most commonly
bring to therapy. In (very) simple terms, Eric Berne described a neurotic as someone
"who thinks everyone else is ok, but there is something wrong with them, while a
psychotic thinks he's ok, it's the rest of the world that's mad."

Neurotransmitter
A substance that transmits nerve impulses across a synapse

Nocebo
Describes the phenomena by which people can take a harmless substance and
respond to it as if it were harmful.

Nominal processing
Taken from the work of Piaget, in the context of this book this is the level of
thinking which defines things in simple, binary terms. Something is black or white,
right or wrong, safe or dangerous. In this book it's suggested this is the level of
thinking present when we are in a state of protection (i.e. fight or flight). This is
what LeDoux referred to as 'fast and dirty' thinking.

O

Open loop learning
A situation where the brain is able to access information from all parts of the
memoragination in order to gain understanding - in contrast to closed loop learning.

Ordinal
Taken from the work of Piaget, this is a higher level of thinking than nominal, where

information can be sorted hierarchically – better/worse than, above/below something else: "I like curry more than pasta."

Orr's Law
Imagine the mind has two elements, the thinker and the prover. "What the thinker thinks, the prover proves."

Outcome
The end point of therapy – the client's solution state.

P

Pattern Hunting
Term used in cognitive Hypnotherapy to describe the purpose of the therapist when listening to a client. A problem comprises a pattern made of context, structure, process and consequence. The therapist's task is to hunt for this pattern within the information the client provides about the problem.

Pattern Interrupt
Any technique or intervention that serves to interrupt the normal process of a client's problem pattern as it happens.

Perception
Our subjective awareness of information derived from sensory processes

Placebo effect
Describes the phenomena by which a person responds to something, believing it to be something else. For example, somebody could take a sugar pill believing it to be a pain killer, and experience a lessening of cessation of their pain.

Pleasure Principle
Freudian idea (that still holds true). We are motivated to move towards pleasure and away from pain. The primary reflex of the unconscious.

Post Traumatic Stress Disorder (PTSD)
A severe anxiety disorder that can develop after exposure to any event that results in psychological trauma.

Premature Evaluation
Where the immature mind draws conclusions from its limited understanding of the

world. These conclusions often drive problematic behaviour in adulthood and are the target of techniques aimed at reframing the beliefs that arise from them.

Presuppositions
The linguistic equivalent of assumptions. Things in a sentence we tend to unconsciously accept as true in order to make sense of that sentence.

Priming
Priming is an acuteness to stimuli because of exposure to a certain event or experience. For example, an individual who has just purchased a new car may now start to notice with more frequency other people driving her same make and model. This person has been primed to recognize more readily a car like hers because of the experience she has driving and owning one.

Problem Pattern
The total experience of the client's issue. In Cognitive Hypnotherapy it's divided into four quadrants of information: context, structure, process and consequence.

Process
One of the four categories of information that comprise a problem pattern. Process describes the 'doing' of the client's problem as it occurs. Process is what the matrix model describes.

Protection
In the context of this book, one of the two basic responses have to stimuli – to either grow towards it, or to move away to protect themselves. Bruce Lipton suggests that organisms as a whole are either in a state of growth or protection. In the latter state natural processes are shut down which can lead to a plethora of mental and physical problems.

Protectionplex
A term coined by the author to make the point that over time our beliefs tend to organise themselves into a system that either leaves us living a life in growth, or in protection. If our sense of self is as a 'protectionplex' we are likely to live a life of negativity, and pessimism, and ill-health.

Prover
See Orr's Law

Psychosomatic
Describes a physical disorder that is created and maintained by unconscious mental processes

R

Rapport
The positive connection that can grow between people, often as a result of largely unconscious processes.

Ratio processing
From the work of Piaget, a level of thinking above nominal, ordinal and interval processing. This is where the most sophisticated thinking is possible, with the maximum amount of flexibility. The best level for reframing to take place.

Reality tunnel
The means by which the brain creates a moment-by-moment illusion of reality that guides our actions and ideas about our self. We tend to be mainly aware of the present moment of the tunnel, but through trance can be made aware of the past and future sections of it.

Recoding
The act of changing mental programming so that a thought is stored and experienced in a different way.

Reconsolidation
A memory process whereby a retrieved memory is able to be changed and then re-stored in its updated form.

Reference experience
An experience that is significant enough to an individual to become something used by the mind to measure the meaning of subsequent events.

Reframing
Taking a piece of information and changing the meaning of it by offering a new perspective.

Regression
The guiding of a client back to a past experience.

Remembered present
A phrase used by Edelman to make the point that what we perceive around us in the present is simply a rehash of what we have already experienced.

Replicator
Something that acts to produce copies of itself. In Dawkins view there are two on this planet: genes and memes (ideas).

Representational System
From NLP. The sense (visual, auditory, kinaesthetic etc) that a person is representing the world through at any particular moment. NLP postulates that most people have a preference for which sense they pay most attention to, and that this has a big impact on how they interact with the world.

Resistance
In many schools of therapy resistance is seen as an attempt by the unconscious to prevent thoughts, feelings or memories from being brought into consciousness. In Cognitive Hypnotherapy it is just another item of information of which the question "What's that about?", is asked.

Response
Part of the matrix model, describes the behaviour created by the unconscious in response to a particular stimuli.

S

Scale network
Term used in network theory to describe a structure of relationships that can be mapped as a bell curve. An example is the connections between airports in the world.

Scale-free network
Term used in network theory to describe a structure of relationships where an average cannot be mapped - an example is the connections between sites on the internet.

Secondary gain
The idea that a problem can have a purpose that is often hidden from the conscious. i.e a person may suffer from a bad back and be keen to recover, but the unconscious seeks to maintain the symptom because it desires the attention it brings.

Somnambulists
A term used to describe a class of people who tend to access trance naturally, to a very deep level, and quickly. The subject of choice for a stage hypnotist.

SEE
See Significant Emotional Event.

Selfplex
A term coined by Blackmore to describe the self in terms of memetics - as an emergent property of a system (complex) of memeplexes.

Sensory Distortion
Trance phenomenon where information from a sense other than visual is changed into something other than how it would normally be perceived e.g. getting chocolate to taste of lard.

Significant Emotional Event (SEE)
An event that the unconscious takes to be important as a reference experience in relation to emotions such as anger, fear, sadness guilt, not being loved etc.

Single loop learning
A model developed by Argyris and Schon describing a situation where all that is available for the brain to learn from is contained with a single, closed loop of information. In Cognitive Hypnotherapy memory loops which contain a negative SEE, causing the brain to trigger a state of protection, are examples of this model, and are referred to as 'closed loops'.

Solution State
The point of therapy. The evidence by which the client would know that they no longer have the problem.

Stimulus
Starting point of the Matrix model. The situation, person or object that is matched by the unconscious, using the three algorithms of the mind, to something from the past, which causes a response to be generated.

Structure
One of the four categories of information that comprise a problem pattern. Structure is about how we subjectively experience a thought. Submodalities are usually the means to describe the structure of a problem pattern.

Submodalities
The building blocks of meaning. Where the 5 senses can be described as modalities, sub-modalities (smds) describe the qualities which make up our perception of a thought, such as whether we think of it in black and white or colour. NLP suggests some smds are key to the meaning we give to the thought. These are known as drivers.

Suggestion loop
One wordweaving pattern that incorporates at least one suggestion from each of the Neuro-logical levels, using cause and effect or complex equivalence to connect the lower three to a new belief, value or sense of identity.

Survival calculator
A term used in this book to describe the major purpose of the brain

T

TAOTM (The Algorithms Of The Mind)
The three ways the mind assesses information flowing through the senses by matching it against information stored in the memory; cause and effect (this is because of that), complex equivalence (this is the same as that), and this is different to that.

Termination
From the matrix model. The point at which the response to the stimulus ceases.

Thinker
See Orr's Law.

Trance
A term used to describe an altered state of consciousness associated with hypnosis. In Cognitive Hypnotherapy trance is viewed as a normal phenomenon that is part of our everyday experience. We are in such states 90% of each day, and such states accompany most, if not all, problems that clients bring to therapy.

Trance induction
A formal means of moving a client from a present, conscious, state, to another, less conscious one.

Trance Phenomena
An everyday part of our mental processes through which our model of the world is created and perceived. They are the means by which our reality tunnels are created and are used deliberately in Cognitive Hypnotherapy, particularly with Wordweaving™, to guide the client to a more positive perception.

U

Universal modelling processes
Bandler and Grinder's model of how the mind reduces the 2 million bits of information flowing through its senses each moment, down to roughly 7±2, and by doing so creates a model of reality that we mistake for the whole thing. The processes are deletion, distortion and generalisation.

V

Values
Part of the Neuro-logical levels. Values are the things we use to gauge the importance of things. They motivate us to act, and offer a means of evaluation.

Notes

1. Merel Kindt: *Nature Neuroscience* 12, 256 - 258 (2009)
2. http://www.saffo.com/journal/entries/898.html
3. Bertrand Russell, "Christian Ethics" from *Marriage and Morals* (1950)
4. *Embracing Uncertainty* by Susan Jeffers, Mobius (2003)
5. *Leviathan* by Thomas Hobbes, Oxford Paperbacks (2008)
6. *Why Choose this Book* by Read Montague, E P Dutton & Co Inc (2006)
7. *The User Illusion* by Tor Norretranders, Penguin Books Ltd (1999)
8. The Magical Number Seven, Plus or Minus Two: Some Limits on Our Capacity for Processing Information by George A. Miller *The Psychological Review*, (1956), vol. 63, pp. 81-9
9. *Why Choose this Book* by Read Montague, E P Dutton & Co Inc (7 Dec 2006)
10. *The User Illusion* by Tor Norretranders, Penguin Books Ltd; New edition (26 Aug 1999)
11. *The Times* Rose Wild (Jan 7 2010) Why inventors weren't always hailed as heroes.
12. *Proceedings of the National Academy of Sciences* vol 104 p642
13. As above
14. As above
15. *Darwin's Dangerous Idea* by Daniel Dennett, Penguin (1995)
16. *Emergence* by Steven Johnson, Penguin (2002)
17. *Proceedings of the National Academy of Sciences* vol 104 p.1726
18. *The Psychobiology of mind/body healing* by Ernest Rossi, Norton & Co (1994)
19. *Mind Wide Open* by Steven Johnson, Penguin (2005)
20. *The Emotional Brain* by Joseph LeDoux, Phoenix (1999)
21. *Strangers to Ourselves: Discovering the Adaptive Unconscious* by Timothy Wilson, Harvard University Press (2004)
22. Timewarp: How your brain creates the fourth dimension by Douglas Fox, *New Scientist* (21st October 2009)
23. *Wider than the Sky: A revolutionary view of consciousness* by Gerald Edelman, Penguin (2005)
24. *Man on his Nature* by Sir Charles S Sherrington, Cambs University Press (2009)
25. *Wider than the Sky: A revolutionary view of consciousness* by Gerald Edelman, Penguin (2005)
26. *Trances People Live* by Stephen Wolinsky, Bramble Books (1991)
27. To be honest I can't find where I read this. All my online research led me to people who were quoting me! If you know where this is published please let me know - although Bruce Lipton does say something similar here: *Succeed magazine* (Oct 07)
28. *Monsters and Magical Sticks* by Stephen Heller and Terry Steele, New Falcon Publications (2001)
29. *Did you Spot the Gorilla?* by Prof Richard Wiseman, Arrow Books (2004)
30. *Wider than the Sky: A revolutionary view of consciousness* by Gerald Edelman, Penguin (2005)
31. *Computing machinery and intelligence Mind*, (October 1950) http://en.wikipedia.org/wiki/Computational_theory_of_mind
32. *Why Choose this Book* by Read Montague, E P Dutton & Co Inc (2006)
33. As above
34. *Unpopular Essays, "An Outline of Intellectual Rubbish"* by Bertrand Russell, (1950)
35. *Causal Models* by Steven Sloman, OUP USA (2005)

36. *The Child's Concept of the World* by J Piaget Littlechild, Adams & Co (1965)
37. *The secret life of the brain* by Douglas Fox, New Scientist 2681 (5/11/08)
38 *The Emotional Brain* by Joseph LeDoux, Phoenix (1999)
39. *Bodily Changes in Pain, Hunger, Fear, and Rage* by Walter B. Cannon, D. Appleton and Company, New York and London (1915)
40. *Theory in Practice* by Chris Argyris and Donald A. Schon Bass (1992)
41. *Kluge* by Gary Marcus, Faber and Faber (2009)
42. *The Emotional Brain* by Joseph LeDoux, Phoenix (1999)
43. *The Feeling of What Happens* by Anthony Damasio, Vintage; New edition (2000)
44. *Why Choose this Book* by Read Montague, E P Dutton & Co Inc (2006)
45. As above
46. *Journal of Comparative and Physiological Psychology* 'Positive Reinforcement Produced by Electrical Stimulation of the Septal Area and other regions of rat brain' (1954)
47. 'Predictive Reward Signal of Dopamine Neurons' *Journal of Neurophysiology 80* (1998) 1-27 Wolfram Schultz For source of interview see reference 45
48. *The Decisive Moment* by Jonah Lehrer, Canongate Books (2009)
49. *The Scientist in the Crib* by Alison Gopnik, Ph.D, Andrew Meltzoff, Ph.D, and Patricia Kuhl, Ph.D. Harper Paperbacks (2001)
50. *Causal Models* by Steven Sloman, Oxford University Press USA 2009
51. *Mirroring People* by Marco Iacoboni, Picador USA (2009)
52. As above
53. As above
54. *Psychological Science* Libby, Shaeffer and Slemmer (2004)
55. Argyle, Michael, Veronica Salter, Hilary Nicholson, Marylin Williams & Philip Burgess (1970): The communication of inferior and superior attitudes by verbal and non-verbal signals. *British journal of social and clinical psychology* 9: 222-231.
56. LM DeBruine (2002). Facial resemblance enhances trust. *Proceedings of the Royal Society of London* B, 269(1498)
57. Mimicry turns computers into everyone's best mate by Anil Ananthaswamy, *New Scientist* (2003)
58. *The Selfish Gene* by Richard Dawkins, Oxford Paperbacks (2006)
59. *The User Illusion* by Tor Norretranders, Penguin Books Ltd; New edition (1999)
60. *Prometheus Rising* by Robert Anton Wilson, New Falcon Publications,U.S (1988)
61. *Urban shaman* by Serge Kahili King, Simon & Schuster (1990)
62. *Linked The New Science of Networks* by Albert Laszlo Barabasi, Perseus Books (2002)
63. "The Small World Problem" Stanley Milgram *Psychology Today* (May 1967)
64. *The Kevin Bacon Game* invented by Craig Fass, Brian Turtle, and Mike Ginelli, Allbright College (1994)
65. All the world's a net by David Cohen *New Scientist* (13th April 2002)
66. Edward Lorenz *New York Academy of Sciences* (1963)
67.Arthur Winfree *Journal of Theoretical Biology* no 230
68. Child of Our Time BBC Productions
69. Not-so total recall by John McCrone *New Scientist* (3rd May 2003)
70. As above
71. As above
72. LSD Psychotherapy by Stanislas Grof *MAPS* (2001)
73. African herb yields its anti-addiction secret by Bob Homes *New Scientist* (22nd January 2005)
74. *The Scientist in the Crib* by Alison Gopnik, Ph.D, Andrew Meltzoff, Ph.D, and Patricia Kuhl, Ph.D. Harper Paperbacks (2001)

75. Lilienfeld, S. O. (2007): Psychological treatments that cause harm. *Perspectives on Psychological Science*, 2, 53-70 and *The Other Side of Sadness: What the new science of sadness tells us about life after loss* by George A Bonanno, Basic (Books 2009)

76. *The Lost Symbol* by Dan Brown, Corgi (2010)

77. As above (so below)

78. *Striking Thoughts* by John Little, Tuttle Publishing (2000)

79. Inception Christopher Nolan, Warner Bros (2010)

80. As above

81. http://www.saffo.com/journal/entries/898.html

82. *Prometheus Rising* by Robert Anton Wilson, New Falcon Publications, U.S New Ed (1988)

83. *Mans Search for Meaning* by Victor E. Frankl, Rider & Co (2004)

84. Lilienfeld, S. O. (2007): Psychological treatments that cause harm. *Perspectives on Psychological Science*, 2, 53-70 and *The Other Side of Sadness: What the new science of sadness tells us about life after loss* by George A Bonanno, Basic Books (2009)

85. *Transforming Therapy* by Gil Boyne, Westwood Publishing (1989)

86. As above

87. *Enchiridion* by Epitctetus, Dover Publications Inc. (2004)

88. Picture Yourself at the Polls: Visual Perspective in Mental Imagery Affects Self-Perception and Behavior Libby, Shaeffer, Eibach and Slemmer *Psychological Science* volume 18 issue 3

89. *The Journey* by Brandon Bays, Thorsons (1999)

90. *Metaphors in Mind* James Lawley and Penny Tompkins, Developing Company Press (2006)

91. *Emotions Revealed* by Paul Ekman, Phoenix (2004)

92. *The Artistry of Milton Erickson*, DVD (1975)

93. *Authentic Happiness* by Martin Seligman Ph. D, Nicholas Brealey Publishing (2003)

94. As above

95. *Outliers* by Malcolm Gladwell, Penguin (2009)

96. The science of voodoo:when mind attacks the body, Helen Pilcher *New Scientist* (2009)

97. *What Mad Pursuit* by Francis Crick, Basic books (1990)

Bibliography

Aleksander, Igor, *The World in my Mind*, Imprint Academic (2007)

Argyris, Chris and Schon, Donald, *Theory in Practice*, Bass (1992)

Barabasi, Albert-Laszlo *Linked,* Perseus Publishing (2002)

Bays, Brandon *The Journey*, Thorsons (1999)

Blackmore, Susan Dr. *The Meme Machine*, Oxford Paperbacks (2000)

Bonanno, George A *The Other Side of Sadness*, Basic Books (2009)

Boyne, Gil *Transforming Therapy,* Westwood Publishing (1989)

Brown, Dan *The Lost Symbol* , Corgi (2010)

Buchanan, Mark *Nexus* W.W Norton & Co (2003)

Damasio, Antonio R. *The Feeling of What Happens* Vintage (2000)

Dawkins, Richard *The Selfish Gene* Oxford Paperbacks (2006)

Dennett, Daniel *Kinds of Minds*, Phoenix (1997)

Dennet, Daniel *Darwin's Dangerous Idea* Penguin (1996)

Doidge, Norman *The Brain that Changes Itself* Penguin Books (2008)

Edelman, Gerald M. *Wider than the sky* Penguin Books (2005)

Ekman, Paul *Emotions Revealed* Phoenix (2004)

Frankl, Victor E. *Mans Search for Meaning* Rider & Co (2004)

Freeman, Walter J. *How brains make up their minds* Phoenix (2000)

Frith, Chris *Making up the Mind* Blackwell Pub Ltd (2007)

Gardner, Daniel T*he Science of Fear* Plume Books (2009)

Gigerenzer, Gerd *Gut Feelings* Penguin Group (2008)

Gladwell, Malcolm *Blink* Penguin Group (2006)

Gladwell, Malcolm *Outliers* Penguin (2009)

Gopnik Ph.D, Alison, Meltzoff, Ph.D, Andrew Kuhl Ph.D, Patricia *The Scientist in the Crib* Harper Paperbacks (2001)

Gregory, Richard L. *Seeing through illusions* Oxford University Press (2009)

Heller, Steven and Steele, Terry *Monsters & Magical Sticks* New Falcon Publications (2001)

Hirstein, William *Brain Fiction* MIT Press (2006)

Hobbes, Thomas *Leviathan* Oxford Paperbacks (2008)

Hobson, J. Allan *The Chemistry of Conscious States* Little, Brown & Co (1994)

Hofstadter, Douglas *I am a Strange Loop* Basic Books (2007)

Hood, Bruce *Supersense* Constable & Robinson (2009)

Iacoboni, Marco *Mirroring People* Picador USA (2009)

Jeffers Ph.D, Susan *Embracing Uncertainty* Mobius (2003)

Johnson, Steven *Emergence* Penguin Books (2002)

Johnson, Steven *Mind Wide Open* Penguin Books (2005)

Kahili King, Serge *Urban Shaman* Simon & Schuster (1990)

Kluger, Jeffrey *Simplexity* John Murray (2008)

Lawley, James and Tompkins, Penny *Metaphors in Mind* Developing Company Press (2006)

LeDoux , Joseph *The Emotional Brain* Phoenix (1999)

Little, John *Striking Thoughts* Tuttle Pubs (2000)

Lehrer, Jonah *The Decisive Moment* Canongate Books Ltd (2009)

Piaget, J *The Child's Concept of the World* Adams & Co (1965)

Lipton Ph.D, Bruce *The Biology of Belief* Hay House (2007)

Lynch, Aaron *Thought Contagion* Basic Books (1996)

Marcus, Gary *Kluge* Houghton Mifflin (2008)

McCrone, John *Going Inside* Faber & Faber (1999)

Metzinger, Thomas *The Ego Tunnel* Basic Books (2009)

Montague, Read *Why choose this Book* Dutton (2006)

Norretranders, Tor *The User Illusion* Penguin Books Ltd Aug (1999)

Pert, PH.D Candace B. The *Molecules of Emotion* Pocket Books (1999)

Piattelli-Palmarini, Massimo *Inevitable Illusions* John Wiley & Sons (1996)

Robertson, Ian *Mind Sculpture* Bantam Books (2000)

Rose, Steven *The 21st-Century Brain* Vintage (2006)

Schacter, Daniel L. *The Seven Sins of Memory* Souvenir Press Ltd (2003)

Schwartz MD, Jeffrey and Begley, Sharon *The Mind & The Brain* Harper Collins (2004)

Seligman Ph.D, Martin *Authentic Happiness* Nicholas Brealey Pubs (2003)

Sherrington, Sir Charles *Man on his Nature* Cambs Uni Press (2009)

Sloman, Steven *Causal Models* Oxford Uni Press USA (2009)

Watzlawick, Paul *The Invented Reality* W.W Norton & Co. (2008)

Wegner, Daniel M. *The Illusion of Conscious Will* MIT Press (2003)

Wilson, Robert Anton *Prometheus Rising* New Falcon Pubs (1988)

Wilson, Timothy D. *Strangers to Ourselves* Harvard University Press (2002)

Wiseman, Prof Richard *Did you Spot the Gorilla?* Arrow Books Ltd (2004)

Wolinsky Ph.D, Stephen and Ryan, Margaret *Trances People Live* Bramble Books (1991)

INDEX